Essential
A2 Biology
for OCR

Published in 2004 by:
Nelson Thornes Ltd
Delta Place
27 Bath Road
CHELTENHAM
GL53 7TH
United Kingdom

05 06 07 08 / 10 9 8 7 6 5 4 3

A catalogue record for this book is available from the British Library

ISBN 0 7487 8518 3

Illustrations by IFA Design

Page make-up by Tech-Set Ltd

Printed and bound in Croatia by Zrinski

Contents

Introduction

Essential A2 Biology for OCR has been written specifically to meet the Oxford, Cambridge and RSA (OCR) specification for Advanced (A2) Biology. It covers fully the requirements of this specification and has been endorsed by OCR. It follows on from its partner book *Essential AS Biology for OCR* and is therefore intended for use by students who have studied AS Biology. The subject content corresponds to the module 'Central Concepts' and is divided into six chapters that exactly correspond to the sub-divisions of this module. As with *Essential AS Biology for OCR*, the layout of the book is designed to present information in a clear way that is easy to access. Its features include:

- **Double page spreads** to divide the material into manageable portions by covering a single topic within the pages on view.
- **Full colour diagrams** to illustrate points made in the text, to aid understanding and improve clarity.
- **Colour photographs** to improve understanding further and add realism to the information and ideas.
- **Numbered headed sections** to sub-divide the topic further into bite-sized pieces. This makes accessing material simpler and allows for easy cross referencing of information.
- **Extensive use of bullet points** to produce easy to follow lists of information. They permit quick referencing and often have key introductory words that make learning, and hence revision, easier.
- **Extensive cross referencing** to link different topics and provide a fully integrated understanding of biology as a whole.
- **Accessible language** to improve comprehension and understanding.
- **Bold type** to emphasise key words in the text and make revision more effective.

- **Purple type** to highlight biological words that are not defined within a specific topic, but which can be found in the glossary. This enables the reader easily to access a full explanation of biological terms used in the text.
- **Comprehensive glossary** to provide a clear and concise definition of over 250 biological terms used throughout the book.
- **Summary tests** to provide a quick check on how well the factual content of each unit has been learned. Where there is no room within a unit, these can be found at the back of the book (pages 144–48). Answers are provided at the back of the book, so that the accurately completed test forms a concise summary of the information in each unit.
- **OCR examination questions** to provide practice of the type of questions to be expected in the final examination. Arranged at the back of the book, these questions test the full range of skills expected at A2, including application of knowledge, understanding, analysis, synthesis and evaluation.
- **Extension material** to expand knowledge beyond the strict boundaries of the specification. The content of 'Extensions' is not part of the Central Concepts Module and will not form part of these examination papers. Reading the material should, however, help you to widen your horizons and stimulate an interest in broader aspects of biology.

We trust that you will enjoy using this book and find it interesting and informative. We hope that it will build upon the knowledge and skills that you acquired at AS level and so stimulate a further interest in biology that encourages you to pursue your study beyond this level. Above all, we hope it will contribute to your success in the A level examinations.

Glenn and Susan Toole

Energy and respiration

Energy

All living organisms require energy in order to remain alive. This energy comes initially from the Sun (or in a few instances from chemicals). Plants use solar energy to combine water and oxygen into complex organic molecules by the process of **photosynthesis**. Both plants and animals then break down these organic molecules to make **adenosine triphosphate (ATP)** that is used as the energy source to carry out processes that are essential to life.

1.1.1 What is energy?

Energy is defined as 'the ability to do work'. It can be considered to exist in two states:

- **Kinetic energy** is the energy of motion. Moving objects perform work by making other objects move.
- **Potential energy** is stored energy. An object that is not moving may still have the capacity to do so and therefore possesses potential energy.
  A stone on a hillside has potential energy. If it is set in motion, gravity will cause it to roll downhill and some of its potential energy will be converted into kinetic energy.

Other facts about energy include:
- it takes a variety of different forms, e.g. light, heat, sound, electrical, magnetic, mechanical, chemical and atomic
- it can be changed from one form to another
- it cannot be created or destroyed
- it is measured in Joules (J).

1.1.2 Why do organisms need energy?

Without some input of energy, natural processes tend to break down in randomness and disorder. A building left alone soon becomes derelict – tiles fall off the roof, water penetrates, fungi rot woodwork and climbing plants encroach on brickwork, causing it to crack and fall down. If energy is constantly put into the building, i.e. builders put the tiles back in place, heating is used to prevent dampness and the owners cut down the climbing plants, then the property remains in an ordered state. Living organisms are highly ordered systems that require a constant input of energy to prevent them becoming disordered – a condition that would lead to their death. More particularly energy is needed for:

- **Metabolism** – especially the process of **anabolism**, in which simple substances are built up into complex ones (section 1.1.3), e.g. monosaccharides are built up into polysaccharides, amino acids are built up into polypeptides.
- **Movement** both within an organism (e.g. circulation of blood) and of the organism itself (e.g. locomotion due to muscular contraction or movement of cilia and flagella).
- **Active transport** of ions and molecules against a concentration gradient across cell membranes, e.g. the **sodium–potassium pump**.
- **Maintenance, repair and division** of cells and the organelles within them.
- **Production of substances** used within organisms, e.g. enzymes and hormones.

EXTENSION
Laws of thermodynamics

The first law of thermodynamics states that energy cannot be created or destroyed, but only converted from one form to another. The amount of energy in the universe is always the same, although that on Earth may fluctuate slightly. The Earth obtains the majority of its energy in the form of light from our nearest star – the Sun.

Most of the energy used by mankind comes ultimately from the sunlight via a series of energy conversions. If you are reading this page by artificial light you are likely to be using energy that came to Earth from the Sun, a long time ago. Light energy from the Sun was converted into chemical energy by photosynthesis carried out by giant ferns millions of years ago. The compression of dead ferns over millions of years produced coal. The coal was mined and the chemical energy of plants that made it was converted into heat energy by burning it in a power station. The heat energy became the kinetic (moving) energy of water molecules as liquid water was converted into steam. This in turn was converted into electrical energy by turbines and finally the energy was converted back to its original form, light, by the bulb you are reading by.

The second law of thermodynamics states that disorder (more technically called **entropy**) in the universe is continuously increasing. In other words, disorder is more likely than order. For example, a heap of bricks is more likely to fall down and become scattered than it is to arrange itself into a neat column because there is less energy in a disordered system than in an ordered one. When the universe was formed, it possessed the maximum potential energy it has ever had. Since then, it has become increasingly disordered because at each energy conversion the amount of entropy increased.

- **Maintenance of body temperature** in birds and mammals. These organisms are **endothermic** and need energy to replace that lost as heat to the surrounding environment.
- **Bioluminescence** in a few organisms such as glow worms.
- **Production of electricity**, e.g. the electric eel.

1.1.3 Energy and metabolism

The flow of energy through living systems occurs in three stages:

- The Sun's light energy is converted by plants to chemical energy during photosynthesis.
- The chemical energy from photosynthesis, in the form of organic molecules, is converted into ATP.
- ATP is used by cells to perform useful work.

All the reactions that take place within organisms are collectively known as **metabolism**. These reactions are of two types:

- **Anabolism** is the build up of larger, more complex molecules from smaller, simpler ones – a process requiring energy.
- **Catabolism** is the breakdown of complex molecules into simpler ones, with the release of energy.

1.1.4 Free energy

When one form of energy is converted to another, e.g. when electrical energy is converted to light energy in a light bulb, not all the energy is converted into its intended form; some is lost as heat. By 'lost' we mean the energy is no longer available to do useful work because it is distributed evenly. Energy that is available to do work under conditions of constant temperature and pressure is called **free energy**. If the products of a reaction contain more energy than the reactants and free energy must be supplied to make the reaction happen, it is known as an **endergonic (endothermic) reaction**. Reactions in which the products have less energy than the reactants and therefore energy is released, are known as **exergonic (exothermic) reactions**.

1.1.5 Activation energy

A typical chemical reaction may be represented as:

$$A \rightarrow B + C$$

In this case, A represents the **substrate** and B and C are the **products**. Before any chemical reaction can proceed it must be initially activated, i.e. its energy must be increased. The energy required is called the **activation energy**. Catalysts, such as enzymes, lower this activation energy and so enable reactions to take place more rapidly and/or at lower temperatures. These events are summarised in figures 1.1 and 1.2.

Once provided, the activation energy allows the products to be formed with a consequent release of free energy. Chemical reactions are reversible and therefore C and B can be synthesised into A. Such a reaction is not spontaneous, however, and requires an external source of energy if it is to proceed. Most biological processes are in fact a cycle of reversible reactions. As there is inevitably some loss of free energy in the form of heat each time the reaction is reversed, the process cannot continue without a substantial input of energy from outside the organisms. The ultimate source of this energy is the light radiation of the Sun.

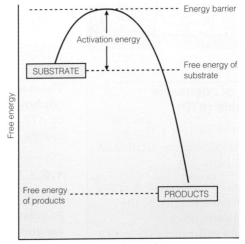

Fig 1.1 Concept of energy activation

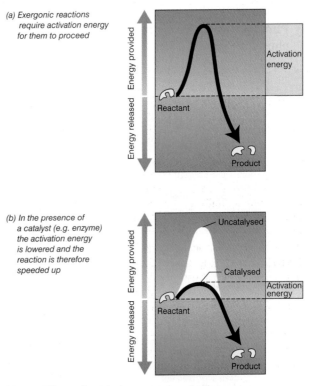

(a) Exergonic reactions require activation energy for them to proceed

(b) In the presence of a catalyst (e.g. enzyme) the activation energy is lowered and the reaction is therefore speeded up

Fig 1.2 Effects of catalysts on energy activation

SUMMARY TEST 1.1

Energy is defined as the ability to do **(1)**. The energy of motion is known as **(2)** energy, whereas **(3)** energy is stored energy. Living organisms need energy for many reasons, including **(4)** reactions in which simple molecules are built up into complex ones and the movement of material by **(5)** against a concentration gradient. Living organisms also use energy for movement and the maintenance of **(6)** in birds and mammals. Before a chemical reaction can take place energy must be provided; this is known as **(7)** energy.

Adenosine triphosphate (ATP)

Structure of adenosine triphosphate (ATP)

The ATP molecule (Fig 1.3) is a phosphorylated macromolecule and it has three parts:

- **Adenine** – a nitrogen-containing organic base belonging to the group called purines.
- **Ribose** – a sugar molecule with a 5-carbon ring structure (pentose sugar) that acts as the backbone to which the other parts are attached.
- **Phosphates** – a chain of three phosphate groups.

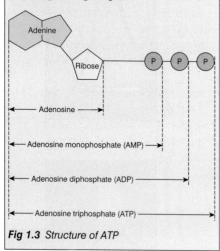

Fig 1.3 Structure of ATP

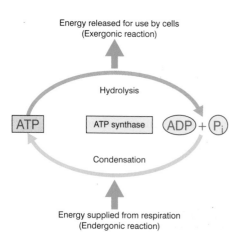

Fig 1.4 ATP cycle

The main energy currency of all cells is a molecule called **adenosine triphosphate (ATP)**. Almost every energy-requiring process in cells is powered by ATP. It is a small water-soluble molecule and therefore easily transported around the cell.

1.2.1 How ATP stores energy

It is the three phosphate groups that are the key to how ATP stores energy. Each one is very negatively charged and so they repel one another. This makes the **covalent bonds** that link them rather unstable – a bit like a coiled spring, with each phosphate straining to break away from its nearest partner. These unstable covalent bonds have a low activation energy, which means they are easily broken. When they do break they release a considerable amount of energy – some $30.6\,\text{kJmol}^{-1}$ for each of the first two phosphates removed and $14.2\,\text{kJmol}^{-1}$ for the removal of the final phosphate. Usually in living cells it is only the terminal phosphate that is removed according to the reversible equation:

$$\begin{array}{ccccccc} \text{ATP} & + & \text{H}_2\text{O} & \rightarrow & \text{ADP} & + & \text{P}_i & + & 30.6\,\text{kJ} \\ \text{adenosine} & & \text{water} & & \text{adenosine} & & \text{inorganic} & & \text{energy} \\ \text{triphosphate} & & & & \text{diphosphate} & & \text{phosphate} & & \end{array}$$

1.2.2 Synthesis of ATP

The conversion of ATP to ADP is a reversible reaction (Fig 1.4) and therefore energy can be used to add an inorganic phosphate to ADP to re-form ATP according to the reverse of the equation above.

The interconversion rate of ATP and ADP is phenomenal. Although there are only around 5 g of ATP in the human body at any point in time, it is thought that, even at rest, a single human uses 40 kg of ATP in a 24 hour period. This means that, on average, a single ATP molecule undergoes around 8000 cycles of synthesis and **hydrolysis** each day. As the synthesis of ATP from ADP involves the addition of a phosphate molecule, it is a **phosphorylation** reaction. This phosphorylation is catalysed by the enzyme ATP synthase (sometimes called ATP synthetase but often just called ATPase) and it occurs in three ways:

- **Photophosphorylation** that takes place in chlorophyll-containing plant cells during photosynthesis.
- **Substrate-level phosphorylation** that takes place in plant and animal cells when phosphate groups are transferred from donor molecules to ADP to make ATP. For example, in the formation of pyruvate at the end of glycolysis (section 1.3.2).
- **Oxidative phosphorylation** that takes place on the mitochondrial membranes of plant and animal cells during the process of electron transport (unit 1.5).

In all three cases, ATP is synthesised using energy released during the transfer of electrons along a chain of electron carrier molecules in either the chloroplasts or the mitochondria. There is a difference in hydrogen ion concentration either side of certain **phospholipid** membranes in chloroplasts and mitochondria and it is essentially the flow of these ions across these membranes that generates ATP. The process was first proposed by Peter Mitchell in 1961 and is referred to as the **chemiosmotic theory of ATP synthesis**. Although it takes place in a similar way in both chloroplasts and mitochondria, the summary account that follows and which is illustrated in figure 1.5 describes the process in mitochondria.

- Hydrogen atoms produced during respiration are carried to the electron transport chain where they are split into **protons** (hydrogen ions – H^+) and electrons.
- As electrons pass along the electron carriers of the electron transport chain, each one being at a lower energy level than the one before, the energy released is used to pump the protons (H^+) into the space between the inner and outer mitochondrial membranes.
- Protons accumulate in the inter-membranal space, leading to a concentration gradient of protons (H^+) between the space and the matrix. This also means that there is an electrochemical gradient between the inter-membranal space and the matrix.
- As the inner mitochondrial membrane is almost impermeable to protons, they can only diffuse back through the **chemiosmotic** channels in the stalked particles.
- As protons flow through these channels their electrical potential energy is used to combine ADP with inorganic phosphate (P_i) to produce ATP.
- The phosphorylation reaction is catalysed by **ATP synthase** found in the bulbous end of the stalked particles.
- Once in the matrix the protons recombine with the electrons on carriers on the inner membrane to form hydrogen atoms, which in turn combine with oxygen to form water.

1.2.3 Role of ATP

The same feature that makes ATP a good energy donor, namely the instability of its phosphate bonds (section 1.2.1), is also the reason it is **not** a good long-term energy store. Fats, and carbohydrates such as glycogen, serve this

purpose far better. ATP is therefore the **intermediate energy source** of a cell. As a result, cells do not store large quantities of ATP, but rather just maintain a few seconds' supply. This is not a problem, as ATP is rapidly re-formed from ADP and inorganic phosphate (P_i) and so a little goes a long way. ATP is the source of energy for:

- **Anabolic processes** – It provides the energy needed to build up macromolecules from their basic units, e.g.
  - polysaccharide synthesis from monosaccharides
  - polypeptide synthesis from amino acids
  - DNA/RNA synthesis from nucleotides.
- **Movement** – ATP provides the energy for muscle contraction, ciliary and flagellar action and contraction of spindle fibres in nuclear division. In muscle contraction, ATP provides the energy for the filaments of striated muscle to slide past one another and therefore shorten the overall length of a muscle fibre. This ATP is regenerated using a substance called phosphocreatine, which is stored in muscle and acts as a reserve store of phosphate and energy. There is, however, a limited quantity of phosphocreatine in a cell and it is replenished when the muscle is relaxed, using phosphate from ATP.
- **Active transport** – ATP provides the energy necessary to move molecules or ions against a concentration gradient. This is an essential role, as every cell must maintain a precise ionic content.
- **Secretion** – ATP is needed to form the vesicles necessary for the secretion of cell products.
- **Activation of chemicals** – ATP makes chemicals react more readily, e.g. the phosphorylation of glucose at the start of glycolysis (section 1.3.2).

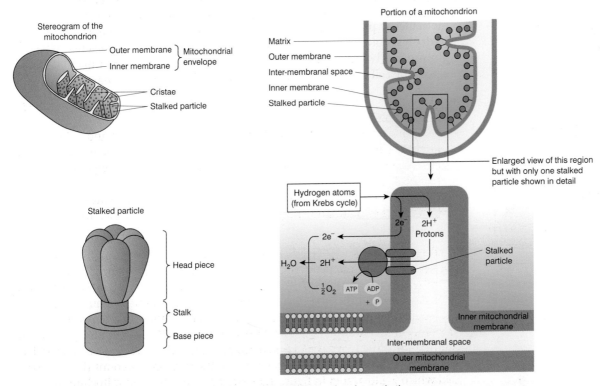

Fig 1.5 *Role of mitochondria in the synthesis of ATP according to the chemiosmotic theory*

Cellular respiration is the process by which the energy in food is converted into the energy for an organism to do biological work. Glucose is the main respiratory substrate and the overall equation for the process is:

$$C_6H_{12}O_6 \; + \; 6O_2 \; \rightarrow \; 6CO_2 \; + \; 6H_2O \; + \; energy$$

glucose   oxygen   carbon dioxide   water

1.3.1 Overview of cellular respiration

Cellular respiration can be divided into four stages:

- **Glycolysis** – the splitting of the 6-carbon glucose molecule into two 3-carbon pyruvate molecules.
- **Link reaction (pyruvate oxidation)** – the 3-carbon pyruvate molecule is converted into carbon dioxide and a 2-carbon molecule called acetyl coenzyme A.
- **Krebs cycle** – the introduction of acetyl coenzyme A into a cycle of nine reactions that yield some ATP and a large number of electrons.
- **Oxidative phosphorylation (electron transport system)** – the electrons are used to synthesise ATP and water is produced.

The main respiratory pathways are summarised in figure 1.6.

1.3.2 Glycolysis

Glycolysis occurs in the cytoplasm of all living cells and is the process by which a hexose (6-carbon) sugar, usually glucose, is split into two molecules of the 3-carbon molecule, pyruvate. Although there are 10 smaller enzyme-controlled reactions in glycolysis, these can be conveniently grouped into four stages:

- **Activation of glucose by phosphorylation**. Before it can be split into two, glucose must first be made more reactive by the addition of two phosphate molecules = **phosphorylation**. The phosphate molecules come from the **hydrolysis** of two ATP molecules to ADP. This provides the energy to activate glucose (**activation energy**) and also prevents glucose from being transported across the cell membrane and out of the cell. In the process glucose is

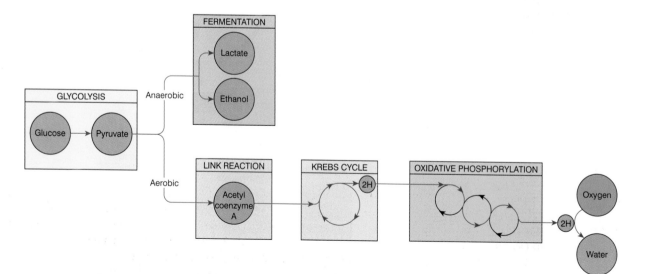

Fig 1.6 *Summary of respiratory pathways*

converted to another hexose sugar called fructose. For ease of understanding, however, we shall refer to most of the sugars in the remainder of this account simply by the number of carbon atoms they contain (hexose = 6, triose = 3).

- **Splitting of the phosphorylated hexose sugar**. The hexose sugar produced has two phosphates attached and is therefore called hexose bisphosphate. This molecule is then split into two 3-carbon molecules known as triose phosphate.
- **Oxidation of triose phosphate**. Hydrogen is removed from each of the two triose phosphate molecules and transferred to a hydrogen carrier molecule called nicotinamide adenine dinucleotide (NAD^+) to form reduced nicotinamide adenine dinucleotide ($NADH + H^+$).
- **The production of ATP**. Four enzyme reactions convert each triose phosphate into another 3-carbon molecule called pyruvate. In the process, two molecules of ATP are regenerated from ADP and two more hydrogens are produced, which become attached to a molecule of NAD^+ to give reduced NAD ($NADH + H^+$). It must be remembered, however, that for each molecule of glucose at the start of the process, there are two molecules of triose phosphate produced. Therefore these yields must be doubled, i.e. 4 × ATP and 2 × reduced NAD ($NADH + H^+$).

The events of glycolysis are summarised in figure 1.7.

The overall yield from one glucose molecule undergoing glycolysis is therefore:

- 2 molecules of ATP (four molecules of ATP are produced, but two were used up in the initial phosphorylation of glucose and so the net increase is two molecules)
- 2 molecules of reduced NAD ($NADH + H^+$) (these have the potential to produce more ATP)
- 2 molecules of pyruvate.

Glycolysis is a universal feature of every living organism. It was one of the earliest biochemical processes to evolve. It occurs in the cytoplasm of cells and does not require any organelle or membrane for it to take place. As it does not require oxygen it can proceed in both **aerobic** and **anaerobic** conditions. In the absence of oxygen the pyruvate produced by glycolysis can be converted into either lactate or alcohol by a process called fermentation. This is necessary in order to re-oxidise NAD so that glycolysis can continue. This is explained, along with details of the reactions, in unit 1.6. These reactions, however, yield only a small fraction of the potential energy stored in the pyruvate molecule. In order to release this energy, most organisms use oxygen to break down pyruvate further in a process called the Krebs cycle.

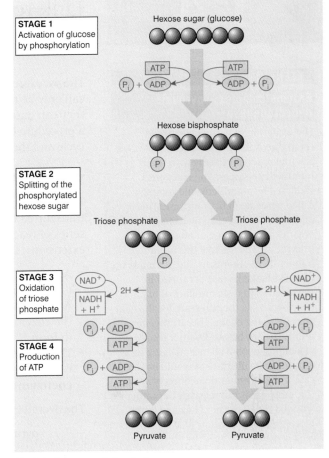

Fig 1.7 *Summary of glycolysis*

SUMMARY TEST 1.3

Glycolysis takes place in the **(1)** of cells and begins with the activation of the main respiratory substrate, namely the hexose sugar called **(2)**. This activation involves the addition of two **(3)** molecules provided by two molecules of **(4)**. The resultant molecule is known as **(5)** and in the next stage of glycolysis it is split into two molecules called **(6)**. The third stage entails the oxidation of these molecules by the removal of **(7)**, which is transferred to a carrier called **(8)**. The final stage is the production of the 3-carbon molecule **(9)**, which also results in the formation of two molecules of **(10)**.

1.4 Link reaction and Krebs cycle

The pyruvate molecules produced during **glycolysis** possess potential energy that can only be released using oxygen in a process called the **Krebs cycle**. Before they can enter the Krebs cycle, these pyruvate molecules must first be oxidised in a procedure known as the **link reaction**. In **eukaryotic cells** both the Krebs cycle and the link reaction take place exclusively inside mitochondria.

1.4.1 The link reaction

The pyruvate molecules produced in the cytoplasm during glycolysis are actively transported into the matrix of mitochondria. Here pyruvate undergoes a complex series of reactions that are catalysed by a **multienzyme complex** (see extension). During these reactions the following changes take place:

- A carbon dioxide molecule is removed from each pyruvate (= **decarboxylation**) by means of the enzyme pyruvate decarboxylase.
- A pair of hydrogens are removed from pyruvate (= **dehydrogenation**) using the enzyme pyruvate dehydrogenase. These hydrogens are picked up by NAD^+ to form $NADH + H^+$, which is later used to produce ATP (section 1.5.1).
- The 2-carbon molecule called an acetyl group that is thereby formed combines with a cofactor called coenzyme A (CoA) to produce a compound called **acetyl coenzyme A**.

The overall equation can be summarised as:

$$\text{pyruvate} + NAD^+ + \text{CoA} \rightarrow \text{acetyl CoA} + \text{reduced NAD} + CO_2$$

1.4.2 The importance of acetyl coenzyme A

Coenzyme A is made up of vitamin B_5 (pantothenic acid), the organic base adenine and the sugar ribose. It carries the acetyl group made from pyruvate into the Krebs cycle in the form of acetyl coenzyme A. The acetyl coenzyme molecule is important because most molecules that are used by living organisms for energy are made into acetyl coenzyme A before entering the Krebs cycle. Most carbohydrates and fatty acids can be metabolised into acetyl coenzyme A to release energy. In the case of fats, these are first hydrolysed into glycerol and fatty acids. The glycerol can then be converted into triose phosphate that can be broken down during glycolysis, while the fatty acids are progressively broken down in the matrix of the mitochondria into 2-carbon fragments that are converted into acetyl coenzyme A. The reverse is also true, namely that excess carbohydrate can be made into fats via acetyl coenzyme A, making it a pivotal molecule in the interconversion of major substances in eukaryotic cells.

1.4.3 Krebs cycle

The Krebs cycle was named after the British biochemist, Hans Krebs, who worked out its sequence in 1937. A central element of aerobic respiration, the Krebs cycle involves a series of nine small steps that take place in the matrix of mitochondria. Its events are illustrated in figure 1.8 and can be summarised as:

- The 2-carbon acetyl coenzyme A from the link reaction combines with a 4-carbon molecule (oxaloacetate) to produce a 6-carbon molecule (citrate).
- This 6-carbon molecule (citrate) is decarboxylated (loses CO_2) and dehydrogenated (loses two hydrogens) to give a 5-carbon compound, carbon dioxide and reduced NAD.

SUMMARY TEST 1.4

Pyruvate molecules produced during **(1)** are moved into the **(2)** of the mitochondria by the process of **(3)**. Before pyruvate can enter the Krebs cycle, it first has a carbon dioxide molecule removed – a process known as **(4)**, and also has a pair of hydrogen atoms removed – a process called **(5)**. The resultant molecule that enters the Krebs cycle is called **(6)**. This molecule is important because it can also be made from alternative respiratory substrates such as other carbohydrates and **(7)**. This 2-carbon molecule enters the Krebs cycle and combines with a 4-carbon molecule called **(8)** to produce a 6-carbon molecule called **(9)**. The progressive loss of two carbon dioxide molecules and eight hydrogen atoms produces the original 4-carbon molecule. Most of the hydrogen atoms are transferred to a hydrogen carrier called **(10)**.

- Further decarboxylation and dehydrogenation produces a 4-carbon molecule (oxaloacetate), carbon dioxide, reduced NAD and reduced FAD and a single molecule of ATP produced as a result of substrate-level phosphorylation (section 1.2.2).
- The 4-carbon molecule (oxaloacetate) can now combine with a new molecule of acetyl coenzyme A to begin the cycle again.

For each molecule of pyruvate, the Krebs cycle therefore produces:

- 4 molecules of reduced NAD (which includes one molecule produced in the link reaction). These have the potential to produce a total of 10 ATP molecules (section 1.5.2)
- 1 molecule of reduced FAD which has the potential to produce 1.5 ATP molecules (section 1.5.2)
- 1 molecule of ATP
- 3 molecules of carbon dioxide (including one produced in the link reaction).

As two pyruvate molecules are produced for each original glucose molecule, these quantities must be doubled when the yields from a single glucose molecule are being calculated.

1.4.4 Hydrogen carrier molecules

There are a number of small, non-protein organic molecules found in cells whose role it is to carry hydrogen atoms from one compound to another. Examples include:

- **nicotinamide adenine dinucleotide (NAD)**, which is important in respiration
- **flavine adenine dinucleotide (FAD)**, important in aerobic respiration
- **nicotinamide adenine dinucleotide phosphate (NADP)**, important in photosynthesis.

In respiration, NAD is the most important carrier. It works with dehydrogenase enzymes that catalyse the removal of hydrogen ions from substrates such as citrate and transfer them to other molecules such as the hydrogen carriers involved in oxidative phosphorylation (unit 1.5). The process works as follows:

- The two hydrogen atoms removed by the dehydrogenase enzyme dissociate into hydrogen ions (**protons**) and **electrons**:

$$
\begin{array}{ccccc}
2H & \rightleftharpoons & 2H^+ & + & 2e^- \\
\text{hydrogen} & & \text{hydrogen} & & \text{electrons} \\
\text{atoms} & & \text{ions (protons)} & &
\end{array}
$$

- Each NAD molecule in a cell exists in a form in which it has lost an electron, i.e it is oxidised and therefore exists as NAD^+.

- NAD^+ combines with the hydrogen ions (protons) and electrons to form NADH and a hydrogen ion (proton):

$$ NAD^+ + 2H^+ + 2e^- \rightarrow \text{reduced NAD (NADH + H}^+) $$

- When the hydrogen ion is transferred to a new molecule, the reduced NAD is re-oxidised, by the reversal of the above process, to re-form NAD^+.

1.4.5 The significance of the Krebs cycle

The Krebs cycle performs an important role in biochemistry for four reasons:

- It breaks down macromolecules into simpler ones; pyruvate is broken down into carbon dioxide.
- It produces hydrogen atoms that are carried by NAD to the electron transport chain for oxidative phosphorylation and the production of ATP by chemiosmosis, which provides metabolic energy for the cell.
- It regenerates the starter material (oxaloacetate), which would otherwise be completely used up.
- It is a source of intermediate compounds used by cells in the manufacture of other important substances such as fatty acids, amino acids and chlorophyll.

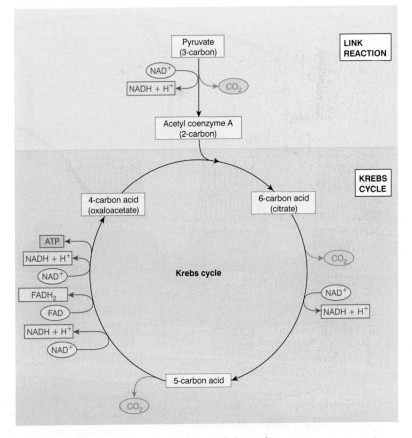

Fig 1.8 *Summary of link reaction and Krebs cycle*

1.5 Oxidative phosphorylation

So far in the process of cellular respiration, we have seen how hexose sugars such as glucose are split (**glycolysis**) and how the 3-carbon pyruvate that results is fed into the **Krebs cycle** to yield carbon dioxide and hydrogen atoms. The carbon dioxide is a waste product and is removed during the process of gaseous exchange (*Essential AS Biology*, units 4.6 and 4.7). The hydrogen atoms, or more precisely the **electrons** they contain, are however valuable as a potential source of energy. **Oxidative phosphorylation** (Fig 1.9), also known as the **electron transport system**, is the mechanism by which the energy of these electrons is converted into a form, adenosine triphosphate (ATP), that cells can use.

1.5.1 Krebs cycle, oxidative phosphorylation and mitochondria

Mitochondria are rod-shaped organelles, between 1 μm and 10 μm in diameter, that are found in all but a few eukaryotic cells. Details of their structure are given in *Essential AS Biology for OCR*, section 1.5.3, and in summary here. Each mitochondrion is bounded by a smooth outer membrane and an inner one that is folded into extensions called **cristae** (Fig 1.10). On the large surface area provided by the cristae are stalked particles (Fig 1.11). The inner space, or **matrix**, of the mitochondrion is made up of a semi-rigid material of protein, lipids and traces of DNA.

Mitochondria are the sites of the Krebs cycle and **oxidative phosphorylation**. More specifically:

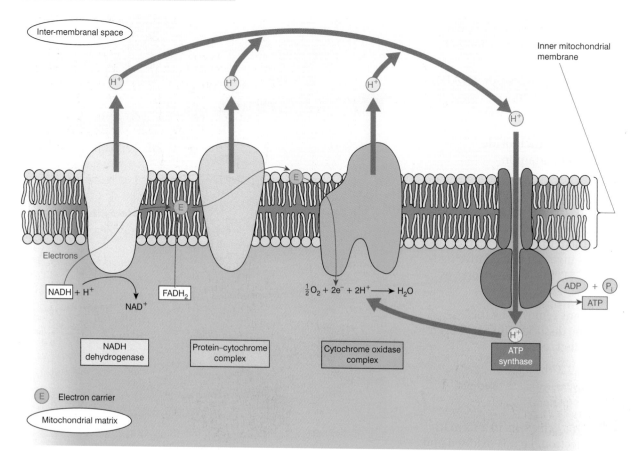

Fig 1.9 *Summary of oxidative phosphorylation*

- **The inner folded membrane (cristae)** has attached to it the proteins involved in the electron transport chain and therefore enables oxidative phosphorylation to take place.
- **The stalked particles** contain the enzymes involved in ATP synthesis and therefore are responsible for producing ATP by the chemiosmotic method (section 1.2.2).
- **The matrix** possesses the enzymes needed for the link reaction (section 1.4.1) and Krebs cycle (section 1.4.3) and is hence where these processes occur. In addition, the energy required to synthesise ATP results from the hydrogen ion (pH) gradient that exists between the matrix and inter-membranal space (section 1.2.2).

As mitochondria play such a vital role in respiration and the release of energy, it is hardly surprising that they occur in greater numbers in metabolically active cells such as those of the muscles, liver and epithelial cells that carry out active transport. The mitochondria in these cells also have more densely packed cristae that provide a greater surface area for the attachment of proteins and enzymes involved in oxidative phosphorylation.

1.5.2 The process of oxidative phosphorylation

- The hydrogen atoms produced during glycolysis and Krebs cycle are combined with special molecules called **carriers** that are attached to the mitochondrial membranes. Most hydrogen atoms are combined with **nicotinamide adenine dinucleotide (NAD)**, although one pair from the Krebs cycle combines with **flavine adenine dinucleotide (FAD)**. These carriers are proteins with a haem prosthetic group. This haem group possesses an iron atom that can change between the Fe^{2+} and Fe^{3+} state as it respectively accepts and donates an electron. The hydrogen atoms split into their protons (H^+) and electrons (e^-).
- The first carrier to accept electrons is a complex called **NADH dehydrogenase**.
- The electrons then pass via a carrier to a protein–cytochrome complex and finally, via another carrier to the cytochrome oxidase complex.
- The sequence of transfer of electrons from one carrier to the next is called the **electron transport chain**. The

enzymes that catalyse these reactions are called **oxidoreductases** (see extension).
- Each of the three complexes in the chain acts as a proton pump using energy from the electrons to drive the protons (H^+) from the mitochondrial matrix into the inter-membranal space.
- The protons (H^+) accumulate in the inter-membranal space before they diffuse back into the mitochondrial matrix through special protein channels.
- As these protons pass through these channels, ADP is combined with inorganic phosphate (P_i) to produce ATP. As this ATP is formed using a diffusion force similar to osmosis the process is called **chemiosmosis** (section 1.2.2).
- At the end of the chain the protons and electrons recombine and the hydrogen atoms so formed link with oxygen to form water.

These events are summarised in figure 1.9. This diagram indicates that 3 ATP molecules are produced for each reduced NAD and 2 ATP are produced for each reduced FAD molecule (fewer because reduced FAD enters further along the electron transport chain). Recent research suggests that these figures are more accurately 2.5 and 1.5 ATP molecules respectively. Not all the potential energy in the 32 ATP molecules produced for each glucose molecule (section 1.6.3) is a net yield. Around 25% of the energy produced is needed to transport ADP into the cell so that it can combine with inorganic phosphate to form ATP.

The importance of oxygen in respiration is to act as the final acceptor of the hydrogen atoms produced in glycolysis and Krebs cycle. Without its role in removing hydrogen atoms at the end of the chain, the hydrogen ions and electrons would 'back up' along the chain and the process of respiration would come to a halt. This point is illustrated by the effect of cyanide on respiration. Most people are aware that cyanide is a very potent poison that causes death rapidly. It is lethal because it is an inhibitor of the final dehydrogenase enzyme in the electron transport chain, namely **cytochrome oxidase**. This enzyme catalyses the addition of the hydrogens to oxygen to form water. Its inhibition causes hydrogen ions and electrons to accumulate on the carriers, bringing cellular respiration to a halt.

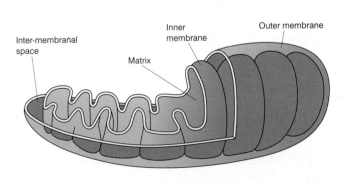

Fig 1.10 *Structure of a mitochondrion*

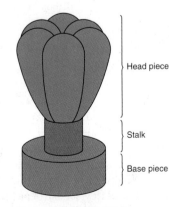

Fig 1.11 *Stalked particle*

We saw in unit 1.5 that oxygen is needed if the hydrogen atoms produced in **glycolysis** and **Krebs cycle** are to be converted to water and thereby drive the production of ATP. What happens if oxygen is temporarily or permanently unavailable to a tissue or a whole organism?

In the absence of oxygen, neither the Krebs cycle nor **oxidative phosphorylation** can take place, leaving only the **anaerobic** process of glycolysis as a potential source of ATP. For glycolysis to continue, its products of pyruvate and hydrogen must be constantly removed. In particular, the hydrogen must be released from the reduced **NAD** (NADH + H$^+$) in order to regenerate NAD$^+$. Without this the already tiny supply of NAD$^+$ in cells will be entirely converted to NADH$^+$ + H$^+$, leaving no NAD$^+$ to take up newly produced hydrogen from glycolysis. Glycolysis will then grind to a halt. The replenishment of NAD$^+$ is achieved by the pyruvate molecule from glycolysis accepting the hydrogen from reduced NAD in a process called fermentation.

There are a number of types of fermentation – various bacteria carry out over a dozen different forms. In eukaryotic cells, however, only two types occur with any regularity:

- alcoholic fermentation
- lactate fermentation.

1.6.1 Alcoholic fermentation

Alcoholic fermentation occurs in organisms such as certain bacteria and fungi (e.g. yeast) as well as in some cells of higher plants, e.g. root cells under waterlogged conditions.

The pyruvate molecule formed at the end of glycolysis first loses a molecule of carbon dioxide (decarboxylation) to form ethanal and then accepts hydrogen from NADH + H$^+$ to produce ethanol. The summary equation for this is:

$$\overset{\displaystyle \text{NADH} + \text{H}^+ \qquad \text{NAD}^+}{\underset{\text{(CH}_3\text{COCOOH)}}{\text{pyruvate}} \longrightarrow \underset{\text{(C}_2\text{H}_5\text{OH)}}{\text{ethanol}} + \underset{\text{(CO}_2)}{\text{carbon dioxide}}}$$

The overall equation using glucose as the starting point is:

$$\underset{\text{glucose}}{\text{C}_6\text{H}_{12}\text{O}_6} \rightarrow \underset{\text{ethanol}}{2\text{C}_2\text{H}_5\text{OH}} + \underset{\text{carbon dioxide}}{2\text{CO}_2}$$

Alcoholic fermentation in yeast has been exploited by humans for thousands of years, in both the brewing and baking industries. In brewing, ethanol is the important product. Yeast is grown in anaerobic conditions in which it ferments natural carbohydrates in plant products such as grapes (wine production) or barley seeds (beer production) into ethanol. The ethanol produced kills the yeast cells that

make it when its concentration reaches around 15%. Higher alcohol concentrations such as those found in spirits are achieved by distilling the ethanol solution.

1.6.2 Lactate fermentation

Lactate fermentation occurs in animals as a means of overcoming a temporary shortage of oxygen. Clearly, such a mechanism has considerable survival value, for example for a baby mammal in the period immediately after birth or an animal living in water where the amount of oxygen fluctuates. However, lactate fermentation occurs most commonly in muscles as a result of strenuous exercise. In these conditions oxygen may be used up more rapidly than it can be supplied and therefore an **oxygen deficit** occurs. It may be essential, however, that the muscles continue to work despite the lack of oxygen – for example if the organism is fleeing from a predator. In the absence of oxygen, each pyruvate molecule produced takes up the two hydrogen atoms from glycolysis to form lactate as shown below:

$$\overset{\displaystyle \text{NADH} + \text{H}^+ \qquad \text{NAD}^+}{\underset{\text{(CH}_3\text{COCOOH)}}{\text{pyruvate}} \longrightarrow \underset{\text{(CH}_3\text{CHOHCOOH)}}{\text{lactate}}}$$

The lactate produced will cause cramp and muscle fatigue if it is allowed to accumulate in the muscle tissue. Although muscle has a certain tolerance to lactate, it is nevertheless important that it is removed by the blood and taken to the liver. Here it is converted to glycogen in a process called the Cori cycle. Some lactate may also be oxidised to pyruvate and then enter the Krebs cycle. The individual incurs an **oxygen debt**, which is later repaid when oxygen is available again. Figure 1.12 shows how the NAD$^+$ needed for glycolysis to continue is regenerated in both common forms of fermentation.

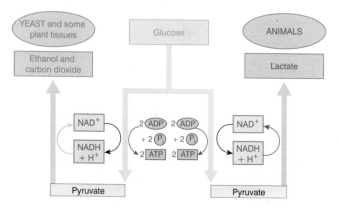

Fig 1.12 *How the NAD$^+$ needed for glycolysis is regenerated during fermentation in yeast and animals*

1.6.3 Energy yields from anaerobic and aerobic respiration

Energy from cellular respiration is derived in two ways:

- **Phosphorylation** – the direct linking of inorganic phosphate (P_i) to ADP to produce ATP.
- **Oxidative phosphorylation** – the indirect linking of inorganic phosphate to ADP to produce ATP using the hydrogen atoms from glycolysis and Krebs cycle that are carried on NAD and FAD.

To calculate the total number of ATP molecules produced, we need to know how many are produced from each pair of hydrogen atoms during oxidative phosphorylation. Historically, the number has been put at 3 ATP molecules for every pair of hydrogens carried on NAD and 2 for every pair carried on FAD. Recent thinking suggests that the figures are more accurately 2.5 and 1.5 molecules for hydrogen atoms carried on NAD and FAD respectively. It is these latter figures that are used in the following calculations.

During strenuous exercise, muscle may temporarily respire anaerobically

In anaerobic respiration there are 2 ATPs produced by phosphorylation but none by oxidative phosphorylation, because in the absence of oxygen this process cannot take place. The total yield is therefore 2 ATP. With each ATP producing 30.6 kJmol^{-1} of energy the total energy produced is 61.2 kJmol^{-1}. This compares with a theoretical value of 2870 kJmol^{-1} for the complete breakdown of glucose. Anaerobic respiration is therefore around 2% efficient.

In aerobic respiration the number of ATP molecules produced for each glucose molecule is:

- Substrate-level phosphorylation during
  - glycolysis   =   2
  - Krebs cycle   =   2
- Oxidative phosphorylation of
  - 2 reduced NAD from glycolysis   =   5
  - 8 reduced NAD from Krebs cycle   =   20
  - 2 reduced FAD from Krebs cycle   =   3
  -               TOTAL   32

Of these 32 ATP molecules, the equivalent of one ATP is used in transporting some of the chemicals involved, giving a net yield of 31 ATP.

The 31 molecules of ATP each producing 30.6 kJmol^{-1} of energy give a total yield of 948.6 kJmol^{-1}, compared with the theoretical maximum yield of 2870 kJmol^{-1} for each

glucose molecule, which makes aerobic respiration 33% efficient. This may appear a poor return, but compares favourably with most machines – a car engine, for example, is around 25% efficient.

1.6.4 Energy yields from other respiratory substrates

Although we normally think of glucose as the main respiratory substrate, other carbohydrates, as well as lipids and protein, may also be used in certain circumstances, without first being converted to glucose.

As lipids contain relatively more hydrogen than an equivalent mass of carbohydrate, their breakdown produces more hydrogen atoms for the electron transport chain and hence more energy. As a result, lipids release more than twice as much energy (39.4 kJg^{-1}) than the same mass of carbohydrate (15.8 kJg^{-1}). Once the immediate stores of carbohydrate, such as glycogen in the liver, have run out, organisms start to metabolise lipids for energy. Hence athletes in a long distance race may resort to their lipid reserves to give them energy in the latter stages of their run.

Protein is normally only metabolised for energy in extreme situations such as starvation. When all carbohydrate and lipid reserves have been exhausted, organisms will, as a last resort, break down their protein into amino acids. These then have the amino groups (NH_2) removed before entering the respiratory pathway at a number of different points depending on their carbon content. The 4-carbon and 5-carbon amino acids are converted to Krebs cycle intermediates, whereas 3-carbon amino acids are converted to pyruvate. Amino acids with large numbers of carbons are first converted to 3-, 4- and 5-carbon amino acids. Although the energy yield depends upon the exact composition of each protein, they normally yield around 17.0 kJg^{-1} – slightly more energy than carbohydrates.

SUMMARY TEST 1.6

In the absence of oxygen neither the Krebs cycle nor **(1)** can take place, leaving only glycolysis as a source of ATP. To allow glycolysis to continue, the hydrogen attached to **(2)** must be removed. In microorganisms such as **(3)**, this is achieved by first removing **(4)** from pyruvate to form ethanal and then reducing it with hydrogen to form **(5)** in a process called **(6)** fermentation. Animals use a different form of fermentation in which pyruvate accepts hydrogen to form **(7)**. Anaerobic respiration yields far less energy, with only a total of **(8)** ATP being made from each glucose molecule as opposed to a total of **(9)** ATP in aerobic respiration, although one of these is used to transport some chemicals needed in the process. When immediate supplies of carbohydrate, such as **(10)** in the liver, have been used up, organisms will release energy by metabolising firstly **(11)** and then, as a last resort, **(12)**.

The rate of respiration in an organism can be determined either by measuring the volume of oxygen taken in or the volume of carbon dioxide produced. Measurements can be taken on an instrument called a **respirometer**.

1.7.1 A simple respirometer

One type of simple respirometer is illustrated in figure 1.13. It consists of two identical chambers – an experimental one containing the respiring organisms and a control one containing an equal volume of non-respiring material such as glass beads. The two chambers are connected by a U-shaped manometer tube that contains a coloured fluid. This type of respirometer is sometimes referred to as a **differential respirometer** because it has a built-in control chamber that ensures any fluctuation in temperature or pressure affects both sides of the manometer equally and so they cancel each other out. An equal volume of some carbon dioxide absorbing material such as soda-lime is added to each chamber. In figure 1.13 the apparatus has been set up to measure the rate of respiration of small organisms such as woodlice at different temperatures.

A simple respirometer is used as follows:

- The apparatus is left in the water bath for about 10 minutes to allow it to reach the desired temperature.
- Screw clips A and B are kept open during this time to allow air to escape as it expands.
- Both screw clips are closed at the end of the 10 minutes.
- The woodlice respire, absorbing oxygen and giving out the same volume of carbon dioxide.
- The carbon dioxide given off by the woodlice in chamber B is absorbed by the soda-lime. There is hence a reduction in the volume of air in chamber B, due to the oxygen being absorbed by the woodlice.
- As chamber B is airtight, this leads to a reduction in pressure within it.
- The pressure in chamber A (control) is now greater than that in chamber B (experimental) and so air moves towards chamber B, pushing the liquid in the manometer towards chamber B as it does so.
- The distance moved by the liquid in a given time is measured.
- At the end of this period, the screw clip A is opened and the syringe attached to chamber A is drawn upwards to reduce the pressure in it until it is again equal to that in chamber B, i.e. the liquid in the manometer is at an equal height in both tubes.
- The complete process is repeated 2 or 3 times and the measurements taken are averaged.
- Both screw clips are re-opened to allow oxygen to diffuse into the chambers and to allow the air to expand/contract when the temperature of the water bath is raised/lowered to a new value.

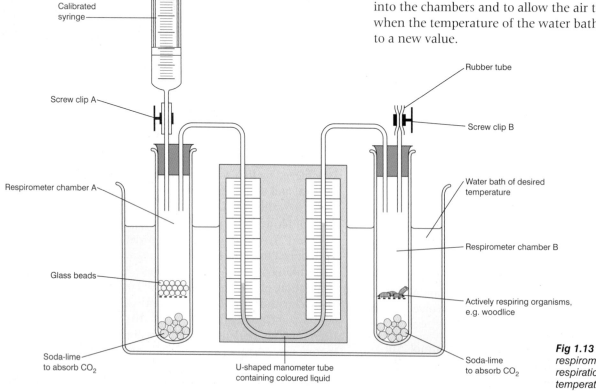

Calibrated syringe

Screw clip A

Respirometer chamber A

Glass beads

Soda-lime to absorb CO_2

U-shaped manometer tube containing coloured liquid

Rubber tube

Screw clip B

Water bath of desired temperature

Respirometer chamber B

Actively respiring organisms, e.g. woodlice

Soda-lime to absorb CO_2

Fig 1.13 *A simple respirometer used to measure respiration rate at different temperatures*

- The experiment is repeated at the new temperature.

The actual volume of oxygen taken in by the woodlice can be found in two ways:

- We can calculate the volume using the equation:

$$\text{volume} = \pi r^2 h$$

  (where h is the distance moved by the liquid in the manometer and r is the internal radius of the manometer tube).
- We can simply measure on the calibrated syringe the volume of air needed to equalise the levels in the manometer tubes.

1.7.2 Respiratory quotients

The **respiratory quotient (RQ)** is a measure of the ratio of carbon dioxide given out by an organism to the oxygen consumed over a given period:

$$RQ = \frac{\text{volume of } CO_2 \text{ given out}}{\text{volume of } O_2 \text{ taken in}}$$

Although the term respiratory quotient is used, the ratio should more accurately be called the **respiratory exchange ratio (RER)**. This is because some of the gases being expired may come from non-respiratory sources. The RQ should not include these gases. In most cases the RQ and the RER are the same.

Different RQs give an indication of the type of substrate being respired. For example, a typical sugar such as glucose is oxidised according to the following equation:

$$C_6H_{12}O_6 + 6O_2 \rightarrow 6CO_2 + 6H_2O$$

The RQ is therefore: $\dfrac{6CO_2}{6O_2} = 1.0$

Lipids however, have less oxygen relative to carbon and hydrogen. A greater volume of oxygen is therefore required to oxidise a lipid completely and their RQs are therefore lower than those of carbohydrates:

$$C_{18}H_{36}O_2 + 26O_2 \rightarrow 18CO_2 + 18H_2O$$

The RQ is therefore: $\dfrac{18CO_2}{26O_2} = 0.7$

Proteins have a very varied structure depending on the number and types of each amino acid in the protein molecule. Their RQs are therefore equally varied but most have values around 0.9.

The usefulness of RQs in determining the substrate being respired is limited because:

- substances are rarely completely oxidised and partial oxidation gives a different value
- organisms rarely, if ever, respire a single food substance and the RQ therefore reflects the proportions of the different substrates being respired.

Most resting animals have an RQ of between 0.8 and 0.9. Although these values would suggest that protein was being respired, we know that protein is used only in extreme situations such as starvation. We must assume, therefore, that these values are due to a mixture of carbohydrate (1.0) and lipid (0.7) being respired.

In anaerobic respiration, carbon dioxide is produced but no oxygen is taken in. If only anaerobic respiration takes place, then the RQ will be infinity. Where there is a mixture of aerobic and anaerobic respiration, RQ values are greater than 1.0. Some of these various values and their explanations are shown in table 1.1, which shows the RQ of germinating seeds.

Most resting animals like this leopard and spotted bush snake have an RQ between 0.8 and 0.9 as a result of respiring a mixture of fat and carbohydrate

Table 1.1 *Showing the RQ values of germinating seeds*

Time	RQ	Possible explanations
Seeds soaked in water	7.2	With little dissolved oxygen in water, respiration is a mixture of aerobic ($\leqslant 1.0$) and anaerobic (infinity)
After 14 hours in soil	1.5	As oxygen becomes available, the amount of aerobic respiration ($\leqslant 1.0$) increases, whereas anaerobic respiration (infinity) decreases
After 48 hours in soil	0.7	A mixture of lipids (0.7) and carbohydrate (1.0) from the stores in the seed is being respired. The conversion of stored lipid to carbohydrate (0.35) is also taking place
After 14 days	1.0	The leaves have emerged and photosynthesis is producing carbohydrate (1.0), which is being respired

Photosynthesis

An overview of photosynthesis

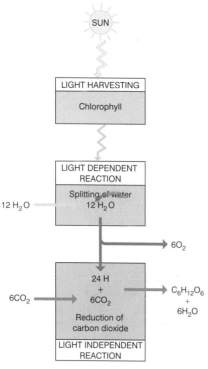

Fig 2.1 Overview of photosynthesis

Green plants use sunlight to produce complex organic molecules from simple ones which then provide food for heterotrophs such as this bird and insect

Humans, along with almost every other living organism, owe their very existence to photosynthesis. The energy we use, whether from the food we respire or from the wood, coal, oil or gas that we burn in our homes, has been captured by photosynthesis from sunlight. Photosynthesis likewise produces the oxygen we breathe by releasing it from water molecules.

2.1.1 Autotrophic nutrition

The nutrition of organisms can be divided into two broad categories:

- **Autotrophic nutrition** involves the build-up of simple inorganic molecules such as carbon dioxide and water into complex organic ones like lipids, carbohydrates and proteins. Plants, algae and some bacteria are autotrophs.
- **Heterotrophic nutrition** involves the breakdown of complex organic molecules into simple soluble ones. Animals, fungi and some bacteria are heterotrophs.

The word autotroph means '*self-feeding*' and refers to those organisms like plants that have no obvious means of obtaining or digesting food – no mouth, teeth, alimentary canal etc. Instead of obtaining their food by consuming complex organic molecules, they manufacture their own from simple inorganic substances using energy from two possible sources:

- **Photoautotrophs** use light as their source of energy to drive the process of photosynthesis. Examples of photoautotrophs include green plants, algae and photosynthetic bacteria (e.g. cyanobacteria).
- **Chemoautotrophs** use energy from certain chemical reactions. The process is far less common than photosynthesis, but takes place in certain bacteria such as the **nitrifying** and **denitrifying** bacteria that are important in the nitrogen cycle (*Essential AS Biology for OCR*, unit 7.4).

2.1.2 An outline of photosynthesis

The overall equation for photosynthesis is:

$$\underset{\text{carbon dioxide}}{6CO_2} + \underset{\text{water}}{6H_2O} + \underset{\text{light}}{\text{energy}} \longrightarrow \underset{\text{glucose}}{C_6H_{12}O_6} + \underset{\text{oxygen}}{6O_2}$$

Experiments using radioactive **isotopes** show that all the oxygen produced ($6O_2$) comes from water molecules and not the carbon dioxide molecules. However, the $6H_2O$ in the equation only provides six oxygen atoms, rather than the 12 produced. What happens in practice is that 12 water molecules are used to produce the oxygen, and the hydrogens from the water are used to reduce the carbon dioxide and produce the six water molecules. The equation for photosynthesis is therefore more accurately represented by the equation:

$$6CO_2 + 12H_2O + \text{energy} \rightarrow C_6H_{12}O_6 + 6O_2 + 6H_2O$$

Photosynthesis is a process of energy **transduction** in which light energy is firstly changed into electrical energy and then into chemical energy. There are three main stages to photosynthesis (Fig 2.1):

- **Capturing of light energy (light harvesting)** by chloroplast pigments such as chlorophyll and carotenoids.

- **The light dependent reaction**, in which light energy is converted into chemical energy. During the process an electron flow is created by the effect of light on chlorophyll and this causes water to split (**photolysis**) into hydrogen ions and oxygen. The products are reduced NADP and ATP from chemiosmosis (section 1.2.2).
- **The light independent reaction**, in which these hydrogen ions are used to reduce carbon dioxide to produce sugars and other organic molecules.

2.1.3 Measuring photosynthesis

The rate of photosynthesis is usually found by measuring the volume of oxygen produced by an aquatic plant such as Canadian pondweed (*Elodea*). This does not give an altogether accurate measure because:

- dissolved oxygen, nitrogen and other gases are often released from the leaf and surrounding water and become included in the gas volume measured
- some oxygen produced in photosynthesis will be used up in respiration.

The following account outlines how the rate of photosynthesis at different light intensities can be measured.

- The apparatus, known as an **Audus microburette** or **photosynthometer** is set up as in figure 2.2, taking care not to introduce any air bubbles into it and that the apparatus is completely air-tight.
- The water bath is used to maintain a constant temperature throughout the experiment and should be adjusted as necessary. Better still, a thermostatically controlled bath should be used.
- Potassium or sodium hydrogencarbonate solution can be used around the plant to provide a source of carbon dioxide – especially important if the experiment is to extend over a long period.
- A source of light, such as a lamp that can have its voltage adjusted to change its intensity, is arranged close to the apparatus, which is kept in a dark room to prevent other light (which may vary in intensity) falling on the plant.
- The apparatus is kept in the dark for 2 hours to prevent photosynthesis and allow oxygen produced by the plant to disperse.
- The light source is switched on and a stop clock started.
- Oxygen produced by the plant during photosynthesis collects in the funnel end of the capillary tube above the plant.
- After 30 minutes this oxygen is drawn up the capillary tube by gently withdrawing the syringe until its volume can be measured on the scale. This can be done directly (if the scale is calibrated in mm³) or, if the scale is not calibrated, calculated using the formula r^2h (where r is the internal radius of the tube and h is the length of the column of oxygen collected).

- The gas is drawn up into the syringe, which is then depressed again before the process is repeated at the same light intensity four or five times and the average volume of oxygen produced per hour is calculated.
- The apparatus is left in the dark for 2 hours before the procedure is repeated with the light source set at a different light intensity. The actual light intensity can be measured by a light meter placed in the same position relative to the light source as the plant was during the experiment.
- An alternative method of varying the light intensity is to change the distance of the light source relative to the plant. The light intensity is inversely proportional to the square of the distance from the plant to the light source, i.e. doubling the distance apart reduces the light intensity by a quarter.

The experiment can be modified to measure the effect of other factors on the rate of photosynthesis as follows:

- **Wavelength of light** – the experiment is repeated using different light sources that emit specific wavelengths or using filters of different colours between the light source and the photosynthometer.
- **Temperature** – the temperature of the water bath can be varied and the rates of photosynthesis compared.
- **Carbon dioxide concentration** – different concentrations of potassium or sodium hydrogencarbonate can be used to compare the rate of photosynthesis at different carbon dioxide concentrations.

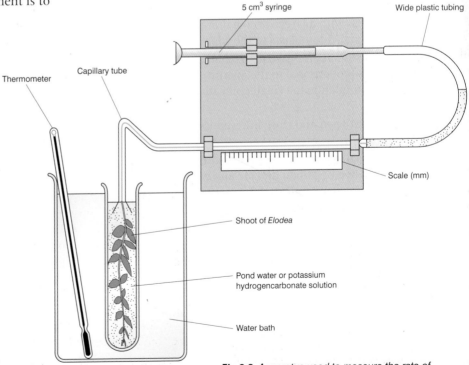

Fig 2.2 Apparatus used to measure the rate of photosynthesis under various conditions

2.2 Leaf and chloroplast structure

The leaf is the main photosynthetic structure of the plant, although stems, sepals and other parts may also photosynthesise. The cellular organelles within the leaf where photosynthesis takes place are the chloroplasts.

2.2.1 Structure of the leaf

Photosynthesis takes place largely in the leaf, the structure of which is shown in figure 2.3. Leaves are adapted to bring together the three raw materials of photosynthesis (water, carbon dioxide and light) and remove its products (oxygen and glucose). These adaptations include:

- a large surface area that collects as much sunlight as possible
- a mosaic arrangement on the plant that minimises overlapping and so avoids the shadowing of one leaf by another
- a thin lamina (leaf blade), as most light is absorbed in the first few millimetres of the leaf and the diffusion distance is thus kept short
- a transparent cuticle and epidermis that let light through to the photosynthetic palisade cells beneath
- long thin palisade cells that form a continuous layer collecting sunlight
- palisade cells packed with chloroplasts that can move within the cells and so arrange themselves in the best positions to collect the maximum amount of light (Fig 2.3c)
- palisade cells with a large vacuole that pushes the cytoplasm and chloroplasts to the edge of the cell
- numerous stomata for gaseous exchange – the rate of diffusion is proportional to the aperture periphery and so is greater through many small pores than through a few large ones
- stomata that open and close in response to changes in light intensity
- many air spaces, especially in the spongy mesophyll, to allow diffusion of carbon dioxide and water
- a network of vascular tissue made up of xylem that brings water to the leaf cells and phloem that carries away the sugars produced in photosynthesis.

2.2.2 Structure and role of chloroplasts in photosynthesis

Photosynthesis takes place within cell organelles called **chloroplasts**, the structure of which is shown in figure 2.3d. These vary in shape and size but are typically disc-shaped, 2–10 μm long and 1 μm in diameter. They are surrounded by a double membrane called the **chloroplast envelope**. The inner membrane is folded into a series of lamellae and is highly selective in what it allows to enter and leave the chloroplast. Inside the chloroplast envelope are two distinct regions:

- **The stroma** is a fluid-filled matrix where the light independent stage of photosynthesis takes place. Within the stroma are a number of other structures such as starch grains and oil droplets.
- **The grana** are stacks of up to 100 disc-like structures called **thylakoids**. Within the thylakoids are the chloroplast pigments (sections 2.3.1 and 2.3.2), which are arranged in a structured way and form a complex called photosystem II. Some thylakoids have tubular extensions that join up with thylakoids in adjacent grana. These are called **inter-granal lamellae** and are the sites of photosystem I. Chloroplasts also contain a small quantity of DNA and ribosomes that manufacture some chloroplast proteins.

Chloroplasts are adapted to their function of harvesting sunlight and carrying out the light dependent and light independent reactions of photosynthesis in the following ways:

- The granal membranes provide a large surface area for the attachment of the photosynthetic pigments (chlorophyll and carotenoids), electron carriers and enzymes that carry out the light dependent reaction.
- A network of proteins in the grana hold the photosynthetic pigments in a very precise manner that forms special units called **photosystems** (section 2.3.4), allowing maximum absorption of light.
- The granal membranes have many ATP synthase enzymes attached to them, which help manufacture ATP by **chemiosmosis**.
- The fluid of the stroma houses all the enzymes needed to carry out the light independent reaction (reduction of carbon dioxide).
- The stroma fluid surrounds the grana and so the products of the light dependent reaction in the grana can readily pass into the stroma.
- Chloroplasts contain both DNA and ribosomes so they can quickly and easily manufacture some of the proteins needed for photosynthesis.

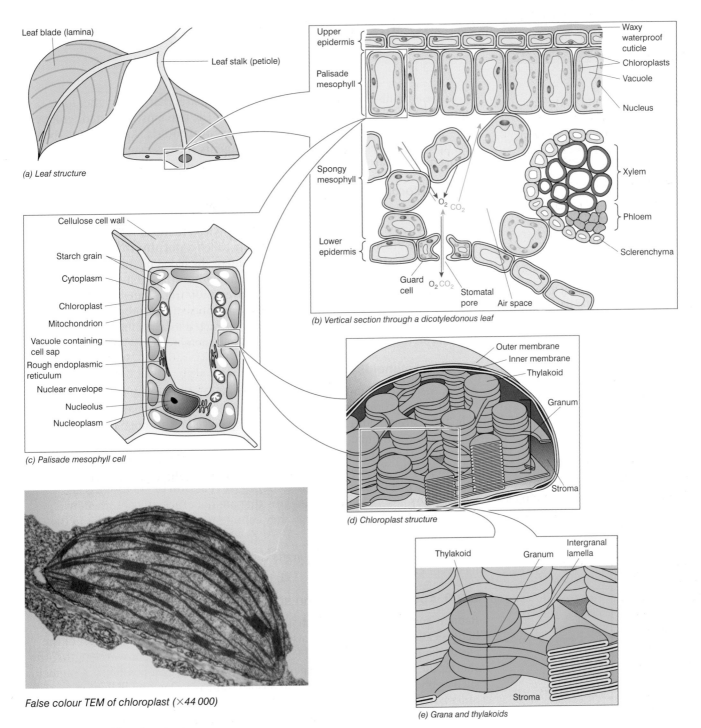

(a) Leaf structure

(b) Vertical section through a dicotyledonous leaf

(c) Palisade mesophyll cell

(d) Chloroplast structure

False colour TEM of chloroplast (×44 000)

(e) Grana and thylakoids

Fig 2.3 *Leaf and chloroplast structure*

SUMMARY TEST 2.2

Leaves are the main site of photosynthesis, which occurs mainly in their **(1)** cells. They have numerous **(2)** that allow exchange of gases between themselves and the air around them and a network of veins made up of the tissue called **(3)** that brings water into the leaf and the tissue called **(4)** that carries away **(5)** produced in photosynthesis. Chloroplasts are the organelles that carry out photosynthesis. They are surrounded by a double membrane or **(6)** and possess both **(7)** and **(8)** that enable them to make their own proteins. Inside, there is a fluid-filled matrix called the **(9)** that carries out the **(10)** reaction and also contains other structures like **(11)** grains and oil droplets. Within this matrix are disc-like structures called **(12)** that are stacked in groups of up to 100 to form structures called **(13)** where the **(14)** reaction of photosynthesis takes place.

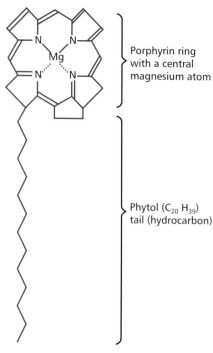

Fig 2.4 *General structure of the chlorophyll molecule*

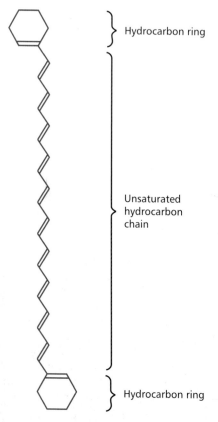

Fig 2.5 *General structure of a carotenoid molecule*

There are a number of pigments found in chloroplasts that act together to capture the light necessary for photosynthesis. The two most important groups of these pigments are the **chlorophylls** and the **carotenoids**. Apart from carbon, hydrogen and oxygen, they also contain elements such as magnesium and nitrogen, which are obtained from minerals taken up from the soil by the roots.

2.3.1 Chlorophyll

Chlorophyll is not a single substance, but rather a group of similar green pigments of which chlorophyll *a* and chlorophyll *b* are the most common. Chlorophylls are made up of a complex ring called a **porphyrin** ring, which has the same basic structure as the 'haem' group of the blood pigment **haemoglobin**. To this ring is attached a long hydrocarbon chain (Fig 2.4). This chain is lipid soluble and hydrophobic (moves away from water) and therefore embeds itself in the lipid-rich thylakoid membranes of a chloroplast. The porphyrin ring, by contrast, is hydrophilic (attracted to water) and therefore remains on the watery surface of the thylakoid membrane.

2.3.2 Carotenoids

Again, there are a number of different types of carotenoids, all of which have a basic structure comprising two small rings linked by a long hydrocarbon chain (Fig 2.5). Carotenoids range in colour from pale yellow, through orange to red. The greater the number of double bonds in the hydrocarbon chain, the deeper the colour. There are two main types of carotenoids, the **carotenes** and the **xanthophylls**. Carotenoids are known as **accessory pigments** because they are not directly involved in the **light dependent reaction** of photosynthesis. Instead they absorb light wavelengths that are not efficiently absorbed by chlorophyll *a* and pass the energy they capture to chlorophyll *a* for use in the light dependent reaction.

The various photosynthetic pigments can be separated from one another by means of **chromatography**.

2.3.3 Absorption and action spectra

Radiant energy comes in discrete packages called quanta. A single quantum of light is called a **photon**. Light also has a wave nature and so forms part of the electromagnetic spectrum. Visible light is made up of different wavelengths. The shorter the wavelength the greater the quantity of energy it possesses. A pigment, such as one of the chlorophylls, will absorb some wavelengths of light more than others. If the amount of light it absorbs at each wavelength is plotted on a graph, we obtain what is called the **absorption spectrum**.

We can also plot the effectiveness of different wavelengths of light in bringing about photosynthesis. This is called the **action spectrum** and shows that blue and red light are most effective in bringing about photosynthesis.

These two spectra are shown in figure 2.6 and can be seen to follow a similar pattern, suggesting that the pigments shown are responsible for absorbing the light used in photosynthesis.

2.3.4 Light harvesting

In 1932, plant physiologists Emerson and Arnold discovered that it took hundreds of chlorophyll molecules to produce a single molecule of oxygen. This led them to conclude that light for photosynthesis, rather than being absorbed by independent pigment molecules, is captured by groups of chlorophyll molecules

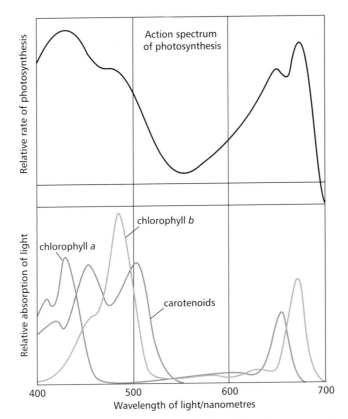

Fig 2.6 Action spectrum for photosynthesis and absorption spectrum of common plant pigments

along with their accessory pigments. These groups are now known as **photosystems** and they operate as follows:

• Each photosystem is a collection of chlorophyll *a* molecules, accessory pigments and associated proteins all fixed within a protein matrix on the surface of the photosynthetic membrane.

• One particular chlorophyll molecule, known as a **primary pigment**, acts as a **reaction centre** for each photosystem.

• The remaining pigment molecules (**accessory pigments**) of the photosystem absorb light energy (**photons**). These molecules are called the **antenna complex**. They are held tightly together by proteins that act as a framework holding the pigment molecules in the best positions to allow energy to be transferred between them.

• The photon absorbed by an accessory pigment creates an excitation energy that is passed along a chain of pigment molecules to the reaction centre. It is the energy and not the electrons that are transferred in this way – rather like the energy is transferred in Newton's cradle or when a cue ball hits one end of a row of touching snooker balls and all remain in place except the one at the other end, which shoots away from the chain.

• Energy from many pigment molecules in the antenna complex is funnelled in this way to the reaction centre at the heart of the photosystem.

• This energy from one photon is sufficient to excite a pair of electrons in the primary chlorophyll molecule that is the reaction centre. These electrons move up to a higher energy level within the chlorophyll molecule and play an important part in the light dependent reaction (unit 2.4).

Figure 2.7 illustrates the role of photosystems in light harvesting.

There are two different photosystems involved in photosynthesis:

• **Photosystem I (PSI)** has a chlorophyll molecule that has a light absorption peak of 700 nm as its reaction centre and is therefore known as P700. Photosystem I occurs mostly on inter-granal lamellae of the chloroplast (section 2.2.2).

• **Photosystem II (PSII)** has a chlorophyll molecule that has a light absorption peak of 680 nm as its reaction centre and is therefore known as P680. Photosystem II occurs mostly on the granal lamellae of the chloroplast (section 2.2.2).

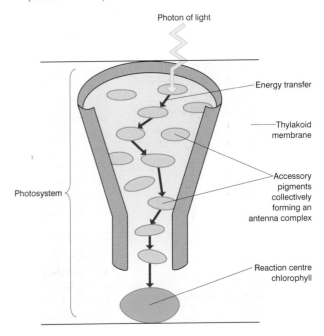

Fig 2.7 Light harvesting system

SUMMARY TEST 2.3

The two most important pigments involved in photosynthesis are chlorophylls and **(1)**. The chlorophyll molecule consists of a complex ring called a **(2)** ring that is attracted to water and therefore is described as **(3)**. It also has a long lipid-soluble chain that is repelled by water and is therefore described as **(4)**. Chlorophyll, as with other pigments, takes in certain wavelengths more than others. A graph of the amount of light of different wavelengths taken in by a pigment is called the **(5)**. Chlorophyll *a* molecules act as **(6)** centres at the heart of a complex of pigment molecules and associated **(7)** known collectively as a photosystem. Around the central chlorophyll molecule in each photosystem are **(8)** pigments that form a unit called an **(9)**. There are two different photosystems. Photosystem I has a chlorophyll molecule that absorbs light of wavelength **(10)** and is found mostly on the **(11)** of the chloroplast. Photosystem II has a chlorophyll molecule that absorbs light of wavelength **(12)** and is found mainly on the **(13)** of the chloroplast.

Photosynthesis – the light dependent reaction

The enhancement effect

The two photosystems in plants use light of different wavelengths. Photosystem I uses light with a peak absorption of 700 nm, whereas photosystem II uses light with a peak absorption of 680 nm. When these two wavelengths of light are provided together, the rate of photosynthesis is greater than the sum of the rates when each wavelength is provided separately (Fig 2.8). This is known as the **enhancement effect** and shows that the two systems act together rather than independently.

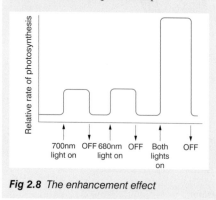

Fig 2.8 *The enhancement effect*

The light dependent reaction of photosynthesis takes place in the thylakoids of the chloroplasts. It involves the capture of light whose energy is used for two purposes:

- To add an inorganic phosphate molecule to ADP, thereby making **ATP**. As this process of phosphorylation is brought about by light it is known as **photophosphorylation**.
- To split water into H^+ ions (protons) and OH^- ions. As the splitting is caused by light, it is known as **photolysis**.

2.4.1 Photophosphorylation

When light is passed to a reaction centre chlorophyll molecule (section 2.3.4), a pair of electrons within this chlorophyll molecule is raised to a higher energy level. These electrons are said to be in an **excited state** and are taken up by a molecule called an **electron carrier** or **electron acceptor**. Having lost a pair of electrons, the chlorophyll molecule has been oxidised while the carrier, which has gained electrons, has been reduced. The electrons are now passed along a number of electron carriers in a series of redox reactions (unit 1.5). Each new carrier is at a slightly lower energy level than the previous one, and so the electrons lose energy at each stage. This energy is used to combine an inorganic phosphate molecule to an ADP molecule in order to make ATP – the process being called **photophosphorylation**. It is essentially the same process as oxidative phosphorylation (section 1.5.2) except that light, rather than oxygen, is the driving force.

The precise mechanism is the chemiosmotic process, whereby **protons** (H^+) from the photolysis of water flow through channels in the stalked particles of the thylakoid membrane, thereby providing the energy to combine inorganic phosphate with ADP to form ATP. The chemiosmotic process is described in full in section 1.2.2 and the events are illustrated in figure 2.9. The question now is, what happens to the electrons? There are two alternative processes they can enter:

- cyclic photophosphorylation
- non-cyclic photophosphorylation.

These are compared in table 2.1.

2.4.2 Cyclic photophosphorylation

Cyclic photophosphorylation uses only photosystem I (section 2.3.4). When light raises an electron in a reaction centre chlorophyll molecule to an excited state, the electron is taken up by an electron acceptor and simply passed back to the same chlorophyll molecule via a sequence of electron carriers, i.e. it is recycled. While this does not produce any reduced NADP, it does generate sufficient energy to combine inorganic phosphate with ADP. The ATP so produced is then utilised in the light independent reaction (unit 2.5) or is used directly, as in guard cells where it is used to pump potassium ions into the guard cells, thereby reducing water potential and leading to water entering them by osmosis and increasing their turgidity, with the result that the stoma opens (unit 6.19).

2.4.3 Non-cyclic photophosphorylation

Non-cyclic photophosphorylation uses both photosystem I and photosystem II (section 2.3.4). Electrons raised to an excited state in both systems are taken up by an electron acceptor and passed along a sequence of electron carriers. These electrons are finally taken up by NADP (nicotinamide adenine dinucleotide phosphate) and passed into the light independent stage of photosynthesis (unit 2.5). This, however, leaves both photosystems short of electrons and therefore positively charged. Before the photosystems can operate again these electrons

Table 2.1 *Comparison of cyclic and non-cyclic photophosphorylation*

	Cyclic	Non-cyclic
Electrons returned to chlorophyll molecule directly	Yes	No
Photosystems involved	I	I and II
Photolysis of water involved	No	Yes
Products	ATP	Reduced NADP + oxygen

must be replaced. The replacement electrons are provided from water molecules that are split using light energy. This photolysis of water also yields hydrogen ions (protons) that enter the light independent reaction along with the electrons from both photosystems.

2.4.4 Photolysis

Photolysis is the splitting of water as a direct consequence of light causing chlorophyll molecules to lose electrons. It occurs only in photosystem II as it alone possesses the necessary enzymes. Having lost an electron, the chlorophyll molecule needs to replace it and, in the case of non-cyclic photophosphorylation, it does this using electrons from water molecules that are split by an enzyme into protons, electrons and oxygen according to the following equation:

$$2H_2O \rightarrow 4H^+ + 4e^- + O_2$$

water   protons   electrons   oxygen

- The electrons replace those lost by the chlorophyll molecule. The protons reduce NADP to NADPH + H⁺, which then enters the light independent reaction where it reduces carbon dioxide.
- The oxygen by-product is either used in respiration or diffuses out of the leaf as a waste product of photosynthesis.

2.4.5 The Z-scheme

The two processes of the light dependent reaction, photophosphorylation and photolysis, are inextricably linked. These events are summarised in figure 2.10, which illustrates the zig-zag energy levels of the electrons. As the diagram resembles a Z on its side, the complete process is called the Z-scheme.

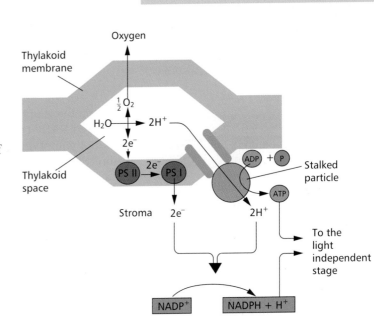

Fig 2.9 ATP production during the light dependent stage of photosynthesis

1. Light energy is trapped in photosystem II and boosts electrons to a higher energy level.
2. The electrons are received by an electron acceptor.
3. The electrons are passed from the electron acceptor along a series of electron carriers to photosystem I. The energy lost by the electrons is captured by converting ADP to ATP. Light energy has thereby been converted to chemical energy.
4. Light energy absorbed by photosystem I boosts the electrons to an even higher energy level.
5. The electrons are received by another electron acceptor.
6. The electrons which have been removed from the chlorophyll are replaced by pulling in other electrons from a water molecule.
7. The loss of electrons from the water molecule causes it to dissociate into protons and oxygen gas.
8. The protons from the water molecule combine with the electrons from the second electron acceptor and these reduce nicotinamide **adenine dinucleotide phosphate. (NADP)**
9. Some electrons from the second acceptor may pass back to the chlorophyll molecule by the electron carrier system, yielding ATP as they do so. This process is called **cyclic photophosphorylation.**

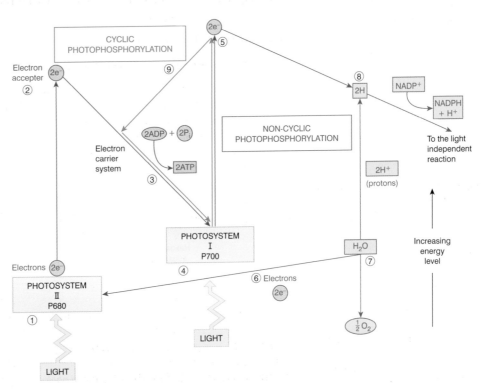

Fig 2.10 Summary of light dependent stage of photosynthesis

2.5

Photosynthesis – the light independent reaction

EXTENSION

Rubisco – the most common protein on Earth?

The enzyme that combines carbon dioxide with ribulose bisphosphate (RuBP) is called ribulose bisphosphate carboxylase (rubisco). By normal enzyme standards rubisco is a slow operator, combining only about three molecules of CO_2 with RuBP each second, compared with 1000 substrate molecules per second for a typical enzyme. To compensate for its sluggishness and to ensure a good conversion rate of CO_2 into sugar, the enzyme is present in phenomenal quantities. Typically, over half the protein of a leaf is rubisco. Given the considerable **biomass** of the world that is leaves, it is not surprising that rubisco is thought to be the most abundant protein on the planet.

The products of the light dependent reaction of photosynthesis, namely ATP and reduced NADP (NADPH + H$^+$) are used to reduce carbon dioxide in the second part of photosynthesis. Unlike the first stage, this stage does not require light directly and, in theory at least, occurs whether or not it is available. It is therefore called the **light independent reaction** (Fig 2.11). In practice, it requires the products of the light dependent stage and so rapidly ceases when light is absent. The light independent reaction takes place in the **stroma** of the chloroplasts. The details of this stage were worked out by Melvin Calvin and his co-workers using his 'lollipop experiment' (Fig 2.12). The process is therefore often known as the **Calvin cycle**.

2.5.1 The Calvin cycle

In the following account of the Calvin cycle, the numbered stages are illustrated in figure 2.11.

1. Carbon dioxide from the atmosphere diffuses into the leaf through **stomata** and dissolves in water around the walls of the **palisade** cells. It then diffuses through the cell membrane, cytoplasm and chloroplast envelope into the stroma of the chloroplast.

2. In the stroma, the carbon dioxide combines with the 5-carbon compound **ribulose bisphosphate (RuBP)** using the enzyme **ribulose bisphosphate carboxylase (rubisco)**, to form an unstable 6-carbon compound.

3. The unstable 6-carbon compound immediately breaks down into two molecules of the 3-carbon **glycerate 3-phosphate (GP)**.

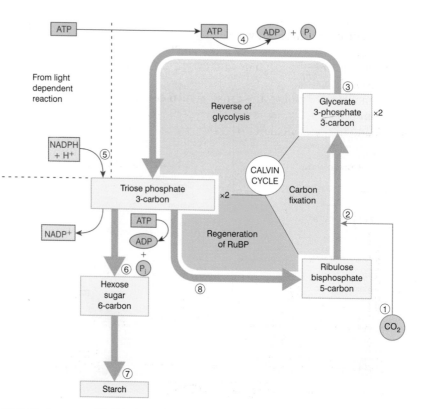

Fig 2.11 *Summary of light independent stage of photosynthesis*

4. Using one of the ATP molecules from the light dependent reaction, the glycerate 3-phosphate is converted into a **triose phosphate (TP)**.

5. Reduced NADP from the light dependent reaction provides hydrogen ions to complete the conversion of glycerate 3-phosphate to triose phosphate.

6. Triose phosphate molecules combine in pairs to form 6-carbon (hexose) sugars.

7. The 6-carbon sugars can be **polymerised** into starch.

8. Five out of every six triose phosphate molecules produced are used to regenerate ribulose bisphosphate using the remainder of the ATP from the light dependent reaction as the source of energy.

A summary of both stages of photosynthesis is given in figure 2.13.

2.5.2 Formation of other substances for use by the plant

Plants, like other organisms, are made up of a range of complex organic molecules. The bulk of these are carbohydrates, lipids and proteins. Unlike animals and other **heterotrophic** organisms, plants cannot obtain these substances by taking them in from the outside. They must synthesise them from the various compounds of the Calvin cycle.

• Carbohydrates such as sucrose (the carbohydrate which is transported in the phloem) are made by combining the two hexose sugars, glucose and fructose.
• Starch (the storage carbohydrate) and cellulose (the essential component of cell walls) are made by polymerising glucose in different ways.
• Lipids are made up of glycerol and fatty acids. Plants make glycerol from triose phosphate and fatty acids from glycerate 3-phosphate (GP).
• Proteins are made up of amino acids that in turn can be produced from glycerate 3-phosphate (GP) via acetyl coenzyme A and the intermediates of **Krebs cycle**.

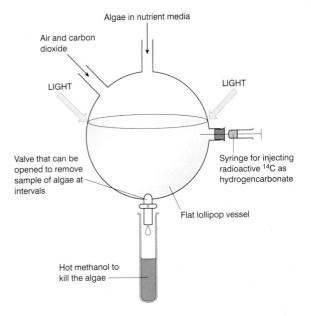

• Algae are grown under light in the thin transparent lollipop

• Radioactive ^{14}C in the form of hydrogencarbonate is injected

• At intervals (seconds to minutes) samples of the photosynthesising algae are dropped into the hot methanol to stop chemical reactions instantly

• The compounds in the algae are separated by two-way chromatography

Fig 2.12 *The 'lollipop' experiment of Melvin Calvin*

SUMMARY TEST 2.5

The light independent reaction is also known as the (**1**) cycle after the person who determined its biochemical sequence. In the process, carbon dioxide combines with a 5-carbon compound called (**2**) to form a 6-carbon intermediate that immediately splits into two molecules of (**3**). By the addition of (**4**) and (**5**) formed in the (**6**) reaction, each of the molecules is then converted into a (**7**) molecule. These combine in pairs to form a (**8**) sugar that is then made into starch by a process called (**9**).

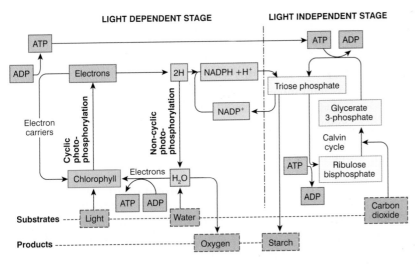

Fig 2.13 *Summary of photosynthesis*

2.6 Environmental factors affecting photosynthesis

Photosynthesis is the process that captures light energy and thereby makes life on Earth possible. It follows that an understanding of those factors which influence the rate of photosynthesis can help ensure that an adequate supply of energy (food) is available, not only to ourselves, but also to those other organisms with which we share this planet. Before we consider some of these factors, it is necessary to understand the **concept of limiting factors**.

2.6.1 Limiting factors

In any complex process such as photosynthesis, the factors that affect its rate all operate simultaneously. However, the rate of the process at any given moment is **not** affected by a combination of all the factors, but rather by just one – the one whose level is at the least favourable value. This factor is called the **limiting factor** because it alone limits the rate at which the process can take place. However much the levels of the other factors change, they do not alter the rate of the process.

To take the example of light intensity limiting the rate of photosynthesis:

- In complete darkness, it is the absence of light alone that prevents photosynthesis occurring.
- No matter how much we raise or lower the temperature or change the concentration of carbon dioxide, there will be no photosynthesis. Light, or rather the absence of it, is the factor determining the rate of photosynthesis at that moment.
- If we provide light, however, the rate of photosynthesis will increase.
- As we add more light, the more the rate increases. This does not continue indefinitely, however, because there comes a point at which further increases in light intensity have no effect on the rate of photosynthesis.
- At this point some other factor, such as the concentration of carbon dioxide, is in short supply and so limits the process.
- Carbon dioxide is now the limiting factor and only an increase in its level will increase the rate of photosynthesis.
- In the same way as happened with light, providing more carbon dioxide will lead to more photosynthesis.
- Further increases in carbon dioxide levels will ultimately fail to have any effect.
- At this point a different factor, such as temperature, is the limiting factor and only an alteration in its level will affect the rate of photosynthesis.

These events are illustrated in figure 2.14.

The law of limiting factors can therefore be expressed as: **At any given moment, the rate of a physiological process is limited by the one factor which is at its least favourable value, and by that factor alone.**

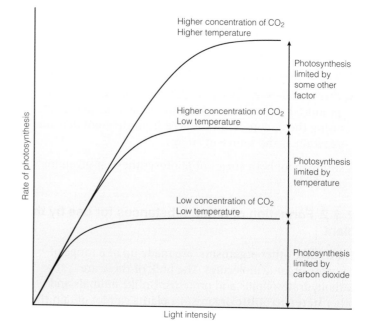

Fig 2.14 *Concept of limiting factors as illustrated by the effects of levels of different conditions on the rate of photosynthesis*

2.6.2 Effect of light intensity on the rate of photosynthesis

When light is the limiting factor, the rate of photosynthesis is directly proportional to light intensity. The rate of photosynthesis is usually measured in two ways:

- the volume of oxygen produced by a plant
- the volume of carbon dioxide taken up by a plant.

These measurements do not, however, provide an absolute measure of photosynthesis because:

- some of the oxygen produced in photosynthesis is used in cellular respiration and so never leaves the plant and therefore cannot be measured
- some carbon dioxide from cellular respiration is used up in photosynthesis and therefore the volume taken up from the atmosphere is less than that actually used in photosynthesis.

As light intensity is increased, the volume of oxygen produced and carbon dioxide absorbed due to photosynthesis will increase to a point at which it is exactly balanced by the oxygen absorbed and carbon dioxide produced by cellular respiration. At this point there will be no net exchange of gases into or out of the plant. This is known as the **light compensation point**. Further increases in light intensity will cause a proportional increase in the rate of photosynthesis and increasing volumes of oxygen will be given off and carbon dioxide taken up. A point will be reached at which further increases in light intensity will have no effect on photosynthesis. At this point some other factor such as carbon dioxide concentration or temperature is limiting the reaction. These events are illustrated in figure 2.15.

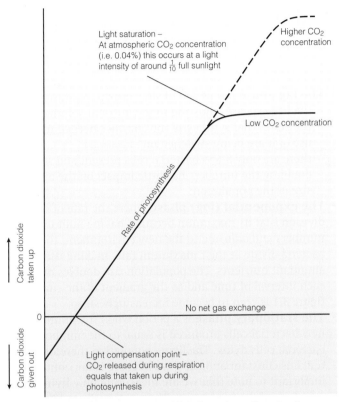

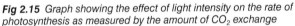

Fig 2.15 *Graph showing the effect of light intensity on the rate of photosynthesis as measured by the amount of CO₂ exchange*

2.6.3 Effect of light wavelength on the rate of photosynthesis

Not all wavelengths of light are equally effective in bringing about photosynthesis. As we saw in section 2.3.3, the action spectrum of photosynthesis shows peaks of activity in the blue region (420–480 nm) and the red region (640–670 nm) of the spectrum. Other wavelengths of light, especially in the green region of the spectrum, do not bring about photosynthesis and so are reflected by plants, giving them their characteristic green colour.

2.6.4 Effect of carbon dioxide concentration on the rate of photosynthesis

Carbon dioxide is present in the atmosphere at a concentration of around 0.04%. This level continues to increase as the result of human activities such as burning fossil fuels and the clearing of rain forests. It is still one of the rarest gases present and is often the factor that limits the rate of photosynthesis under normal conditions. The optimum concentration of carbon dioxide for a consistently high rate of photosynthesis is 0.1% and growers of some greenhouse crops like tomatoes enrich the air in the greenhouses with more carbon dioxide to provide higher yields. Figures 2.14 and 2.15 illustrate the effect of enhanced carbon dioxide levels on photosynthesis.

2.6.5 Effect of temperature on the rate of photosynthesis

Provided that other factors are not limiting, the rate of photosynthesis increases in direct proportion to the temperature. Between the temperatures of 0°C and 25°C the rate of photosynthesis is approximately doubled for each 10°C rise in temperature. Above the optimum temperature of 25°C the rate levels off and then declines – largely as a result of enzyme **denaturation**. Purely photochemical reactions are not usually affected by temperature, and so the fact that photosynthesis is temperature sensitive suggested to early researchers that there was also a totally chemical process involved as well as a photochemical one. We now know that this chemical process is the light independent reaction (unit 2.5).

The burning of rain forests contributes to an increase in atmospheric CO₂, both by releasing it directly and by removing trees that absorb it during photosynthesis

SUMMARY TEST 2.6

At any given moment the rate of a physiological process is restricted by the one factor that is at its least favourable value. This is known as the **(1)**. The rate of photosynthesis can be measured by calculating the volume of **(2)** taken up or the volume of **(3)** produced by a plant. The light intensity at which there is no net exchange of gases into or out of the plant is known as the **(4)**. The wavelengths of light that are most effective together in producing a high rate of photosynthesis occur in the **(5)** and **(6)** regions of the visible spectrum. Carbon dioxide concentration affects the rate of photosynthesis. Normally present in the atmosphere at a proportion of **(7)**%, the optimum for a consistently high rate of photosynthesis is nevertheless **(8)**%.

Populations and interactions

Populations and their growth

A **population** is a group of freely interbreeding individuals of the same species occupying the same place at the same time (*Essential AS Biology for OCR*, section 7.1.3). The number of individuals in a population is the **population size**, whereas the number of individuals per unit area is the **population density**. All the populations of the different organisms that live and interact together are known as a **community** (*Essential AS Biology for OCR*, section 7.1.2). Communities are found in a particular habitat and are based on dynamic feeding relationships.

3.1.1 Population growth

Imagine the situation in which a single algal cell capable of asexual reproduction is placed in a newly created pond. It is summer and so there is plenty of light and the temperature of the water is around 12°C; mineral nutrients have been added to the water. In these circumstances the algal cell divides rapidly because all the factors needed for the growth of the population are present. There are no limiting factors. In time, however, things change. For example:

- the minerals become used up as the population becomes large
- the population becomes so large that the algae at the surface prevent light reaching those at deeper levels
- other species are introduced into the pond, carried by animals or the wind – some of these may use algae as food or compete for light or minerals
- winter brings much lower temperatures and lower light intensity of shorter duration.

In short, the good life ends and the going gets tough. As a result the growth of the population slows, possibly ceases altogether and the population may even diminish in size. Ultimately the population is likely to reach a relatively constant size. There are many factors, living and non-living, that affect this ultimate size and changes in these factors will influence the population growth of the algae. It is, however, extremely difficult to measure accurately the influence of each of these factors on the growth of these algae in a natural, open environment like a pond. Instead we have to investigate them in an artificial environment. This can be done by growing bacteria in nutrient medium in a container kept under constant conditions in a laboratory. In these circumstances we find that the population growth curve produced is a **sigmoid population growth curve**; it is illustrated in figure 3.1. This type of growth has four main phases:

- **The lag phase** is a period of slow growth because:
  - the bacteria are adjusting to the nutrient solution and the genes that synthesise the enzymes needed to make use of it are being switched on
  - there are only a few bacterial cells present and so even doubling the numbers has little impact on the overall size of the population.
- **The exponential (log) phase** where the rate of cell division is at its maximum because, having built up numbers and adjusted to the new environment, the bacteria divide at their maximum rate, making use of the abundant nutrients. The population size doubles during each interval of time and so the gradient of the curve in figure 3.1 is seen to become increasingly steep.
- **The stationary phase** is a period when the number of new bacterial cells produced is equal to the number of bacterial cells dying. The living population therefore remains constant and the growth curve is horizontal. It is important to note that we are measuring only **living** members of the population. The total number of bacterial cells (living and dead) will of course continue to increase steadily throughout this phase.
- **The death (decline) phase** is the period when the living population size decreases because more bacteria die than are produced, usually as a result of a lack of nutrients or a build-up of toxic waste. The growth curve therefore falls steadily.

The usual pattern of growth for a natural population does not show the death (decline) phase, but rather reaches a

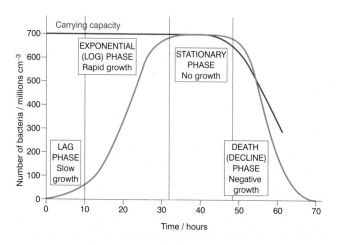

Fig 3.1 *Sigmoid growth of a bacterial population grown in a nutrient medium*

stable situation in which births and deaths are in balance. The graph therefore levels out around the carrying capacity (section 3.1.2), with just cyclic fluctuations due to variations in factors such as food supply. This curve, called the **logistic growth curve**, is shown in figure 3.2.

3.1.2 Limiting factors and carrying capacity

No population continues to grow indefinitely, because certain factors limit growth, e.g. availability of food, light, water, oxygen and shelter, the accumulation of toxic waste, disease and predators. These **limiting factors** are collectively called the **environmental resistance**. Each population therefore has a maximum size that can be sustained over a relatively long period and this is determined by the limiting factors (environmental resistance). This maximum population size is called the **carrying capacity**.

The various limiting factors that affect the size of a population are of two basic types:

- **Density-dependent factors** are factors with effects that depend on the size (density) of the population. The larger the population the greater the effect. For example, a large population will use up the available food more quickly than a small population. The growth of a large population will therefore be checked by the availability of food, whereas a small population can continue growing. Density-dependent factors are usually **biotic** ones such as food availability, predation and disease. These factors cause a population to reach a certain size, at which point it becomes relatively stable.
- **Density-independent factors** have similar effects regardless of the population size (density). For example, a sudden fall in temperature may kill most of a population whether it is large or small. Density-independent factors are usually **abiotic** ones such as climate changes or fire.

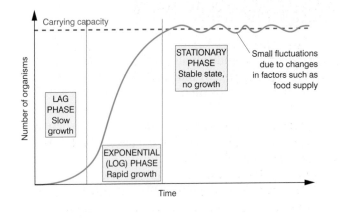

Fig 3.2 Logistic growth curve of most populations

Table 3.1 lists some limiting factors that influence the carrying capacity of populations.

3.1.3 Population size

Any environmental factor, whether density-dependent or density-independent, that affects the size of a population, does so by influencing one or more of four factors:

- **Birth rate (natality)** – the number of offspring produced divided by the total number of adults in the population over a given period, usually a year.
- **Death rate (mortality)** – the number of deaths over a given period, usually a year, divided by the number of adults in the population.
- **Immigration** – the number of individuals joining the population from neighbouring ones.
- **Emigration** – the number of individuals leaving the population to join neighbouring ones. Unlike migration, emigration is a non-reversible, one-way process.

Table 3.1 Limiting factors that influence the carrying capacity of populations

Factors that increase the carrying capacity	Factors that decrease the carrying capacity
Plentiful food / nutrient supply	Inadequate food/nutrient supply
Adequate supply of water	Inadequate supply of water
Favourable intensity and duration of light	Light of inappropriate intensity and duration
Fewer predators	Increased number of predators
Effective means of avoiding predation, e.g. camouflage, escape mechanisms	Ineffective means of avoiding predation
Effective means of resisting disease	Inability to resist disease
Favourable climatic conditions, e.g. suitable temperature, humidity, rainfall	Unfavourable climatic conditions, e.g. extremes of temperature, humidity, rainfall
Constant abiotic conditions, e.g. pH, water potential, climate	Fluctuating abiotic conditions
High reproductive rate	Low reproductive rate

3.2 Intra- and interspecific competition

Where two or more individuals share any resource (e.g. light, food, space, oxygen) that is insufficient to satisfy all their requirements fully, then competition results. Where such competition arises between members of the same species it is called **intraspecific competition**. Where it arises between members of different species it is termed **interspecific competition**.

3.2.1 Intraspecific competition

Intraspecific competition occurs when individuals of the **same** species compete with one another for resources such as food, water, breeding sites etc. It is the availability of such resources that determines the size of a population. Examples of intraspecific competition include:

- Limpets grazing on algae on rocks. Where the density of the population of limpets is greater, the size of each limpet becomes smaller, although the overall **biomass** remains about the same.
- Robins competing for breeding territory. Female birds are normally only attracted to males who have established territories. Each territory provides adequate food for the family of birds. When food is scarce, territories have to become larger to provide enough food. There are therefore fewer territories in a given area and fewer breeding pairs, leading to a smaller population size.
- Frogs in tropical rain forests compete for shelter from predators during the day. When the number of shelter sites is increased, fewer frogs are taken by predators and the population size increases.

3.2.2 Interspecific competition and the competitive exclusion principle

Interspecific competition occurs when individuals of different species compete for resources such as food, light, water etc. In a classic piece of research in 1934, the Russian biologist C.F. Gausse was able to show that when two species were in competition for the same **ecological niche** (*Essential AS Biology for OCR*, section 7.1.5) only one could survive. His series of experiments went as follows:

- Three species of *Paramecium* (*P. aurelia*, *P. caudatum* and *P. bursaria*) were grown alone in separate culture tubes containing bacteria and yeast as food.
- *P. aurelia* and *P. caudatum* were then repeatedly grown together in the same culture tube using the same bacteria and yeast food supply.
- In every case the population of *P. caudatum* declined to the point of extinction, leaving only *P. aurelia*.
- Gausse was able to show that *P. aurelia* survived because it was better adapted to using the limited food available and so grew six times faster than *P. caudatum*.

A graph illustrating these changes in population is shown in figure 3.3.

This research led Gausse to formulate the **competitive exclusion principle**, which states that where two species are competing for limited resources, the one that uses these resources most effectively will ultimately eliminate the other. In other words, **no two species can occupy the same niche indefinitely when resources are limiting**. The sea birds, shags and cormorants, appear to occupy the same niche, living and nesting on the same type of cliff face and eating fish from the sea. Analysis of their food, however, shows that shags feed largely on sand eels and herring, whereas cormorants eat mostly flat fish, gobies and shrimps. They therefore occupy different niches.

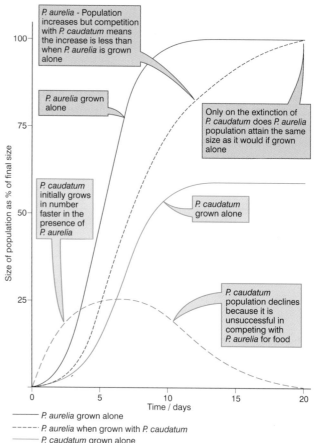

Fig 3.3 *Population growth of* P. aurelia *and* P. caudatum *grown separately and together*

3.2.3 The effects of interspecific competition on population size and distribution

We saw in the previous section that two species, cormorants and shags, appeared to occupy the same niche but in practice there were subtle differences in the way that they lived – in this case the food they ate differed. In these situations, however, the niches of the two species overlap and this has a major effect on the size and distribution of each population. This can be illustrated by further experiments carried out by Gausse on *Paramecium*:

- *P. caudatum* (the species that 'lost out' in the experiment described in section 3.2.2) was repeatedly grown together with a third species, *P. bursaria*, to find out which would best use the bacteria and yeast food supply and therefore oust the other.
- In all cases both species survived.
- Gausse found that this was because the distribution of the food varied.
- In the lower part of the tube, oxygen levels were lower and this favoured the growth of yeast, which was therefore the more abundant food than the bacteria.
- *P. bursaria* was better adapted to feeding on yeast than *P. caudatum* and so survived towards the bottom of the tube.
- In the upper part of the tube, the higher oxygen levels favoured the growth of bacteria over yeast, hence bacterial food predominated in this region.
- *P. caudatum* was better adapted to feeding on bacteria and so survived towards the top of the tube.

It is clear from these experiments that these two species occupied different niches and so both survived. However, as the two niches had some overlap, i.e. the middle region of the tube, there was considerable interspecific competition. This resulted in changes to:

- **the distribution of the two populations** – competition had forced *P. bursaria* to occupy the lower regions of the tube and *P. caudatum* to occupy the upper regions of the tube. When grown separately, each species occupied all regions of the tube.

- **the size of the two populations** – Gausse showed that, when grown separately, *P. bursaria* and *P. caudatum* both achieved a population density three times greater than when they were grown together. Competition had reduced the population size of each by more than the half expected if they had simply shared the tube equally, i.e. the overall population density of the tube had been reduced.

Another example of how competition affects population size and distribution is illustrated by a study carried out by J.H. Cornell of the University of California on the growth of barnacles on rocky sea shores in Scotland. Cornell studied two genera – *Chthamalus* and *Balanus*.

- *Chthamalus* is able to live both low down and high up on the shore.
- *Balanus* can only survive low down on the shore, because it is not well adapted to tolerate exposure to the air at low tide.

Cornell found that, in deeper water, *Balanus* always out-competed *Chthamalus*, eventually replacing it completely on the rocks. If, however, *Balanus* was removed from the lower part of the shore, *Chthamalus* quickly recolonised the area. There was therefore no physiological or environmental reason why *Chthamalus* did not grow in this region – it was simply being ousted by *Balanus* that out competed it, probably because it grows faster and therefore occupies the limited space on the rocks more quickly. Competition from *Balanus* therefore means that, where they coexist, the population of *Chthamalus* is distributed less widely (being confined to the upper shore), and is therefore also smaller in overall size. Figure 3.4 illustrates the distribution of *Chthamalus* and *Balanus*.

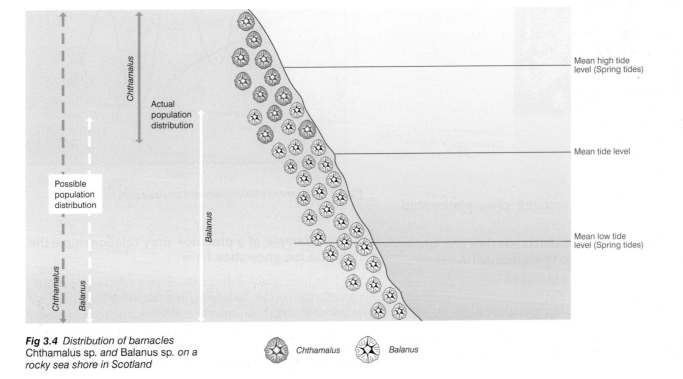

Fig 3.4 *Distribution of barnacles* Chthamalus sp. *and* Balanus sp. *on a rocky sea shore in Scotland*

3.3   The predator–prey relationship

A **predator** is an organism that feeds on another organism known as its **prey**. Although not normally thought of as predators, both herbivores and **parasites** may, for the purposes of this discussion, be considered as such.

Evolution has equipped predators with an ever greater ability to capture their prey – faster movement, camouflage, better means of detecting prey. Prey have equally become more adept at avoiding predators – camouflage, protective features such as spines, concealment behaviour. In other words the predator and the prey have evolved together. Had either party not matched the improvements of the other, it would most probably have become extinct.

3.3.1 Predation

Predation occurs when one organism is consumed by another. When the populations of a predator (e.g. the protoctistan *Didinium*) and the population of its prey (e.g. *Paramecium caudatum*) are brought together in a laboratory, the prey is usually exterminated by the predator. This is largely because the range and variety of the habitat provided is normally limited in the confines of a laboratory. In nature it is different. The area over which the population can travel is far greater and the variety of the environment is much more diverse. In particular, there are many more potential refuges. In these circumstances some prey can escape predation and so, although their population falls to a low level, it rarely, if ever, does so to the point of extinction.

Example of a predator–prey relationship: a bobcat catching a snowshoe hare

3.3.2 The effect of the predator–prey relationship on population size

The relationship between predators and their prey and its effect on population size can be summarised as follows:

- Predators eat their prey, whose population is therefore reduced.
- With fewer prey available the predators are in greater competition with each other for the prey that are left.
- The predator population is reduced as some individuals are unable to obtain enough prey for their survival.

- With fewer predators left, fewer prey are eaten.
- The prey population therefore increases.
- With more prey now available, the predator population in turn increases.

This general predator–prey relationship is illustrated in figure 3.5. In natural **ecosystems**, however, organisms eat a range of foods and therefore the fluctuations in population size shown in the graph are often less severe. Examples of this type of predator–prey relationship include:

- Canadian lynx preying on the snowshoe hare
- *Hydra* preying on the water flea, *Daphnia*
- *Paramecium* preying on yeast cells.

Although predator–prey relationships are significant reasons for cyclic fluctuations in populations, they are not the only reasons; disease and climatic factors also play a part. These periodic population crashes are important in evolution as they create a selection pressure whereby only those individuals who are able to escape predators, or withstand disease or adverse climate, will survive to reproduce. The population therefore evolves to be better adapted to the prevailing conditions.

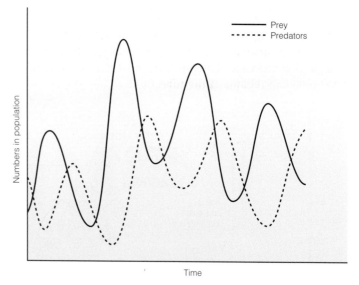

Fig 3.5 *Relationship between prey and predator populations*

3.3.3 Example of a predator–prey relationship – the lynx and the snowshoe hare

The long term study of the predator–prey relationship of the Canadian lynx (*Lynx canadensis*) and the snowshoe hare (*Lepus americanus*) was made possible because records exist of the number of furs traded by companies such as Hudson's Bay Company in Canada over 200 years. The assumption is made that the relative numbers of each type of fur traded represents the relative size of each animal's population at the time. Although this may not be totally true, as economic factors may encourage the capture of one type of animal in preference to the other, it at least gives us a very useful estimate of population size. The trade records of the Hudson's Bay Company were studied by Charles Elton, who compiled graphs to show that:

- The population size of the snowshoe hare fluctuated in a series of peaks and troughs.
- Each peak and trough was repeated about every 10 years.
- The population size of the Canadian lynx also fluctuated in a 10-year cycle of peaks and troughs.
- The relative pattern of peaks and troughs is similar for the lynx and the snowshoe hare.
- The rise in the population size of the snowshoe hare often (but not always) preceded that of the lynx.

These findings show that the size of the population of lynx is, to some degree, determined by the size of the population of its main prey, the snowshoe hare. The lynx, however, has other prey and their population will also influence that of the lynx. For instance, in figure 3.6 you can see that the rise in population of lynx in 1900 **precedes** that of the snowshoe hare, rather than the other way round which is more usually the case. The population of the lynx in this cycle also increases to a size equal to that of the snowshoe hare – another rare event. Both facts suggest that lynx were also feeding on an alternative form of prey that happened to be particularly abundant at this time.

In the same way, the size of the population of the snowshoe hare is determined by the size of the lynx population. Again, though, the snowshoe hare also has other predators whose population size changes and influences its own population size. This situation is further complicated when we consider the fact that snowshoe hares living on islands where there are no lynx or other predators still show cyclic oscillations in their population. A possible reason for this is the abundance of the grass that the hares eat. A large population of hares leads to overgrazing and therefore a lack of food and a consequent fall in population size, i.e. a different sort of 'predator–prey' relationship. Other factors also play a part. For example, overgrazed grasses on these islands produce toxic shoots that make the grass unpalatable to the hares. These toxins are produced for up to three years, during which time the hare population falls as a result of death from starvation. It seems therefore that the hare population size is influenced less by its main predator, the lynx, than by the abundance of its own 'prey', the grasses.

In summary, we can say that while there is a relationship between the population sizes of prey and predator, it is not only the interaction between these two groups that determines population changes, but also the interaction of many other factors, both living and non-living.

SUMMARY TEST 3.3

In laboratory experiments, when prey and predator populations coexist, the prey population usually falls to the point of (1). In nature, this rarely happens because the environment is more (2) and the prey has more places to hide. In a typical relationship between prey and predator, predators eat prey, whose population falls. This in turn leads to a (3) in the predator population and so the prey population is able to (4). An example of such a relationship is between the snowshoe hare and its predator the (5), where the populations of both fluctuate in a series of peaks and troughs over a period of approximately (6) years.

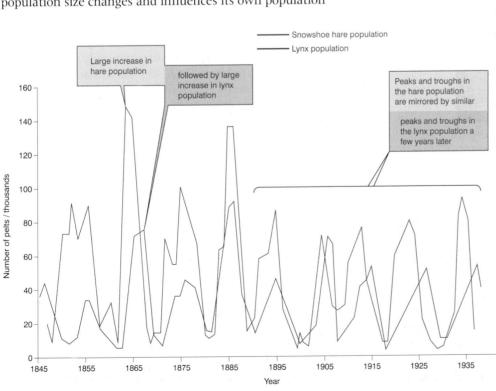

Snowshoe hare population
Lynx population

Large increase in hare population

followed by large increase in lynx population

Peaks and troughs in the hare population are mirrored by similar

peaks and troughs in the lynx population a few years later

Fig 3.6 *The predator–prey relationship illustrated by the number of snowshoe hare and lynx trapped for Hudson's Bay Company between 1845 and 1940*

Succession and climax community

In *Essential AS Biology for OCR*, unit 7.1, we saw that ecosystems are made up of all the interacting **biotic** and **abiotic** factors in a particular area within which there are a number of **communities** of organisms. As we look around at natural ecosystems such as moorland or forest, we may get the impression that they have been there forever. This is far from the case. Ecosystems constantly change, sometimes slowly and sometimes very rapidly. **Succession** is the term used to describe these changes in species of organisms that occupy an area over time.

3.4.1 Primary succession

Primary succession occurs when bare rock or other barren terrain is first colonised. This may occur as a result of:

- a glacier retreating and depositing rock
- sand being piled into dunes by wind or sea
- volcanoes erupting and depositing lava
- lakes or ponds being created by land subsiding
- silt and mud being deposited at river estuaries.

The first stage of primary succession is the colonisation of an inhospitable environment by organisms called **pioneer species**. Pioneer species often have features that suit them to colonisation. These include that they:

Lichens, with their ability to withstand dry conditions and to colonise bare rock, are frequently the first pioneer species on barren terrain

Deciduous woodland is normally the climax community in lowland Britain

Moorland is an example of a deflected climax. Grazing by sheep has prevented shrubs and trees from developing

- produce vast quantities of wind-dispersed seeds or spores and so easily reach isolated situations such as volcanic islands
- do not require a period of dormancy and so germinate quickly on arrival
- are photosynthetic, as light is normally available but other 'food' is not. They are therefore not dependent on animal species
- often fix nitrogen from the atmosphere because, even if there is soil, it has few or no nutrients
- can tolerate extreme conditions
- are unable to compete well for resources.

Succession takes place in a series of stages, each called a **sere**. At each stage, certain species can be identified which change the environment so that it becomes more suitable for other species.

Imagine an area of bare rock. One of the few kinds of organism capable of surviving on such an inhospitable area is lichen. Lichen is therefore a pioneer species. As a symbiotic relationship between an alga and a fungus, a lichen can survive considerable drying out.

In time, weathering of this base rock produces sand or soil, although in itself this cannot support other plants. However, as the lichens die and decompose they release sufficient nutrients to support a community of small plants. Mosses are typically the next stage in succession, followed by ferns. With the continuing erosion of the rock and the increasing amount of organic matter available from these plants, a thicker layer of soil is built up. This then supports small flowering plants such as grasses and, by turn, shrubs and trees. In the UK the ultimate community is most likely to be deciduous oak woodland. The stable state thus formed comprises a balanced equilibrium of species with few, if any, new species replacing those that have become established. This is called the **climax community**. This is a stable state, with many species flourishing. This community consists of animals as well as plants. The animals have undergone a similar series of successional changes, which have been largely determined by the plant types available for food and shelter. Within the climax community there is normally a dominant plant and animal species.

During any succession there are a number of common features that emerge:

- **the abiotic environment becomes less hostile**, e.g. soil forms, nutrients are more plentiful and plants provide shelter from the wind. This leads to
- **a greater number and variety of habitats** that in turn produce
- **increased biodiversity** as different species occupy these habitats. This is especially evident in the early stages,

reaching a peak in mid-succession, but decreasing as the climax community is reached. With increased biodiversity comes
- **more complex food webs**, leading to
- **increased biomass**, especially during mid-succession.

3.4.2 Climatic climax

Climax communities are in a stable equilibrium with the prevailing climate. It is this climate that determines the dominant species of the community and therefore it is known as the **climatic climax**. In the lowlands of the UK, the climatic climax is deciduous woodland; in other climates of the world it may be tundra, steppe or rain forest.

3.4.3 Secondary succession

Secondary succession occurs when land that has already sustained life is suddenly altered. This may be the result of land clearance for agriculture or a forest fire. The process by which the ecosystem returns to its climatic climax is the same as for primary succession, except that it normally occurs more rapidly. This is because spores, seeds and organs

of vegetative propagation often remain alive in the soil, and there is an influx of animals and plants through dispersal and migration from the surrounding area. Secondary succession therefore does not begin with pioneer species, but with organisms from subsequent successional stages. Figure 3.7 summarises the events of ecological succession.

The grassland in the foreground is maintained as a deflected climax by the grazing of sheep. The land behind the fence has not been grazed for many years and has reverted to the climax community of deciduous woodland. This is therefore an example of secondary succession

---

EXTENSION

Deflected climax (Plagioclimax)

Sometimes it is the influence of organisms (mostly humans) rather than climate that determines the dominant species, and hence the nature, of the climax community. These are known as **biotic climaxes** and they are less stable than climatic climaxes.

The burning of heather along with the grazing of moorland by sheep prevent the land from reaching its climax community. Instead it is in an arrested state in which the burning and grazing destroy the young tree saplings and so prevent the natural succession into

deciduous woodland. This type of biotic climax is known as a **deflected climax** or a **plagioclimax**.

Around 4000 years ago, much of lowland UK was a climax community of oak woodland, but most of this forest was cleared to allow grazing and cultivation. The many heaths and grasslands that we now refer to as 'natural' are the result of this clearance and subsequent grazing by animals. They are therefore deflected climaxes.

If the biotic factor that is preventing further succession is removed, then the ecosystem develops naturally into its climatic climax. For example, if grasslands are no longer grazed or mowed, or if farmland is abandoned, shrubs initially take over, followed by deciduous woodland.

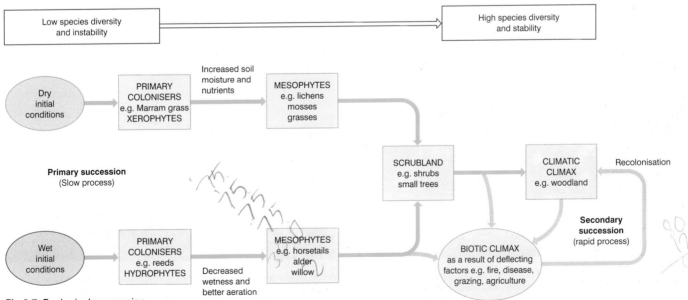

Fig 3.7 *Ecological succession*

3.5 An example of primary succession

In unit 3.4 we saw what succession is and looked at some general examples. While all successions display similar features, each one is unique. To understand the process fully, therefore, we need to consider one example in more detail. One of the best researched examples of primary succession is Glacier Bay on the south east coast of Alaska.

3.5.1 Studying primary succession following the retreat of a glacier

Many glaciers in the northern hemisphere have been melting over the past 200 years. This retreat is, in part, the result of the additional global warming that has taken place since the industrial revolution and the burning of fossil fuels that has accompanied it. When glaciers melt and retreat they leave behind gravel deposits known as moraines. The retreat of the glaciers in Glacier Bay, Alaska has been measured since 1794 and so the age of the moraines in this region is recorded. Although no ecologist has been present to watch the succession that has taken place on these moraines, they can infer the changes that have occurred by examining the plant and animal **communities** on the moraines of different ages. The 'youngest' moraines (those nearest the retreating glacier) have the earliest colonisers (**pioneer species**), whereas those successively further away from the glacier show a chronological sequence of later communities.

3.5.2 Changes as a glacier retreats

Succession occurs in a series of stages (Fig 3.8). Each stage has its own distinctive community of plants and animals that alters the environment in a way that allows the next stage and its community to develop. The stages that follow the retreat of an Arctic glacier are:

- **Pioneer stage** – in the early years after the ice has retreated, photosynthetic bacteria, known as cyanobacteria, and lichen colonise patches of land. Both of these pioneers fix nitrogen that is essential because it is virtually absent from glacial moraines. They also form tough mats that help to stabilise the loose surface of the moraines. When these pioneer species die, they decompose to form **humus** that provides the nutrients that enable mosses to colonise. The pioneer stage occurs when the land has been ice free for 10–20 years.

Lichens are pioneer species that first colonise bare rock

Dryas (mountain avens) is the most common pioneer species in Glacier Bay, Alaska. It is able to fix nitrogen and forms dense mats and therefore enriches and stabilises the thin fragile soil

Arctic poppy (yellow flower) and moss campion (pink flowers) are early flowering pioneer species on Arctic moraines

- **Dryas stage** – some 30 years after the ice has retreated, the ground is an almost continuous mat of the herbaceous plant *Dryas*. Its roots stabilise the thin and fragile soil layer that has formed from the erosion of the rocks that make up the moraine. *Dryas* also fixes nitrogen, further adding nitrogenous nutrients to this poor quality soil. It is considered to be a pioneer species as it can survive on ground with very little soil. Other pioneer flowering plants found at this stage are the Arctic poppy and moss campion.

- **Alder stage** – This arises about 60 years after the ice has retreated. Alder is a small shrub-like tree that has **nitrogen-fixing** nodules on its roots. It therefore further enriches the soil with nitrogen-rich humus as its leaves are shed and decompose. The alder stage occurs some 50–70 years after the retreat of the glacial ice.

- **Spruce stage** – About 100 years after the ice has retreated, spruce trees develop amongst the alder. A period of transition takes place and during the next 50 years or so the taller spruce outcompetes the alder and ultimately displaces it altogether. Provided there is no dramatic climate change, these spruce forests will persist for centuries.

Spruce trees are the final succession stage following the retreat of glacial ice in the Arctic. They begin to grow around 100 years after the ice has retreated and persist as the dominant vegetation for centuries

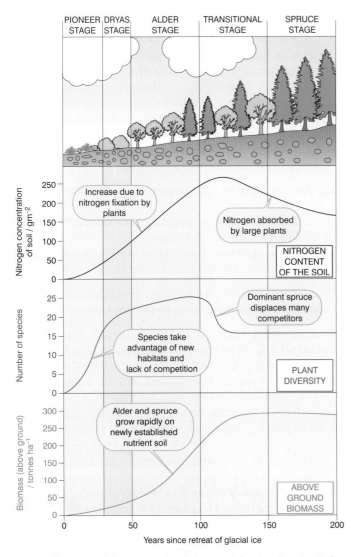

***Fig 3.8** Summary of the successional changes following the retreat of a glacier in Alaska*

SUMMARY TEST 3.5

When a glacier melts it leaves behind gravel deposits called **(1)**. These gravel deposits then undergo a series of successional stages, each of which alters the environment in a way that allows the next **(2)** of plants and animals to develop. The first colonisers after the glacier has retreated are organisms such as **(3)** and **(4)**. These are collectively called **(5)** species and can survive in inhospitable environments. Then, 30 years or so after the glacier has retreated a herbaceous plant called **(6)** develops, followed by the tree-like shrub called **(7)**. All these species survive despite the absence of nutrients in the soil, by carrying out **(8)**. The final stage is development of **(9)** trees some 100 years or so after the melting of the glacier. During the transition to this final stage, the amount of nitrogen in the soil becomes **(10)**, the number of plant species present becomes **(11)** and the biomass increases less rapidly before reaching a constant level.

41

Investigating the abundance and distribution of organisms

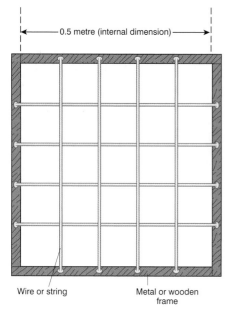

Fig 3.9 A frame quadrat

Table 3.2 ACFOR scale for three seashore organisms

Small barnacles

Abundant	100 or more 0.01 m^{-2}
Common	10–99 0.01 m^{-2}
Frequent	1–9 0.01 m^{-2}
Occasional	1–99 m^{-2}
Rare	Fewer than 1 m^{-2}

Tube worms

Abundant	50 or more 0.01 m^{-2}
Common	1–49 0.01 m^{-2}
Frequent	1–9 0.1 m^{-2}
Occasional	1–9 m^{-2}
Rare	Fewer than 1 m^{-2}

Limpets

Abundant	5 or more 0.1 m^{-2}
Common	1–4 0.1 m^{-2}
Frequent	5–9 m^{-2}
Occasional	1–4 m^{-2}
Rare	Fewer than 1 m^{-2}

It is often necessary to measure the abundance of organisms in particular habitats, and as it is virtually impossible to identify and count every organism, only small samples of the **habitat** are usually studied in detail. Provided these are representative of an area as a whole, any conclusion drawn from the findings will be valid. There are a number of sampling techniques including:

• random sampling using frame quadrats or point quadrats
• systematic sampling along transects.

3.6.1 Random sampling using frame quadrats

A quadrat is a sturdily built square frame (Fig 3.9) divided by string or wire into equally sized subdivisions. It is often designed so that it can be folded to make it more compact for storage and transport. The size of quadrat used will depend upon the size of the plants or animals being counted. Suppose we wish to investigate the effects of grazing animals on the species of plants growing in a field. We would begin by choosing two fields as close together as possible to minimise soil, climatic and other **abiotic** differences. One field should be regularly grazed by animals such as sheep, whereas the other has not been grazed for many years. We would take random samples at many sites on each field by placing the quadrat on the ground and recording the name and abundance of each species found within the area of the quadrat. The problem is: how do we get a truly random sample? We could simply stand in one of our fields and throw the quadrat over our shoulder. Even with the best of intentions, it is difficult not to introduce an element of personal bias using this method. Are we as likely to stand in a muddy wet area as in a dry one? Will we deliberately try to avoid the area covered in sheep droppings or rich in nettles? A better form of random sampling is to:

• Lay out two long tape measures at right angles, along two sides of the study area.
• Using random numbers from a table or generated on a computer or certain types of calculator, obtain a series of coordinates.
• Place a quadrat at the intersection of each pair of coordinates and record the species within it.

Abundance can be measured in a number of ways, depending upon the size of the species being counted and the habitat. Examples include:

• **Density of a species**, which is calculated by counting the number of times a particular species occurs within all the quadrats used and calculating the mean number of individuals per unit area, e.g. 12 per square metre. This method can be time consuming where a species is very small and it is often difficult to determine where one plant ends and the next begins.
• **Frequency of occurrence** is the likelihood of a particular species occurring in a quadrat. If, for example, a species occurs in 15 out of 30 quadrats, the frequency of occurrence is 50%. This method is useful where a species, e.g. grass, is hard to count, but it ignores the density and distribution of a species.
• **Percentage cover** is an estimate of the area within a quadrat that a particular plant species covers. It is useful where a species is particularly abundant or is difficult to count. It is less useful where organisms, more probably plants, occur in several overlapping layers.
• **Abundance scales** are specific measures that give the relative abundance of a particular species. The scales vary from one species to the next. Examples of

'ACFOR' scales (which list organisms as abundant, common, frequent, occasional or rare) for sea shore species are given in table 3.2. The process is simple and easy to use but subjective – individuals often give different values for the same sample quadrat.

To obtain reliable results, it is necessary to ensure that the sample size is large, i.e. many quadrats are used and the mean of all the samples is obtained. The larger the number of samples, the more representative of the field as a whole will be the results obtained.

3.6.2 Point quadrats

A point quadrat consists of a horizontal bar supported by two legs. Within the horizontal bar are ten holes, through which a long pin may be dropped in turn (Fig 3.10). Each species that the pin touches is recorded. The point quadrat is especially useful where there is dense vegetation, growing close to the ground, e.g. grasslands, because it can sample at many different levels. It is not, however, feasible to use it where a species is taller than the height of the frame. It also tends to overestimate the abundance of species with long, narrow, vertical leaves (e.g. grasses) and underestimate those with broader, more horizontal leaves. The point quadrat can be used for random sampling in the same way as a frame quadrat by using random number coordinates. It must be remembered, however, that the values produced are not an absolute measure but only a relative value.

3.6.3 Systematic sampling along transects

It is sometimes more informative to measure the abundance and distribution of a species in a systematic rather than a random manner. For example, the distribution of organisms on a tidal sea shore is determined by the relative periods of time they spend under water and time they spend exposed to the air, i.e. by their vertical height up the shore. In these circumstances more useful data are obtained using a transect, of which there are two main types:

- A **line transect** comprises a string or tape stretched across the ground in a straight line. Any organism over which the line passes is recorded.
- A **belt transect** is a strip, usually a metre wide, marked by putting a second line transect parallel to the first. The species occurring within the belt between the lines are recorded. Alternatively, a metre-square frame quadrat can be laid alongside a single line transect and the species within it recorded. The quadrat is then moved its own length along the line and the process repeated.

Both line and belt transects are of two types:

- **continuous transect** – in which sampling takes place over a relatively short distance and therefore takes place from one end of the line/belt to the other
- **interrupted (ladder) transect** – in which a much larger distance is involved and therefore it is only practical to take samples at intervals, e.g. every 10 metres, along the line/belt.

SUMMARY TEST 3.6

We can measure the abundance of a species within a frame quadrat by counting the number of times it occurs – known as the **(1)** of a species. Where a species is very **(2)** it is preferable to measure its percentage **(3)** within the quadrat. Another type of quadrat consists of a horizontal bar with a total of **(4)** holes through which a long **(5)** is dropped, and the species it touches are recorded. This is called a **(6)** quadrat and is useful where vegetation is low growing and **(7)**. Systematic, rather than random sampling is preferable in places such as a **(8)**. Here a transect is used. Sampling along a transect may be continuous or at intervals, in which case it is known as an **(9)** transect.

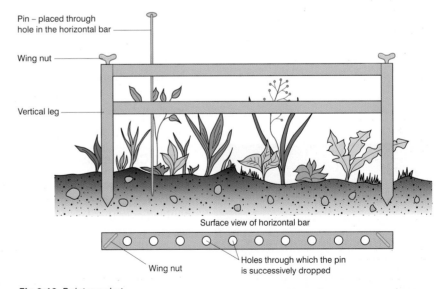

Pin – placed through hole in the horizontal bar

Wing nut

Vertical leg

Surface view of horizontal bar

Wing nut

Holes through which the pin is successively dropped

Fig 3.10 *Point quadrat*

Balancing food production and conservation

Silage production involves maintaining high soil nitrate levels by the application of fertilisers. This favours just a few grass species, with resulting low species diversity

Hay meadows have low soil nitrate levels, allowing a range of other species to compete with the grasses, resulting in high species diversity

As consumers we want a reliable supply of a wide range of food, at minimum cost. We therefore create a highly competitive market, which puts farmers under pressure to cut costs and supply cheap food in order to stay in business. As a result they have had to resort to using intensive methods of food production, with its consequent impact on the environment. There is clearly a conflict between our wish for cheap and plentiful food and our desire to conserve the environment. The question for the future is: how skilfully can we balance these two conflicting needs? Are we prepared to pay a little more for our food to ensure sustainable agriculture that has a reduced impact on wildlife?

3.7.1 Agricultural ecosystems

Agricultural ecosystems are artificially controlled by humans to prevent them from reaching their natural **climax communities**. Instead they are maintained in an arrested state called a **deflected climax** or **plagioclimax** (section 3.4.3). Agricultural ecosystems are made up largely of domestic animals and plants used to produce food for humans. Although governed by the same basic ecological principles as a natural ecosystem, agricultural ones differ in a number of ways, as illustrated in table 3.3.

Table 3.3 Comparison of natural and agricultural ecosystems

Natural ecosystem	Agricultural ecosystem
No additional energy input beyond solar energy	Energy from food (labour) and fossil fuels (machinery and transport) needed in addition to solar energy in order to maintain a plagioclimax (deflected climax)
Lower productivity	Higher productivity
More species diversity	Less species diversity – often a monoculture
More genetic diversity within a species	Less genetic diversity within species that are selectively bred or genetically engineered for a narrow range of desirable characteristics
Nutrients are recycled naturally within the ecosystem with little addition from outside	Natural recycling of nutrients is often supplemented by the addition of fertilisers
Populations are controlled only by natural means such as competition, climate, predation and disease	Populations are controlled by both natural means and the use of other agents such as pesticides
Are natural climax communities	Are plagioclimax (deflected climax) communities, i.e. are prevented from reaching their usual climax

3.7.2 Conflict between intensive food production and conservation

Food is essential for life, and with an ever expanding human population there is pressure to produce it more and more intensively. In the UK, food production has doubled over the past 40 years. This has been achieved by the use of improved genetic varieties of plant and animal species, greater use of chemical fertilisers and pesticides, greater use of biotechnology and changes in farm practices, leading to larger farms. These changes have had many ecological impacts, but the over-riding effect of intensive food production has been to diminish the variety of **habitats** within ecosystems and consequently reduce species diversity.

Certain practices have directly removed habitats and reduced species diversity. For example:

• removal of hedgerows and grubbing out woodland

Large area of arable land without hedgerows

- creating monocultures, e.g. replacing natural meadows with cereal crops or grass for silage
- filling in ponds and draining marsh and other wetland
- over-grazing of land, e.g. upland areas by sheep, thereby preventing regeneration of woodland.

Other practices have had a more indirect effect:

- use of pesticides and inorganic fertilisers
- escape of effluent from silage stores and slurry tanks into water courses
- absence of crop rotation and lack of **intercropping** or undersowing.

Despite the obvious conflicts between intensive food production and conservation, there are a number of management techniques that can be applied to increase species and habitat diversity, without unduly raising food costs or lowering yields. Examples of these conservation techniques include:

- Maintain existing hedgerows at the most beneficial height and shape. An A-shape provides better habitats than a rectangular one.
- Plant hedges rather than erect fences as field boundaries.
- Maintain existing ponds and where possible create new ones.
- Leave wet corners of fields rather than draining them.
- Plant native trees on land with a low species diversity rather than in species-rich areas.
- Reduce the use of pesticides – use biological control where possible or genetically modified organisms that are resistant to pests.
- Use organic, rather than inorganic, fertilisers.
- Use crop rotation that includes a **nitrogen-fixing** crop, rather than fertilisers, to improve soil fertility.
- Use intercropping rather than herbicides to control weeds.
- Create natural meadows and use hay rather than grasses for silage.
- Leave the cutting of verges and field edges until after flowering and when seeds have dispersed.

Farmland with small fields and many hedgerows

It is recognised that these practices will make food slightly more expensive to produce, and therefore to encourage farmers there are a number of financial incentives from the Department for Farming and Rural Affairs (DEFRA) and the European Union.

SUMMARY TEST 3.7

Agricultural ecosystems are examples of a **(1)**, whereby succession is maintained in an arrested state. Compared with a natural ecosystem there is **(2)** productivity, and less **(3)** and **(4)** diversity. The over-riding effect of intensive food production is to reduce the variety of **(5)** where organisms live within ecosystems. This situation has arisen partly because **(6)** have been removed, **(7)** have been filled in and single species crops or **(8)** have been created. Other agricultural practices have had indirect effects on ecosystems. These include the use of **(9)** and inorganic fertilisers, the escape of **(10)** and the absence of farming practices such as **(11)** and **(12)**.

EXTENSION

HEDGE ROWS! – Hedgerows typify the conflict between food production and conservation

They were originally created to mark the boundaries of fields and to contain livestock. Most that are around in the UK today are at least 400 years old. Over the past 50 years there has been a farming revolution with an increase in the use of large farm machinery and larger farm sizes. Small fields are not suited to the new machinery and so hedgerows are removed to make them larger. Hedges are removed because they:

- make it difficult to manoeuvre large machinery
- occupy space that could be used for a crop
- harbour pests, diseases and weeds, especially in winter

- reduce crop yields because they absorb water and nutrients as well as shading some of the crop
- need time and energy to maintain.

Hedges do, however, have a number of uses, some of which help to improve crop yields in the long term. Amongst other things they:

- are a habitat for a wide range of organisms, including some that are natural predators of crop pests and therefore provide a means of **biological control**
- produce food for many animals that do not live in the hedgerow, as well as those that do
- act as corridors along which many species move to disperse themselves
- provide wind-breaks and so reduce soil erosion
- add diversity and interest to the countryside.

3.8 Use and effects of nitrogen-containing fertilisers

Crops grown for food whether directly or as fodder for animals need soil nutrients, especially nitrogen. Where food production is intensive, it is usually necessary to replenish supplies of soil nitrogen. This can have harmful ecological consequences and is another example of the conflict of interests between our need to produce cheap, readily available food and our desire to conserve the environment.

3.8.1 Use of fertilisers

In natural **ecosystems** the minerals that are removed from the soil by plants are returned when the plant is broken down by microorganisms on its death. In agricultural systems the crop is removed, transported and consumed away from its source of origin. The urine and faeces and dead remains of the consumer are rarely returned to the land. Under these conditions the nutrient levels of agricultural land will reduce. To offset this reduction in mineral ions, fertilisers need to be added to the soil. These are of two types:

- **Natural (organic) fertilisers** consist of the dead and decaying remains of plants and animals as well as animal wastes such as manure and bonemeal.

- **Artificial (inorganic) fertilisers** that are mined from rocks and deposits and then converted into different forms and blended together to give the appropriate balance of minerals for the particular crop. Some compound of the three elements, nitrogen, phosphorus and potassium, is almost always present.

The advantages and disadvantages of the use of both types of fertiliser are given in table 3.4.

Research suggests that a combination of natural and artificial fertilisers gives the greatest long term increase in crop yields. However, it is important that nutrients are added in appropriate quantities, as the application of fertiliser is subject to the **law of diminishing returns**. This economic law states that there is a point at which an increase in a particular factor no longer results in a proportionate increase in yield (Fig 3.11). Indeed, with fertilisers, over-application can actually reduce yield because:

- Factors other than the lack of mineral ions are limiting growth, e.g. low temperature, low carbon dioxide levels.

- High mineral levels, especially of nitrate, lead to rapid vegetative growth. Plants grow tall and are easily flattened by wind or rain, with subsequent reduction in photosynthesis.

- Where minerals and water are readily available, roots develop less extensively, plants may be easily uprooted and germination and early growth are slower.

Table 3.4 The advantages and disadvantages of using organic and inorganic fertilisers

	Advantages	Disadvantages
Natural (organic)	• Supply all the necessary nutrients for growth • Increase water retention of the soil • Maintain the air content of the soil directly and by encouraging earthworms • Effective over a long period • Improve the crumb structure of the soil • Improve drainage and so help prevent waterlogging	• Not easily obtained • Bulky and therefore expensive to transport • Slow acting and therefore not effective in a single season • Difficult to handle • Relatively expensive • May contain pathogens, e.g. agents for BSE and *E. coli 157* • Mineral content low and variable • May contribute to eutrophication due to nitrate run-off as it is difficult to measure the exact quantity of nitrate being added
Artificial (inorganic)	• Relatively light and therefore easy to transport and apply • Quick acting • Easy to handle • Relatively cheap • Easily obtained • Do not spread disease • Mineral content can be adjusted to suit crop	• Do not improve the physical characteristics of the soil • Unless they are slow release varieties they can be easily removed by leaching and therefore need to be regularly applied • Run-off can cause pollution of water courses

3.8.2 Effects of nitrogen fertilisers

Nitrogen is an essential component of proteins and is needed for the growth, and therefore the increased area, of leaves. This increases the rate of photosynthesis and improves crop productivity. There can be no doubt that nitrogen fertilisers have been a considerable benefit in providing us with cheaper food. It is estimated that the use of fertilisers has increased agricultural food production in the UK by around 100% since 1955. Most of this increase is due to additional nitrogen (Fig 3.12). The additional use of nitrogen-containing fertilisers has also had some detrimental effects. These include:

- **Reduced species diversity** because nitrogen-rich soils favour the growth of grasses, nettles and other rapidly growing species. These then out-compete many other species that die as a result – a process accelerated by the use of selective weedkillers. Species-rich hay meadows such as the one in the photograph only survive when soil nitrogen levels are low enough to allow other species to compete with the grasses.

- **Increased soil acidity** – ammonium nitrate, a common nitrogen-containing fertiliser, releases ammonia into the atmosphere. This ammonia increases the rate at which

sulphate is deposited in soil and thereby increases its acidity, causing damage to forest trees in particular.
- **Pollution of drinking water** – very high nitrate levels in drinking water can prevent efficient oxygen transport in babies. The evidence that it harms adults is much less clear, although a link to stomach cancer has been suggested.
- **Eutrophication** – as a result of 'run off' of fertiliser into water courses.

3.8.3 Eutrophication by organic effluent and fertilisers

Eutrophication is the process by which salts build up in bodies of water. It is a natural process that occurs mostly in freshwater lakes and the lower reaches of rivers. Where eutrophication occurs the sequence of events is as follows:

- The higher concentration of salts, especially phosphates and nitrates, encourages the growth of algae and species of cyanobacteria.
- This leads to the water becoming densely populated with algae (= **algal bloom**).
- Light is unable to penetrate to any depth and so plants at lower levels die.
- All but the algae at the very surface die, due to lack of light which is necessary for photosynthesis.
- The dead plants of the deeper layers are quickly decomposed by **saprobiontic** bacteria.
- The saprobiontic bacteria use up oxygen for **aerobic** respiration, rapidly creating an increased **biochemical oxygen demand (BOD)**. BOD is a measure of the rate at which oxygen is used up in a volume of water. A rise in BOD means a lower oxygen content of water.
- Aerobic organisms such as fish die due to the lack of oxygen.
- Bacteria now respire anaerobically, producing methane and hydrogen sulphide.

Organic manures, animal slurry, human sewage, ploughing old grassland and natural leaching can all contribute to eutrophication. To help prevent eutrophication, government guidelines to farmers include:

- avoid applying excessive quantities of organic manures
- calculate precisely the amount of inorganic fertiliser needed, having regard to the needs of the crop and amount of nitrate already in the soil
- apply fertiliser when the crop is actively growing
- do not apply fertiliser to bare soil or when it is raining
- do not spread fertiliser within 10 metres of a water course
- avoid ploughing up old grassland where possible.

3.8.4 Alternatives to nitrogen-containing fertilisers

There are a number of farming practices that can be used to reduce the need to use nitrogen-containing fertilisers, including:

- **Crop rotation** – By growing a different crop on a particular area of land each year, soil fertility may be maintained and the risk of disease reduced. A typical rotation might involve four different crops over four years, e.g. wheat, root crop (such as turnip), barley and a crop comprising grass and clover. As clover is a legume that has **mutualistic** bacteria in its root nodules that are able to take nitrogen from the air and incorporate it into the soil as nitrate, this crop improves the nutrient level of the soil, and reduces the need for fertilisers.
- **Intercropping** is based on a principle similar to crop rotation, with two or more crops being grown together. If one crop is a leguminous plant that fixes nitrogen, the nitrate content of the soil is improved.
- **Growing genetically engineered varieties** of a crop that have had a **nitrogen-fixing** gene introduced into them. This technique is in its infancy, but it is likely that most major crops will have varieties that can fix atmospheric nitrogen, leaving little if any nitrate to be absorbed from the soil.

Low species diversity in a field grown for silage that has had nitrogen fertilisers applied

High species diversity in a meadow grown for hay without the addition of fertilisers

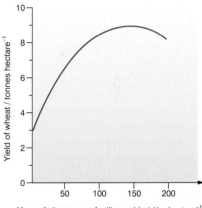

Fig 3.11 *The law of diminishing returns with the use of fertiliser in wheat production*

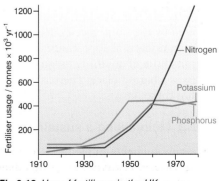

Fig 3.12 *Use of fertilisers in the UK*

Timber is produced from a growing crop – trees. As such it is a **renewable resource**, i.e. as it is removed it replaces itself within a reasonable time scale. This is different from non-renewable resources such as coal and oil whose replacement takes millions of years and therefore we regard them as a limited, finite resource. Renewable resources have a **sustainable yield**. This means that the amount removed (yield) is equal to, or less than, the rate of production. If trees in a forest take 100 years to mature, then only one-hundredth of the forest may be felled each year without the forest becoming smaller. A sustainable yield, if not exceeded, can be taken indefinitely.

3.9.1   Timber production

With over-production of food in much of Europe and therefore less need for intensive production, there is a move to increase the amount of woodland in the UK. This is encouraged by the set-aside scheme, a European Community initiative in 1988 to give grants to farmers who took at least 20% of their land out of food production and used it for other purposes, including woodland.

Timber has many functions; it is a construction material used in houses, and is made into furniture, packaging material and paper, as well as being a source of energy. Globally, woodland makes a considerable contribution to **biodiversity**, the removal of carbon dioxide (a **greenhouse gas**) from the atmosphere and nutrient cycles. It therefore makes sense to use woodland as a sustainable resource. Sustainable timber management maintains the functioning of a woodland ecosystem while allowing timber production. Although wood is a renewable resource, its production is not without ecological problems. Trees grow relatively slowly and so give a small yield for a given area of land. For this reason, it is not economic to use fertile farmland for their cultivation. Instead, poorer quality land typical of upland areas is often used. As conifers grow more rapidly, those softwood species like Scots pine, Norway spruce, Sitka spruce and larches, are more often cultivated than **endemic** hardwoods such as elm, oak, ash and beech. In the UK and northern Europe, large areas have become **afforested**. The trees are often grown in rows and many square miles are covered by the same species. Not only does this arrangement have an unnatural appearance, but the density of trees permits little, if anything, to grow beneath them and the forest is a barren place. There is little diversity of animal life within these forests.

3.9.2   Maintaining a sustainable forest ecosystem

Schemes are being implemented that permit a profit to be taken from woodland without damaging the ecosystem. To be successful these schemes require:

- **Gathering information on biodiversity and wildlife**. It is necessary to know which organisms and **habitats** exist already in order to conserve them.
- **Consideration of transport links and markets**. To be profitable, the timber must have easily reached markets and, because it is heavy and bulky, there must be the means of reaching these markets with minimal environmental impact.
- **Formulation of both ecological and business plans**. These must be considered together to ensure that business considerations do not result in damage to the ecosystem and ecological considerations do not result in the business failing. Compromises are inevitable.
- **Selection of appropriate species to grow**, taking into account the climate, slope of the land, type of soil.
- **Measurement of forest growth and structure**, to manage the woodland in a way that produces the maximum sustainable yield.
- **Application of ecologically sensitive systems**. For example, the use of long rotation times. This entails leaving areas where trees have been completely removed (**clear felling**) for long periods, e.g. up to 100 years, before re-harvesting. This allows the ecosystem time to recover and mature. The use of short-term rotations, e.g. 10 years, never allows a mature climax community (section 3.4.1) to develop, and so some habitats and their communities never return.
- **Careful removal of selected trees**. Rather than all trees in an area being removed (clear felling), selected large trees can be removed from different areas of the woodland (= **selective felling**). Not only are these trees the most commercially valuable, but also the habitats are

Afforested hillside planted with rows of larch. The density of the canopy and the accumulation of needles on the forest floor mean that few other species survive at ground level

kept intact. Selective felling also helps to maintain soil mineral levels and avoids soil erosion that often follows clear felling on steep slopes.

- **Planting and tending of new trees to ensure regeneration of harvested areas**. Large cleared areas need to be replanted with appropriate species and some selective weeding out may be needed to ensure the right mix of species. Distance apart of the saplings is important – too close together and they grow long and thin – too far apart and the venture may be uneconomic. Weeds, pathogens and other pests may need to be controlled.
- **Recreational use of the forests by the public**. Provision of access, parking, picnic sites and nature trails allow individuals to make use of the woodland and serves as an educational resource.
- **Use of broad-leaved deciduous species** around and within coniferous forests to improve their visual appearance and provide more varied habitats and communities.

3.9.3 Coppicing and pollarding

Coppicing is a technique based on the fact that, if a tree is cut down close to the ground, many new shoots develop from the remaining stump. These shoots are then allowed to grow for between 5 and 10 years before being harvested to make fencing and furniture or as fuel (either wood or charcoal). A wide variety of species can be coppiced, including alder, ash, chestnut, hazel, hornbeam, lime and oak. Coppicing is an excellent example of how a sustainable yield can be taken from woodland as, once harvested, the stems quickly grow again. Not all trees are usually coppiced but some, called standards, are left to grow to maturity. The system is known as **coppicing with standards**, but for it to be effective it is important that the mature trees do not form too dense a canopy, as light must penetrate to the coppiced trees. This often requires the mature trees to be harvested as well, although on a much longer rotation cycle of around 70 years. The role of coppicing in increasing species richness includes:

Coppiced trees

- Coppices provide an under storey of vegetation between the tree canopy and the ground that acts as a habitat for many insects and birds.
- Many birds nest in coppiced trees. These include blackbirds, song thrushes and nuthatches.
- Coppices provide insect food for a range of birds, including tits.
- The opening up of the tree canopy means that species normally found only on the edge of woodland can penetrate into it because there is more light.

Pollarding involves cutting branches 2 to 5 metres above the ground rather than at ground level as is the case with coppicing. The poles produced are less straight than with coppicing, but there is no need to protect the shoots from cattle and deer as they are unable to reach the new shoots.

A pair of pollarded willow trees

SUMMARY TEST 3.9

Timber is an example of a **(1)** resource as, once harvested, it replaces itself. If it is not to disappear over time, the amount of timber taken from a woodland must not exceed the **(2)**. Woodland is important globally because it contributes to **(3)**, removes **(4)** – a greenhouse gas – from the atmosphere and plays a role in **(5)**. Areas with many square miles of trees often grown in rows are said to be **(6)**. Conifers are often grown because they are **(7)** species and grow more rapidly than endemic **(8)** species such as oak, ash and beech. The wood of conifers is used for construction and making **(9)**, but the forest floor beneath them is often a barren place. With proper management and the application of the principles of **(10)**, woodlands can both be productive and sustain varied communities of organisms. For example, removing a few, mature trees scattered throughout a woodland – known as **(11)**, creates more diversity than removing all trees from an area – known as **(12)**. The ancient practice of cutting down trees close to the ground and then harvesting the branches that grow after 5–10 years is called **(13)** and increases species diversity. If the tree is cut 2–5 metres above the ground the practice is called **(14)**.

Meiosis, genetics and gene control

Meiosis

The stages of meiosis are described in figure 4.1.

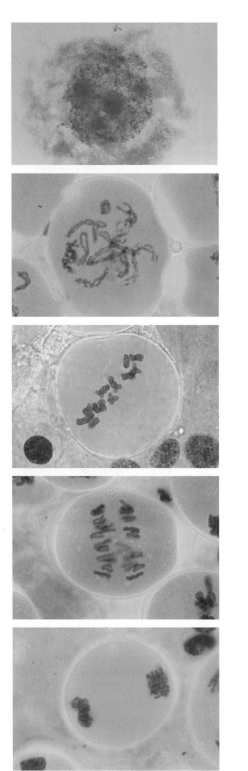

Interphase
Immediately before meiosis DNA replicates so that the cell now contains four, rather than the original two, copies of each chromosome.

Prophase I
The chromosomes shorten and fatten and come together in their homologous pairs to form a bivalent. The chromatids wrap around one another and attach at points called chiasmata. The chromosomes may break at these points and swap similar sections of chromatids with one another in a process called crossing over. Finally the nucleolus disappears and the nuclear envelope disintegrates.

Metaphase I
Centromeres attach to the spindle and the bivalents arrange themselves randomly on the equator of the cell with each of a pair of homologous chromosomes facing opposite poles.

Anaphase I
One of each pair of homologous chromosomes is pulled by spindle fibres to opposite poles.

Telophase I
In most animal cells a nuclear envelope re-forms around the chromosomes at each pole, but in most plant cells there is no telophase I and the cell goes directly into metaphase II.

MEIOSIS I

- Nuclear envelope
- Centrioles moving to opposite ends of the cell
- Point of crossing over
- Chromosomes seen to comprise two chromatids
- Nuclear envelope disintegrating
- Spindle fibres
- Equator
- Centriole
- Piece of sister chromatid exchanged during crossover in prophase 1
- One of the homologous chromosomes being pulled to a pole
- Nuclear envelope re-forming
- Cell divided by constriction

Fig 4.1 Stages of meiosis

SUMMARY TEST 4.1

Meiosis results in a halving of the number of chromosomes. During the first prophase stage the chromosomes come together in their **(1)** pairs to form a **(2)**. The chromatids of each pair attach at points called **(3)** and may exchange equivalent portions in a process called **(4)**. In the next stage called **(5)** the chromosomes line up on the **(6)** of the cell. The following stage, called **(7)**, sees

the chromosomes being pulled by the **(8)** to opposite poles. In the final stage of meiosis I in animals cells, the cell divides into two. The second prophase division involves the breakdown of the re-formed **(9)** and the disappearance of the **(10)**. By the end of meiosis II, four cells, known as a **(11)**, are formed.

Spindle fibres re-forming at right angles to previous spindle axis

MEIOSIS II

Centrioles replicate and move to poles

Prophase II
Where the nuclear envelope has re-formed, it breaks down again. The nucleolus disappears, the chromosomes shorten and thicken and the spindle re-forms.

Chromosomes lying on the equator of the cell

Metaphase II
The chromosomes arrange themselves on the equator of each cell.

Chromatid moving towards the pole

Anaphase II
The centromeres divide and the chromatids are pulled to opposite poles by the spindle fibres.

Telophase II
The tetrad of four cells is formed. Each cell has the haploid number of chromosomes. Crossing over during prophase I has produced genetic variety which, in this example, has given four cells of different genetic composition.

Meiosis and genetic variation

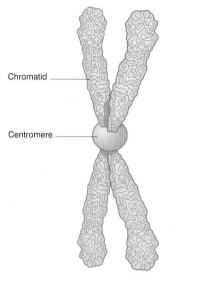

Chromatid

Centromere

Fig 4.2 *Structure of a chromosome*

Division of the nucleus of cells takes place in two ways:

- **Mitosis** produces two daughter nuclei with the same number of chromosomes as the parent and as each other (*Essential AS Biology for OCR*, unit 6.2).
- **Meiosis** produces four daughter nuclei each with half the number of chromosomes of the parent.

The structure of a chromosome is illustrated in figure 4.2, and table 4.1 compares the processes of mitosis and meiosis.

4.2.1 The principles behind meiosis

In sexual reproduction two gametes fuse to give rise to new offspring. It follows that, to maintain the number of chromosomes in the adults of a species constant, the number must be halved at some stage in the life cycle. This halving occurs as a result of meiosis.

Each of the cells of an adult of a species has a fixed number of chromosomes, usually made up of pairs that control the same characteristics. One of each pair is derived from the chromosomes provided in the egg by the mother (maternal chromosomes) and the other of each pair is derived from the chromosomes provided in the sperm by the father (paternal chromosomes). These are known as **homologous pairs** and the total number is referred to as the **diploid** number; in humans this is 46. During meiosis each of the pairs are separated, so that only one enters each gamete. This is known as the **haploid** number and in humans is 23. When two haploid gametes fuse, the diploid number of chromosomes is restored. The zygote then divides by mitosis to maintain the diploid number in all further cells.

4.2.2 Homologous chromosomes

All diploid cells of organisms have two sets of chromosomes, one set provided by each parent. There are therefore always two sets of genetic information for each characteristic of an individual. Any two chromosomes that determine the same characteristics are termed a **homologous pair**. 'Determining the same characteristics' is not the same as being identical. For instance, a homologous pair of chromosomes may each possess information on eye colour and hair texture, but one chromosome may carry the code for blue eyes and curly hair, while the other carries the code for brown eyes and straight hair. During meiosis, the halving of the number of chromosomes is not done randomly. Instead, each daughter cell receives one of each homologous pair of chromosomes. In this way each cell has one set of information on each characteristic of the organism. When these haploid cells (usually gametes) combine, the diploid state, with its paired homologous chromosomes, is restored.

4.2.3 The process of meiosis

Meiosis has two nuclear divisions that normally occur one after the other:

- **The first meiotic division (meiosis I)** is separated for convenience into four stages – prophase I, metaphase I, anaphase I and telophase I. Unlike prophase of mitosis, in prophase I of meiosis homologous pairs come together to form a **bivalent** in a process called **synapsis**. Chromatids of homologous chromosomes wrap around each other and attach at points called **chiasmata** (singular = **chiasma**) and swap equivalent portions of chromatid in a process called **crossing over**.
- **The second meiotic division (meiosis II)** is basically a repeat of meiosis I, but no chiasmata are formed and it is chromatids that move apart, rather than

Table 4.1 *Differences between mitosis and meiosis*

Mitosis	Meiosis
A single division of the chromosome and the nucleus	A single division of the chromosome, but a double division of the nucleus
The number of chromosomes remains the same	The number of chromosomes is halved
Homologous chromosomes do not associate	Homologous chromosomes associate to form bivalents in prophase I
Chiasmata are never formed	Chiasmata may be formed
Crossing over never occurs	Crossing over may occur
Daughter cells are identical to parent cells (in the absence of mutations)	Daughter cells are genetically different from parental ones
Two daughter cells are formed	Four daughter cells are formed, although in females usually only one is functional

whole chromosomes. The four stages – prophase II, metaphase II, anaphase II and telophase II – occur simultaneously in the two daughter cells formed in meiosis I. At the end of this second meiotic division four cells, known as a **tetrad**, are formed.

The events of meiosis are illustrated and explained in unit 4.1.

4.2.4 How meiosis and fertilisation bring about genetic variation

Meiosis halves the number of chromosomes in the gametes and ensures that the diploid number is maintained when haploid gametes fuse. Meiosis also produces variation amongst offspring, allowing an organism to adapt and survive in a changing world. Meiosis brings about this variation by:

- **Crossing over at prophase I.** During prophase I of meiosis, equivalent portions of homologous chromosomes may be exchanged. In this way new genetic combinations are produced and linked genes are separated.
- **Independent assortment of homologous chromosomes at metaphase I**. When the pairs of homologous chromosomes arrange themselves on the equator of the spindle during metaphase I of meiosis, they do so randomly. Although each one of a pair determines the same general features, they differ in the detail of these features. The random distribution, and consequent independent assortment, of these chromosomes produces new genetic combinations. A simple example is shown in figure 4.3.
- **Independent assortment of chromatids at metaphase II** further produces variety in the same manner as independent assortment of **chromosomes** at metaphase I.
- **Production of haploid gametes that fuse randomly at fertilisation**. The haploid gametes produced by meiosis must fuse to restore the diploid state. Each gamete has a different make-up and their random fusion therefore produces variety in the offspring. Where the gametes are from different parents (as is usually the case) two different genetic make-ups are combined and even more variety results.

In **arrangement 1**, the two pairs of homologous chromosomes orientate themselves on the equator in such a way that the chromosome carrying the allele for brown eyes and the one carrying the allele for blood group A migrate to the same pole. The alleles for blue eyes and blood group B migrate to the opposite pole. Cell ❶ therefore carries the alleles for brown eyes and blood group A while cell ❷ carries the ones for blue eyes and blood group B.

In **arrangement 2**, the left-hand homologous pair of chromosomes is shown orientated the opposite way around. As this orientation is random, this arrangement is equally as likely as the first one. The result of this different arrangement is that cell ❸ carries the alleles for blue eyes and blood group A, whereas cell ❹ carries ones for brown eyes and blood group B.

All four resultant cells are different from one another. With more homologous pairs the number of possible combinations becomes enormous. A human, with 23 such pairs, has the potential for $2^{23} = 8388608$ combinations.

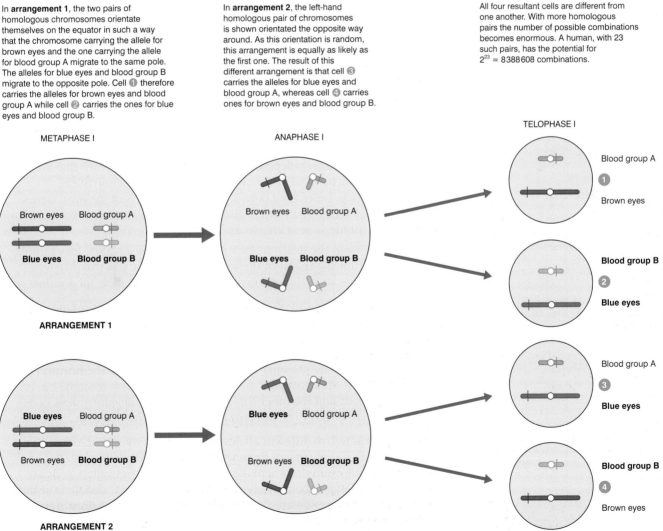

Fig 4.3 *How independent assortment of chromosomes during metaphase I contributes to variety in gametes and hence the offspring*

Genetics – the study of inheritance

The fact that children resemble, to a greater or lesser degree, both parents and yet are identical to neither has long been recognised. However, it took the re-discovery, at the beginning of the last century, of the work of a scientist and monk (living in what was at the time part of Austria) called Gregor Mendel (1822–1884) to establish the basic laws by which characteristics are inherited.

4.3.1 Genotype and phenotype

- **Genotype** is the genetic make-up of an organism. It describes all the alleles (section 4.3.2) that an organism contains. The genotype sets the limits within which the characteristics of an individual may vary. It may determine that a human baby could grow to be 1.8 m tall, but the actual height this individual reaches is affected by other factors such as diet. A lack of an element such as calcium (for bone development) or iodine (for production of the hormone thyroxine) at a particular stage of development could mean that the individual never reaches his/her potential maximum height. Any change to the genotype as a result of a change to the DNA is called a **mutation** and may be inherited if it occurs in the gametes.

- **Phenotype** is the observable characteristics of an organism. It is the result of the interaction between the genotype and the environment, which can modify an organism's appearance. Any change to the phenotype that does not affect the genotype is not inherited and is called a **modification**.

4.3.2 Genes and alleles

- **A gene** is a length of DNA, i.e. a sequence of nucleotide bases that usually determines a single characteristic of an organism (e.g. eye colour). It does this by coding for particular polypeptides that make up the enzymes that are needed in the biochemical pathway leading to the production of the characteristic (e.g. codes for a brown pigment in the iris of the eye). Genes exist in two, or occasionally more, different forms called alleles. The position of a gene on a chromosome is known as the **locus**.

- **An allele** is one of the different forms of a gene. In pea plants, for example, there is a gene for the colour of the seed pod. This gene has two different forms, or alleles – an allele for a green pod and another allele for a yellow pod.

Only one allele of a gene can occur at the locus of any one chromosome. However, in sexually reproducing organisms the chromosomes occur in pairs called homologous pairs. There are therefore two loci that can each carry one allele of a gene. If the allele on each of the chromosomes is the same (e.g. both alleles for green pods are present) then the organism is said to be **homozygous** for the character. If the two alleles are different (e.g. one chromosome has an allele for green pods and the other chromosome has an allele for yellow pods) then the organism is said to be **heterozygous** for the characteristic.

In most cases where two different alleles are present in the genotype (heterozygous state) only one of them shows itself in the phenotype. For instance in our example, where the alleles for green and yellow pods are present in the genotype, the phenotype is always green pods. The allele of the heterozygote that expresses itself in the phenotype is said to be **dominant**, the one that is not expressed is said to be **recessive**. A homozygous organism with two dominant alleles is called **homozygous dominant**, whereas one with two recessive alleles is called **homozygous recessive**. The effect of a recessive allele

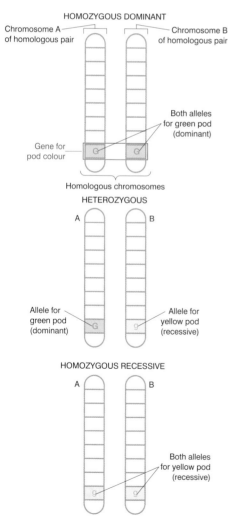

Fig 4.4 Pair of homologous chromosomes showing different possible pairings of dominant and recessive alleles

is apparent in the phenotype of a diploid organism only when it occurs in the presence of another identical allele, i.e. when it is in the homozygous state. These different genetic types are shown in figure 4.4.

In some cases, two alleles both contribute to the phenotype, in which case they are referred to as **co-dominant**. In this situation when both alleles occur together, the phenotype is either a blend of both features (e.g. cattle with a roan-coloured coat resulting from an allele for red-coloured hairs and an allele for white-coloured hairs) or both features are represented (e.g. the presence of both A and B antigens in blood group AB).

Sometimes a characteristic of an organism has more than two possible alleles. The organism is said to have **multiple alleles** for the character. However, as there are always only two chromosomes in a homologous pair, it follows that only two of the three or more alleles in existence can be present in a single organism. Multiple alleles occur in the human ABO blood grouping system (section 4.7.2).

Figure 4.5 summarises the different terms used in genetics.

SUMMARY TEST 4.3

The genetic composition of an organism is called the **(1)** and any change to it is called a **(2)** and may be inherited by future generations. The actual appearance of an organism is called the **(3)** and any change to this that is not inherited is called a **(4)**. A gene is a sequence of **(5)** along a piece of DNA that determines a single characteristic of an organism. This it does by coding for particular **(6)** that make the enzymes needed in a biochemical pathway. Each gene has two or more different forms called alleles. If the two alleles on a homologous pair of chromosomes are the same they are said to be **(7)**, but if they are different, they are said to be **(8)**. An allele that is not apparent in the phenotype when paired with a dominant allele is said to be **(9)**.

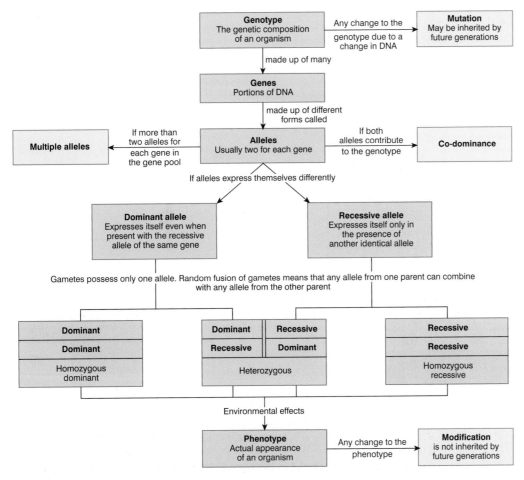

Fig 4.5 Summary of genetic terms

Monohybrid inheritance is the inheritance of a single gene.

4.4.1 Inheritance of pod colour in peas

If pea plants with green pods are bred repeatedly with each other so that they consistently give rise to plants with green pods, they are said to be **pure breeding** for the character of green pods. Pure breeding strains can be bred for almost any character. What it means is that the organisms are homozygous (i.e. they have two **alleles** that are the same) for that particular gene.

If these pure breeding green-pod plants are then crossed with pure breeding yellow-pod plants, all the offspring, known as the **first filial or F₁ generation**, turn out to produce green pods. This means that the allele for green pods is dominant to the allele for yellow pods, which is therefore recessive. This cross is shown in figure 4.6.

When the heterozygous plants (Gg) of the F_1 generation are crossed with one another (= F_1 intercross), the offspring

(known as the **second filial or F₂ generation**) are always in an approximate ratio of 3 plants with green pods to each 1 plant with yellow pods. This cross is shown in figure 4.7.

These observed facts led to the formation of the **law of segregation**, sometimes called Mendel's first law, which states: **In diploid organisms, characteristics are determined by alleles that occur in pairs. Only one of each pair of alleles can be present in a single gamete.**

4.4.2 Representing genetic crosses

Genetic crosses are usually represented in a standard form of shorthand (table 4.2). Although you may occasionally come across some minor variations to this scheme, that outlined in table 4.2 is the one normally used. Always carry out the procedures in their entirety. Once you have practised a number of crosses, you may be tempted to miss out stages or explanations. Not only is this likely to lead to errors, it often makes your explanations difficult for others

Use of the terms F₁ and F₂ generations

The term F_1 should be used only for the offspring of crosses in which the original parents are homozygous, whereas the term F_2 should be used only for the offspring resulting from crossing the F_1 individuals.

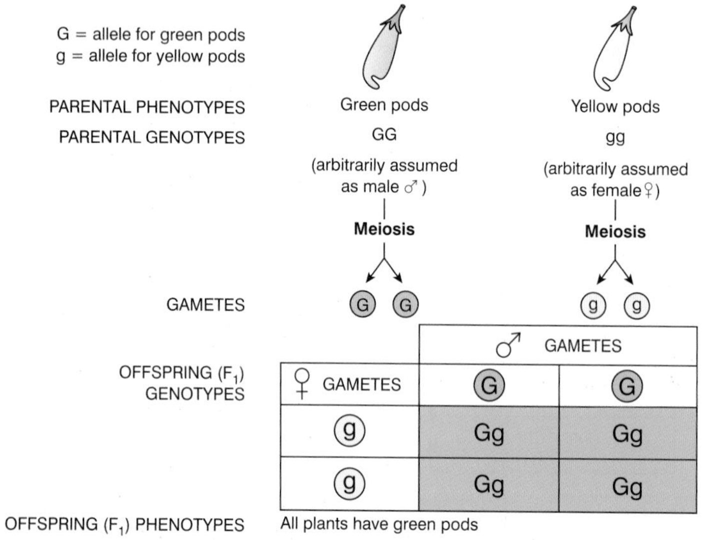

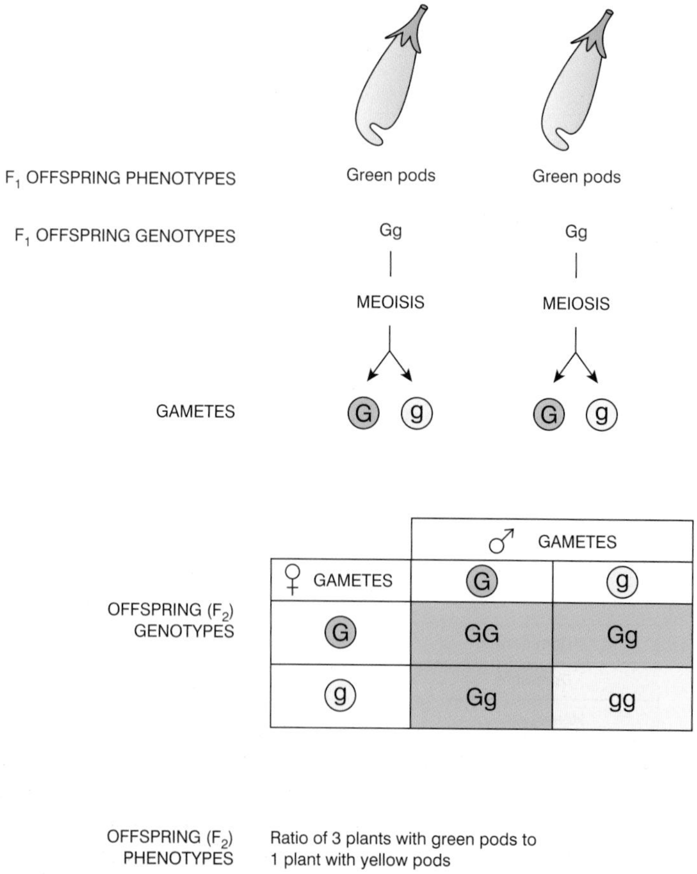

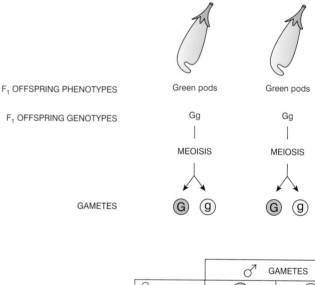

Fig 4.7 F_1 intercross between pea plants that are heterozygous for green pods

Fig 4.6 Cross between a pea plant that is pure breeding for green pods and one that is pure breeding for yellow pods

to follow. **You** may understand what you are doing, but if your teacher or examiner cannot follow it, you are most unlikely to get full credit for your efforts.

Table 4.2 Representing genetic crosses

Instruction	Reason/notes	Example [green pod and yellow pod]
Choose a single letter to represent each characteristic	An easy form of shorthand. In some genetic crosses, e.g. in *Drosophila*, there are set symbols, some of which use two letters	–
Choose the first letter of one of the contrasting features	When more than one character is considered at one time such a logical choice means it is easy to identify which letter refers to which character	Choose G (green) or Y (yellow)
If possible, choose the letter in which the higher and lower case forms differ in shape as well as size	If the higher and lower case forms differ it is almost impossible to confuse them, regardless of their size	Choose G because the higher case form (G) differs in shape from the lower case from (g) whereas Y and y differ only in size and are likely to be confused
Let the higher case letter represent the dominant feature and the lower case letter the recessive one. Never use two different letters where one character is dominant	The dominant and recessive feature can easily be identified. Do not use two different letters as this indicates co-dominance	Let G = green and g = yellow Do *not use* G for green and Y for yellow
Represent the parents with the appropriate pairs of letters. Label them clearly as 'parents' and state their phenotypes	This makes it clear to the reader what the symbols refer to	Green pod Yellow pod Parents GG × gg
State the gametes produced by each parent. Label them clearly, and encircle them. Indicate that meiosis has occurred	This explains why the gametes only possess one of the two parental factors. Encircling them reinforces the idea that they are separate	Meiosis Meiosis Gametes (G) (G) (g) (g)
Use a type of chequerboard or matrix, called a **Punnett square**, to show the results of the random crossing of the gametes. Label male and female gametes even though this may not affect the results	This method is less liable to error than drawing lines between the gametes and the offspring. Labelling the sexes is a good habit to acquire – it has considerable relevance in certain types of crosses, e.g. sex-linked crosses	♂ GAMETES (G) (G) ♀GAMETES (g) Gg Gg / (g) Gg Gg
State the phenotypes of each different genotype and indicate the numbers of each type. Always put the higher case (dominant) letter first when writing out the genotype	Always putting the dominant feature first can reduce errors in cases where it is not possible to avoid using symbols with the higher and lower case letters of the same shape	All offspring are plants producing green pods (Gg)

SUMMARY TEST 4.4

When representing a genetic cross, there is a standard form of shorthand that is normally used. Where the allele for one characteristic is dominant to the allele for another, it is normal to use an **(1)** case letter to represent the dominant allele and a **(2)** case letter to represent the **(3)** allele. Where gametes are involved, the letter for the allele should be **(4)**. To show all the possible outcomes of different gametes fusing, a type of chequerboard called a **(5)** is used. The inheritance of a single gene is known as **(6)** inheritance. One example is a cross between pea plants with yellow seed pods and ones with green pods. The first generation of plants produced is called the **(7)** generation and all have pods coloured **(8)**. When these offspring are crossed with one another the next generation, called the **(9)** generation, has a ratio of three **(10)** coloured pods to one **(11)** pod.

4.5 The test cross

An organism whose phenotype displays a dominant characteristic may possess either of two **genotypes**:

- two dominant **alleles** (homozygous dominant)
- one dominant allele and one recessive allele (heterozygous).

It is not possible to tell which genotype an organism has from outward appearances. It is, however, possible to determine the actual genotype by carrying out a specific genetic cross called a **test cross**.

4.5.1 Carrying out a test cross

To look at how we carry out a test cross, let us use the example in unit 4.3 of pea plants with different seed pod colours. Suppose we have a plant from the F_2 generation that produces green seed pods. This plant has two possible genotypes with respect to pod colour:

- homozygous dominant (GG)
- heterozygous (Gg).

To discover its actual genotype, we cross the plant with an organism displaying the recessive **phenotype** of the same character, i.e. in our case with a pea plant producing yellow pods (gg). Figure 4.8 shows that:

- if the organism is homozygous dominant (GG), then all the offspring will be heterozygous (Gg) and will show the dominant feature (green pods)

- if the organism is heterozygous (Gg), then it would be expected that half the offspring would be heterozygous (Gg) and show the dominant feature (green pods) while half the offspring would be homozygous recessive (gg) and show the recessive feature (yellow pods).

The test cross is so called because it 'tests' the unknown genotype of a dominant character. Is the test cross foolproof? The answer is 'yes and no':

- **Yes**, if any single offspring displays the recessive character (in our case yellow pods). This plant is homozygous recessive and must have obtained one recessive allele from each parent. Our unknown parental genotype must therefore have a recessive allele and be heterozygous (in our case Gg). Assuming no mutations, we can say with absolute certainty that our unknown genotype is heterozygous (Gg).
- **No**, if all the offspring display the dominant character (in our case green pods). While the likelihood is that the unknown genotype is homozygous dominant (in our case GG), we cannot completely discount the possibility that it could be heterozygous (Gg). This is because the gametes produced from our parent of unknown genotype contain alleles of two types, either dominant (G) or recessive (g). It is a matter of chance which of these gametes fuses with those from our recessive parent – all these gametes have a recessive allele (g). It is just possible that in every case it is

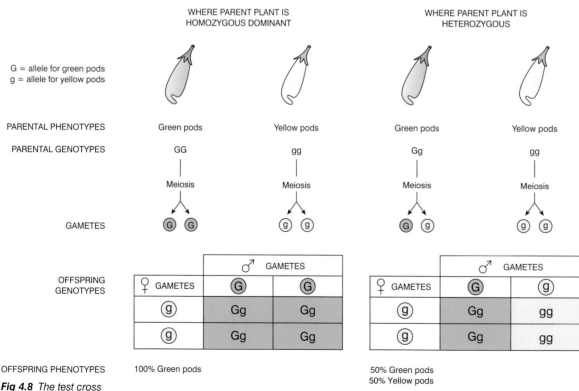

	WHERE PARENT PLANT IS HOMOZYGOUS DOMINANT		WHERE PARENT PLANT IS HETEROZYGOUS	
PARENTAL PHENOTYPES	Green pods	Yellow pods	Green pods	Yellow pods
PARENTAL GENOTYPES	GG	gg	Gg	gg
	Meiosis	Meiosis	Meiosis	Meiosis
GAMETES	G G	g g	G g	g g

G = allele for green pods
g = allele for yellow pods

OFFSPRING GENOTYPES

♀ GAMETES	♂ GAMETES	
	G	G
g	Gg	Gg
g	Gg	Gg

♀ GAMETES	♂ GAMETES	
	G	g
g	Gg	gg
g	Gg	gg

OFFSPRING PHENOTYPES   100% Green pods   50% Green pods
50% Yellow pods

Fig 4.8 *The test cross*

58

the gametes with the dominant allele that fuse and so all the offspring show the dominant character. Provided the sample of offspring is large enough, however, we can be reasonably sure that the unknown genotype is homozygous dominant.

4.5.2 Why actual results of genetic crosses are rarely the same as the predicted results

If you look at table 4.3, you will see the results that Gregor Mendel actually obtained in his experiments. Our knowledge of genetics tells us that for each cross we would expect that, in the F_2 generation, there would be three offspring showing the dominant feature to every one showing the recessive feature. However, in no case did Mendel obtain an exact 3:1 ratio. The same is true of almost any genetic cross. These discrepancies are due to statistical error.

Imagine tossing a coin 20 times. In theory you would expect it to come down heads on 10 occasions and tails on 10 occasions. In practice it rarely does – try it. This is because each toss of the coin is an independent event that is not affected by what went before. If the coin has come down heads 9 times out of 19 tosses, there is still a 50% chance it will come down tails, rather than the head needed to complete the 1:1 ratio. The coin does not 'know' it is expected to come down heads.

The same is true of gametes. It is chance that determines which ones fuse with which. In our cross between the heterozygote (Gg) and the homozygous recessive (gg), all the gametes of the homozygous parent are recessive (g), whereas the heterozygote parent produces gametes of

which half are dominant (G) and half are recessive (g). If it is the dominant gamete that meets the recessive one, plants with green pods are produced (Gg). If it is the recessive gamete, the plants have yellow pods. The larger the sample, the more likely are the actual results to match the theoretical ones. It is therefore important to use large numbers of organisms in genetic crosses if representative results are to be obtained. It is no coincidence that the two ratios nearest to the theoretical value of 3:1 in Mendel's experiments were those with the largest sample size, whereas the ratio furthest from the theoretical value had the smallest sample size (table 4.3).

SUMMARY TEST 4.5

Suppose the appearance, otherwise known as the (1), of an organism displays a feature that is determined by a dominant allele. This organism may have a genotype that is either (2) or (3) for this feature. To determine which genotype it has we can carry out a (4) cross. To do this we cross our organism of unknown genotype with an organism of the same species that has a genotype that is (5) for the feature. The gametes of this organism will all contain recessive (6) for this feature. If some of the resultant offspring from the cross show the recessive feature, then the unknown genotype must have been (7). If, however, all the resultant offspring show only the dominant feature, then it is most probable that the unknown genotype was (8). This becomes increasingly probable when the number of offspring is (9).

Table 4.3 Actual results of Mendel's crosses in pea plants

Character	F_2 results		Ratio
Cotyledon colour	6002 yellow	2001 green	3.01:1
Seed type	5474 smooth	1850 wrinkled	2.96:1
Pod type	882 inflated	299 constricted	2.95:1
Flower position	651 axial	207 terminal	3.14:1
Petal colour	705 purple	224 white	3.15:1
Stem height	787 long	277 short	2.84:1
Pod colour	428 green	152 yellow	2.82:1

Humans have 23 pairs of chromosomes. 22 of these pairs have partners that are identical in appearance whether in a male or a female. These are known as **autosomes**. The remaining pair are referred to as **heterosomes** or the **sex chromosomes**. In females, the two sex chromosomes appear the same and are called the **X chromosomes**. In males there is a single X chromosome like those in females, but the second one of the pair is smaller in size and shaped differently. This is the **Y chromosome**.

SEM of human X and Y chromosomes as found in a male

4.6.1   Sex determination

Unlike other features of an organism, sex is determined by chromosomes, rather than genes. In humans:

- Females have two X chromosomes and hence the gametes are all the same in that they contain a single X chromosome. Females are therefore the **homogametic sex**.
- Males have one X chromosome and one Y chromosome and hence they produce two different types of gamete – half with an X chromosome and half with a Y chromosome. Males are therefore the **heterogametic sex**.

Sex determination (Fig 4.9) is fundamentally the same in other organisms, but the heterogametic and homogametic sexes may be reversed. In birds, many reptiles and all butterflies it is the female who is the heterogametic sex (XY) and the male is homogametic (XX). Sometimes the Y chromosome is absent; in some insects, for example, the female has two X chromosomes (XX) while the male has just one (XO). Amongst fish and some reptiles, environmental conditions such as temperature can affect sex determination.

4.6.2   Sex linkage – haemophilia

Any gene that is carried on either the X or Y chromosome is said to be sex linked. In practice, very few genes are carried on the Y chromosome in humans. Those that are, such as the SRY gene (sex-determining region on the Y chromosome), are only ever found in males. They also always show themselves, even if **recessive**, because there is no **homologous chromosome** that might have the dominant **allele**.

By contrast the X chromosome carries many genes. One example in humans is the condition called **haemophilia**, in

which the blood does not clot, leading to slow and persistent bleeding, especially in the joints. As such it is potentially lethal if not treated. This has resulted in some selective removal of the gene from the population, making its occurrence relatively rare (about 1 person in 20 000 in Europe). Although haemophiliac females are known, the condition is almost entirely confined to males.

One of a number of causes of haemophilia is the result of a recessive allele with altered DNA bases that do not function properly and therefore result in an individual being unable to produce a clotting factor known as **anti-haemophiliac globulin (AHG)** or **factor VIII**. The extraction of factor VIII from blood donations means that it can now be given to haemophiliacs, allowing them to lead near normal lives. Figure 4.10 shows the inheritance of haemophilia. Note that the alleles are shown in the usual way (H = dominant allele for production of factor VIII and h = recessive allele for non-production of factor VIII). However, as they are linked to the X chromosome, they are not shown separately, but always attached to the X chromosome, i.e. as X^H and X^h respectively. There is no equivalent allele on the Y chromosome.

As males can only obtain their Y chromosome from their father, it follows that their X chromosome comes from their mother. As the allele for non-production of factor VIII, along with other sex-linked characters, is linked to the X chromosome, males always inherit the disease from their mother. As the mothers do not suffer the disease, they must be heterozygous for the character ($X^H X^h$). Such females are called **carriers** because they carry the allele without showing any signs of the character in their **phenotype**.

PARENTAL PHENOTYPES   Male   Female

PARENTAL GENOTYPES   XY   XX

GAMETES   X   Y   X   X

OFFSPRING GENOTYPES

♀ GAMETES	♂ GAMETES	
	X	Y
X	XX	XY
X	XX	XY

OFFSPRING PHENOTYPES

50% Male
50% Female

Fig 4.9 *Sex determination in humans*

As males pass the Y chromosome on to their sons, they cannot pass haemophilia to them. However they can pass the allele to their daughters, via the X chromosome, who would then become carriers of the disease (Fig 4.11).

4.6.3 Pedigree charts

One useful way to trace the inheritance of sex-linked characters such as haemophilia is to use a pedigree chart. In these a male is represented by a square and a female by a circle. Shading within either shape indicates the phenotypic presence of a character such as haemophilia. A dot within a circle signifies a normal phenotype who carries the allele for non-production of factor VIII. A famous pedigree chart showing the inheritance of haemophilia from Queen Victoria in members of various European royal families is shown in figure 4.12.

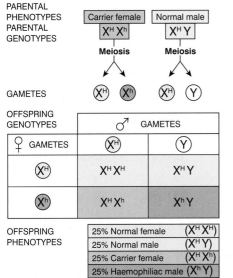

Fig 4.10 *Inheritance of haemophilia from a carrier female*

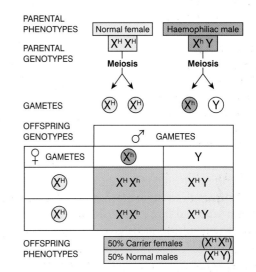

Fig 4.11 *Inheritance of the haemophiliac allele from a haemophiliac male*

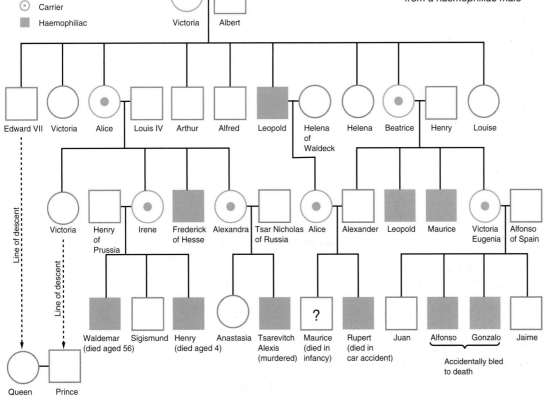

Fig 4.12 *Pedigree chart showing the transmission of haemophilia from Queen Victoria*

N.B. Not all members of each family are shown.

61

4.7   Co-dominance and multiple alleles

Units 4.4, 4.5 and 4.6 dealt with the straightforward situations in which there were two possible **alleles** at each **locus** on a chromosome, one of which was dominant and the other recessive. We shall now look at situations in which both alleles are equally dominant, called **co-dominance**, and where there are more than two alleles, of which only two may be present at the loci of an individual's **homologous chromosomes** – **multiple alleles**.

4.7.1 Co-dominance

Co-dominance occurs when both alleles of a gene are expressed in the phenotype. One example occurs in the snapdragon plant, in which one allele codes for an enzyme that catalyses the formation of a red pigment in flowers. The other allele codes for an altered enzyme that lacks this catalytic activity and so does not produce the pigment. In plants that are homozygous for this second allele, no pigment is made and the flowers are white. Heterozygous plants, with their single allele for the functional enzyme, produce just sufficient red pigment to produce pink flowers. If a snapdragon with red flowers is crossed with one with white flowers, the resulting seeds give rise to plants with pink flowers (Fig 4.13).

Note that we cannot use upper and lower case letters for the alleles, as this would imply that one (the upper case) was dominant to the other (the lower case). We therefore use different letters – R for red and W for white – and use

these as superscripts on a letter that represents the gene, in this case C for colour. Hence the allele for red pigment is written as C^R and the allele for no pigment as C^W. Figure 4.13 shows a cross between a red and a white snapdragon and figure 4.14 a cross between the resultant pink-flowered plants.

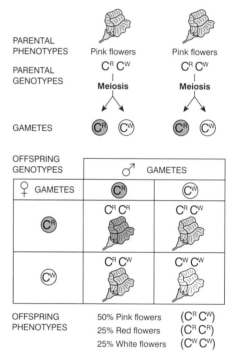

Fig 4.14 *Cross between two snapdragons with pink flowers*

4.7.2 Multiple alleles

Sometimes a gene has more than two alleles, i.e. it has **multiple alleles**. The inheritance of the human ABO blood groups is an example. There are three alleles associated with the immunoglobulin gene (I), which lead to the production of different **antigens** on the surface membrane of red blood cells:

- **allele I^A** leads to the production of antigen A
- **allele I^B** leads to the production of antigen B
- **allele I^O** does not lead to the production of any antigens.

Table 4.4 *Possible genotypes of blood groups in the ABO system*

Blood group	Possible genotype
A	$I^A I^A$ or $I^A I^O$
B	$I^B I^B$ or $I^B I^O$
AB	$I^A I^B$
O	$I^O I^O$

C^R = allele for red pigment production
C^W = allele for no pigment production

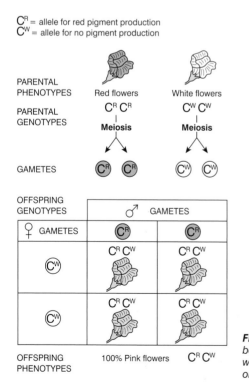

Fig 4.13 *Cross between snapdragons with red flowers and ones with white flowers*

62

Although there are three alleles, only two can be present in an individual at any one time, as there are only two homologous chromosomes and therefore only two gene loci. The alleles I^A and I^B are co-dominant, whereas the allele I^O is recessive to both. The possible **genotypes** for the four blood groups are shown in table 4.4. There are obviously many different possible crosses between different blood groups, but two of the most interesting are:

- A cross between an individual of blood group O and one of blood group AB, rather than producing individuals of either of the parental blood groups, produces only individuals of the other two groups, A and B (Fig 4.15).
- When certain individuals of blood group A are crossed with certain individuals of blood group B, their children may have any of the four blood groups (Fig 4.16).

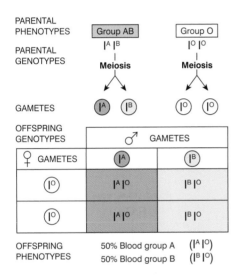

Fig 4.15 *Cross between an individual of blood group AB and one of blood group O*

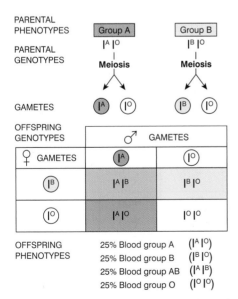

Fig 4.16 *Cross between an individual of blood group A and one of blood group B*

4.7.3 **Multiple alleles and a dominance hierarchy**

In blood groups alleles I^A and I^B are co-dominant and I^O is recessive to both. Sometimes, however, there may be more than three alleles, each of which is arranged in a hierarchy with each allele being dominant to those below it and recessive to those above it. One example is coat colour in rabbits. The gene for coat colour (C) has four alleles. In order of dominance they are:

Agouti coat	C^A
Chinchilla coat	C^{Ch}
Himalayan coat	C^H
Albino coat	C^a

Table 4.5 shows the possible genotypes of rabbits with each of these coat colours.

Table 4.5 *Possible genotypes of various coat colours in rabbits*

Coat colour	Possible genotypes
Full colour (Agouti)	C^AC^A, C^AC^{Ch}, C^AC^H, C^AC^a
Chinchilla	$C^{Ch}C^{Ch}$, $C^{Ch}C^H$, $C^{Ch}C^a$
Himalayan	C^HC^H, C^HC^a
Albino	C^aC^a

EXTENSION

Genetic incompatibility in transfusions and transplants

Every organism, except identical twins, has its own unique genetic makeup. Its immune system recognises its own cells (self) and rejects material that is not its own (non-self) (*Essential AS Biology for OCR*, section 16.2.3). It is important therefore that when blood is transfused from one individual to another the blood groups are matched to ensure they are compatible. If it is not matched, it will agglutinate (clump together) and could block vital organs such as the kidneys, resulting in death.

The same is true of other tissue and organ transplants although, as these are usually genetically more variable, perfect cross matching is all but impossible, except for identical twins. To help cross matching, surgeons look at the **human leucocyte antigen (HLA) system,** also called the major histocompatibility complex (MHC). This comprises four gene families (A–D) that code for antigens on cell surface membranes. Successful transplants require minimal HLA differences between the donor and the recipient. Where tissues have very similar HLA systems they are said to be **histocompatible** and their tissues will be tolerated by the other's immune system.

Unit 4.4 explained how a single character is passed on from one generation to the next (monohybrid inheritance). In practice, many thousands of characters are inherited together. In this unit we shall look at how two characters, determined by two **genes** located on different chromosomes, are inherited. This is referred to as **dihybrid inheritance**.

4.8.1 An example of dihybrid inheritance

In one of his experiments, Gregor Mendel investigated the inheritance of two characters of a pea plant at the same time. These were:

- **seed shape** – where round shape is dominant to wrinkled shape
- **seed colour** – where yellow-coloured seeds are dominant to green-coloured ones.

Table 4.6 Results obtained by Gregor Mendel when he crossed F_1 generation plants with round shaped, yellow coloured seeds

Appearance of seeds	Condition	Number produced
Round Yellow	Dominant Dominant	315
Round Green	Dominant Recessive	108
Wrinkled Yellow	Recessive Dominant	101
Wrinkled Green	Recessive Recessive	32

R = allele for round shaped seeds
r = allele for wrinkled shaped seeds
G = allele for yellow coloured seeds
g = allele for green coloured seeds

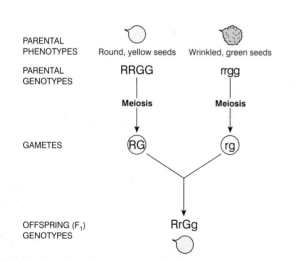

Fig 4.17 Genetic explanation of Mendel's cross between a pure breeding plant for round, yellow seeds and a pure breeding one for wrinkled, green seeds

He carried out a cross between the following two pure breeding types of plants:

- one producing round-shaped, yellow-coloured seeds (both dominant features)
- one producing wrinkled-shaped, green-coloured seeds (both recessive features).

In the F_1 generation he obtained plants all of which produced round-shaped, yellow-coloured seeds, i.e. both dominant features.

He then raised the plants from these seeds and crossed them with one another to obtain the results shown in table 4.6.

The explanation for these results is given in figures 4.17 and 4.18.

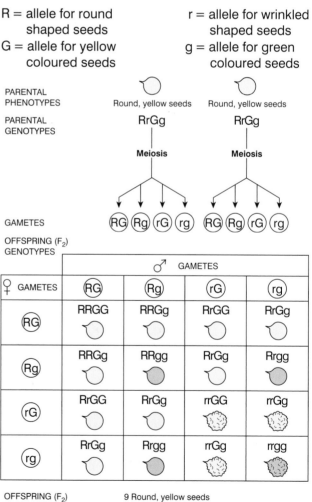

Fig 4.18 Genetic explanation of Mendel's intercross between plants of the F_1 generation

From figure 4.18 it can be seen that the plants of the F_1 generation produce four types of gamete (RG, Rg, rG, rg). This is because the gene for seed colour and the gene for seed shape are on separate chromosomes. As the chromosomes arrange themselves randomly on the equator during meiosis (unit 4.1), any one of the two **alleles** of the gene for seed colour (G and g) can combine with any one of the alleles for seed shape (R and r). Fertilisation is also random, so that any of the four types of gamete (with respect to seed colour and seed shape) of one plant can combine with any of the four types from the other plant.

The theoretical ratio produced of 9:3:3:1 is close enough, allowing for statistical error (section 4.5.2), to Mendel's observed results of 315:108:101:32. Mendel's observations led him to formulate his **law of independent assortment** which, written in today's biological language states: **Each member of a pair of alleles may combine randomly with either of another pair.**

4.8.2 Dihybrid test cross

We saw in unit 4.5 that it is possible to determine whether the **genotype** of an organism that exhibits a dominant character is either homozygous dominant or **heterozygous**. This involved crossing the organism of unknown genotype with one that is homozygous recessive for the same feature. In the same way it is possible to perform a dihybrid test cross.

In our example, a plant that produces round, yellow seeds (i.e. has both dominant alleles) has four possible genotypes:

RRGG
RrGG
RRGg
RrGg.

To find out the actual genotype of this plant, it can be crossed with one displaying the recessive character for both seed colour and seed shape, i.e. a plant producing wrinkled, green seeds. This plant has only one possible genotype – rrgg – and therefore all its gametes are rg with respect to these features. The outcome of each of the four crosses is shown in table 4.7. From the table it can be seen that the unknown genotypes may be identified from examining the seeds produced by the offspring of each cross. The presence of even one plant producing wrinkled green seeds (rrgg) indicates that the unknown genotype can only have been RrGg. To identify the other possible genotypes it is necessary to count a large sample of seeds – say in excess of 100 – and check the ratios of each type against the table of theoretical ratios. Even then we cannot be sure that some statistical fluke has not produced a totally unexpected result. There is, however, a statistical test called the **chi-squared (χ^2) test** that enables us to test the statistical validity of our results. Its use is explained in the next unit.

Table 4.7 Dihybrid backcross

Possible genotypes of plant producing round, yellow seeds	Possible gametes	Genotypes of offspring crossed with plant producing wrinkled, green seeds (gamete = (rg))	Phenotype (type of seeds produced)
RRGG	(RG)	RrGg	All round and yellow
RrGG	(RG)	RrGg	$\frac{1}{2}$ round and yellow
	(rG)	rrGg	$\frac{1}{2}$ wrinkled and yellow
RRGg	(RG)	RrGg	$\frac{1}{2}$ round and yellow
	(Rg)	Rrgg	$\frac{1}{2}$ round and green
RrGg	(RG)	RrGg	$\frac{1}{4}$ round and yellow
	(Rg)	Rrgg	$\frac{1}{4}$ round and green
	(rG)	rrGg	$\frac{1}{4}$ wrinkled and yellow
	(rg)	rrgg	$\frac{1}{4}$ wrinkled and green

SUMMARY TEST 4.8

The inheritance of two characters, determined by two genes located on different chromosomes is referred to as **(1)** inheritance. Mendel investigated two such characters, seed shape, where round shape is **(2)** to wrinkled shape, which is therefore **(3)**, and seed colour where green is **(4)** and yellow is **(5)**. In a cross between a plant producing round-shaped, yellow-coloured seeds (genotype RRGG) and one producing wrinkled-shaped, green-coloured seeds (genotype rrgg), all the offspring produced seeds that were **(6)** in shape and **(7)** in colour. Each of these plants could produce four types of gametes depending on the **(8)** of the two genes that they possess. These four types are represented as **(9)**, **(10)**, **(11)** and **(12)**. When these gametes fuse randomly with one another, the offspring produce seeds, of which nine in every 16 are **(13)** in shape and **(14)** in colour, whereas only one in every 16 is **(15)** in shape and **(16)** in colour. If a plant that is heterozygous for seed shape and homozygous dominant for seed colour is crossed with a plant producing green, wrinkled seeds, the offspring produce either **(17)**-shaped and **(18)**-coloured seeds or **(19)**-shaped and **(20)**-coloured seeds.

If you toss a coin 100 times it would be reasonable to expect it to land heads on 50 occasions and tails on 50 occasions. In practice, it would be unusual if these exact results were obtained (try it if you like!). If it lands heads 55 times and tails only 45 times, does this mean that the coin is weighted or biased in some way, or is it purely a chance deviation from the expected result? How can we test which of these two options is correct?

4.9.1 What is the chi-squared test?

The chi-squared (χ^2) test is used to test the null hypothesis. The null hypothesis is used to examine the results of scientific investigations and is based on the assumption that there will be no statistically significant difference between sets of observations, any difference being due to chance alone. In our coin tossing example, the null hypothesis would be that there is no difference between the number of times it lands heads and the number of times it lands tails. The chi-squared test is a means of testing whether any deviation between the observed and the expected numbers in an investigation is significant or not. It is a simple test that can be used only if certain criteria are met:

- the sample size must be relatively large, i.e. over 20
- the data must fall into discrete categories – i.e. there is discontinuous variation (section 5.4.2)
- only raw counts and not percentages, rates etc. can be used
- it is used to compare experimental results with theoretical ones, e.g. in genetic crosses with expected Mendelian ratios

The formula is:

$$\text{chi squared} = \text{sum of } \frac{[\text{observed numbers (O)} - \text{expected numbers (E)}]^2}{\text{expected numbers (E)}}$$

summarised as:

The different types of comb in domestic fowl are the result of dihybrid inheritance

$$\chi^2 = \sum \frac{(O - E)^2}{E}$$

The value obtained is then read off on a chi-squared distribution table (table 4.8) to determine whether any deviation from the expected results is significant or not. To do this we need to know the number of **degrees of freedom**. This is simply the number of classes (categories) minus one, i.e. if a human can have blood group A or B or AB or O, there are 4 classes and 3 degrees of freedom in this case.

Table 4.8 *Part of a χ^2 table (based on Fisher)*

Degrees of freedom	Number of classes	χ^2							
1	2	0.00	0.10	0.45	1.32	2.71	3.84	5.41	6.64
2	3	0.02	0.58	1.39	2.77	4.61	5.99	7.82	9.21
3	4	0.12	1.21	2.37	4.11	6.25	7.82	9.84	11.34
4	5	0.30	1.92	3.36	5.39	7.78	9.49	11.67	13.28
5	6	0.55	2.67	4.35	6.63	9.24	11.07	13.39	15.09
Probability that deviation is due to chance alone		0.99 (99%)	0.75 (75%)	0.50 (50%)	0.25 (25%)	0.10 (10%)	0.05 (5%)	0.02 (2%)	0.01 (1%)

← Accept *null* hypothesis?
(Any difference is due to chance and not significant)

↑
CRITICAL
VALUE

→ Reject *null* hypothesis and therefore accept experimental hypothesis that
'There will be a significant difference'

of χ^2 at 0.05 p level as this is the smallest value accepted by statisticians for results being due to chance

4.9.2 Calculating chi squared

Using our example of the coin tossed 100 times, we can calculate the chi-squared value:

Class (category)	Observed (O)	Expected (E)	O − E	(O − E)²	$\frac{(O-E)^2}{E}$
Heads	55	50	+5	25	0.5
Tails	45	50	−5	25	0.5
					$\Sigma = 1.0$

Therefore the value of $\chi^2 = 1.0$.

4.9.3 Using the chi-squared table

To find out whether this value of 1.0 is significant or not we use a chi-squared table, part of which is given in table 4.8. Before trying to read this table it is necessary to decide how many **classes of results** there are. In our case there are two classes of results, 'heads' and 'tails'. This corresponds to one **degree of freedom**, as the degrees of freedom are the number of classes minus one. We now look along the row showing 2 classes (i.e. one degree of freedom) for our calculated value of 1.0. This lies between the values of 0.50 (50%) and 0.25 (25%). This means that the probability that chance alone could have produced the deviation is between 0.50 (50%) and 0.25 (25%). In the chi-squared test the critical value is p = 0.05. This is the attribution to chance accepted by statisticians, i.e. 5% due to chance. If the probability that the deviation is due to chance is greater than 0.05 (5%), the deviation is said to be **not significant** and the null hypothesis would be accepted. If the deviation is less than 0.05 (5%), the deviation is said to be **significant**. In other words, some factor other than chance is affecting the results and the null hypothesis must be rejected. In our example the value is greater than 0.05 (5%) and so we assume the deviation is due to chance and accept the null hypothesis. Had we obtained 60 heads and 40 tails, a chi-squared value of slightly less than 0.05 (5%) would be obtained, in which case the null hypothesis would be rejected and we would assume that the coin might be weighted or biased in some way.

4.9.4 Chi-squared test in genetics

The chi-squared test is especially useful in genetics. To take the example of the genetic cross described in section 4.8.1. If we cross F_1 plants producing round, yellow seeds that we know are **heterozygous** we could expect an F_2 ratio of:

9 round, yellow seeds (186)   3 wrinkled, yellow seeds (72)
3 round, green seeds (48)   1 wrinkled, green seeds (14)

Suppose we obtained 320 plants in the ratio 186:48:72:14 as shown in the brackets. Could this variation be due to statistical chance or could some other factor be the reason for the differences? Our null hypothesis states that there is no significant difference between the observed and the expected results. Applying the chi-squared test:

Class (category)	Observed (O)	Expected (E)	O − E	(O − E)²	$\frac{(O-E)^2}{E}$
Round, yellow seeds	186	180	+6	36	0.2
Round, green seeds	48	60	−12	144	2.4
Wrinkled, yellow seeds	72	60	+12	144	2.4
Wrinkled, green seeds	14	20	−6	36	1.8
					$\Sigma = 6.8$

In this example there are 4 classes and therefore 3 degrees of freedom. Using the chi-squared table (table 4.8) we see that our value falls between 6.25 and 7.82 shown on the row for 3 degrees of freedom and that these values correspond to between 0.1 (10%) and 0.05 (5%) probability that the deviation is due to chance alone. In this case there is between a 5% and 10% probability that the deviation is due to chance. Therefore we accept the null hypothesis and accept that the results are a 9:3:3:1 ratio.

In another experiment domestic fowl with walnut combs were crossed with each other. The expected offspring ratio of comb types was 9 walnut, 3 rose, 3 pea and 1 single. In the event, the 160 offspring produced 103 walnut combs, 20 rose combs, 33 pea combs and 4 single combs (see photos). The null hypothesis states that there is no significant difference between the observed and the expected results. Applying the chi-squared test:

Class (category)	Observed (O)	Expected (E)	O − E	(O − E)²	$\frac{(O-E)^2}{E}$
Walnut comb	103	90	+13	169	1.88
Rose comb	20	30	−10	100	3.33
Pea comb	33	30	+3	9	0.30
Single comb	4	10	−6	36	3.60
					$\Sigma = 9.11$

These results give us a chi-squared value of 9.11. In this instance there are four classes of results (walnut, rose, pea and single comb) and this is equivalent to 3 degrees of freedom. We must therefore use this row to determine whether the deviations are significant. The value of 9.11 lies between 7.82 and 9.84, which is equivalent to a probability of 0.05 (5%) and 0.02 (2%) that the deviation is due to chance alone. This deviation is significant and we must reject the null hypothesis. Instead we must look for some other genetic explanation than the parents being heterozygous for the two alleles involved.

SUMMARY TEST 4.9

In *Drosophila*, normal (wild type) wings are dominant to vestigial wings. In a cross between two normal winged individuals, both believed to be heterozygous for this character, we obtain 30 offspring with normal wings and 18 with vestigial wings. Are these numbers close enough to the 3:1 ratio we would expect if the parents are heterozygous? Carry out a chi-squared test to decide whether the parents are likely to be heterozygous.

Any change to the quantity or the structure of the DNA of an organism is known as a **mutation**. Mutations arising in body cells will not be passed on to the next generation. Those occurring during the formation of gametes may, however, be inherited, often producing sudden and distinct differences between individuals. Changes in the structure or number of whole chromosomes are called **chromosome mutations**, whereas changes to DNA that affect a single **locus** and therefore produce a different **allele** of a **gene** are called **gene mutations** or **point mutations**.

4.10.1 Chromosome mutations

Chromosome mutations can take a number of forms:

*   **Changes in whole sets of chromosomes** occur when organisms have three or more sets of chromosomes rather than the usual two. This condition is called **polyploidy** and occurs mostly in plants.
*   **Changes in the number of individual chromosomes**. Sometimes individual chromosomes fail to segregate during the anaphase stage of **meiosis**. This is known as **non-disjunction** and results in an organism having one or more additional chromosomes. This is called **polysomy**. Where polysomy in humans occurs with the larger chromosomes, the developmental defects are so severe that infants with them die within a few months. The smaller autosomes, such as numbers 13, 15, 18, 21 and 22, can however be present as three copies and the individual may survive for some time; in the case of chromosomes 21 and 22 they usually survive to adulthood. An example of a non-disjunction in humans is **Down's syndrome** in which the effect on the phenotype is that individuals have a broad, flat face, learning difficulties, an increased risk of infections and a shorter life expectancy.

4.10.2 Gene mutations – additions and deletions

A gene mutation that arises when a pair of nucleotides is added to the normal DNA sequence is called an **addition**. Where a pair of nucleotides is lost from the normal DNA sequence it is called a **deletion**. Both mutations completely alter the way the triplets of bases are 'read' and hence the sequence of amino acids that make up the polypeptide after transcription and translation. Figure 4.19 illustrates how an addition or a deletion completely alters the amino acids that are coded for and hence the nature of the protein that is produced. Additions or deletions result in a **frame shift** in the DNA code, whereby every triplet of bases that follows the change is altered. An example of a deletion mutation is cystic fibrosis. The effect of this on the phenotype is the production of stickier than normal mucus, leading to lung congestion, reduced gaseous exchange and blocked pancreatic ducts.

4.10.3 Gene mutations – substitutions

If a nucleotide in a DNA molecule is replaced by another that has a different base, the type of mutation is known as a substitution. Depending upon which new base substitutes for the original one, there are three possible consequences. For example, if we take the triplet of bases in the DNA template strand, guanine-thymine-cytosine (GTC) that codes for the amino acid glutamine, a change to a single base could result in one of the following:

*   **A nonsense mutation** occurs if the base change results in the formation of one of the three stop codons that mark the end of a polypeptide chain (*Essential AS Biology for OCR*, section 5.5.3). For example if the first base, guanine, is substituted by adenine, then GTC becomes ATC. The triplet ATC gives rise to one of the three stop codons on mRNA. As a result the production of the polypeptide would be stopped prematurely. The final protein would almost certainly be significantly shortened and the protein could not perform its usual function.
*   **A mis-sense mutation** arises when the base change results in a different amino acid being coded for. In our example, if the final base, cytosine, is substituted by guanine, then GTC becomes GTG. The amino acid histidine is coded for by GTG and this then replaces the original amino acid, glutamine. The polypeptide produced as a consequence will be different. How significant this change proves to be will depend upon the precise role of the original amino acid. If it is important in forming the bonds that determine the three-dimensional shape of the final protein, then the protein may not function. For example, if the protein is an enzyme, it may no longer have an active site that is complementary to its substrate molecule and so will not catalyse a reaction. Section 4.10.4 illustrates an example of how a mis-sense substitution mutation may affect the function of a protein.
*   **A silent mutation**. Also called a **synonymous** mutation, a silent mutation is one in which the substitution results in a different base occurring in a DNA triplet but one that still codes for the same amino acid. The final polypeptide produced is identical to the

Table 4.9 Different types of substitution mutation

	Usual triplet of DNA bases	Nonsense mutation	Mis-sense mutation	Silent mutation
Sequence of bases in DNA coding strand	CAG	TAG	CAC	CAA
Sequence of bases in DNA template strand	GTC	ATC	GTG	GTT
Sequence of bases in mRNA	CAG	UAG	CAC	CAA
Amino acid in polypeptide	GLUTAMINE	STOP CODE	HISTIDINE	GLUTAMINE

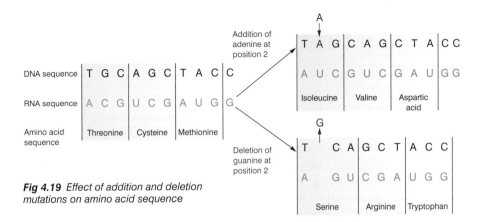

Fig 4.19 *Effect of addition and deletion mutations on amino acid sequence*

original and no effects are apparent. For instance, if the final base in our example is replaced by thymine then GTC becomes GTT. However, as both these triplets code for glutamine, there is no change to the polypeptide produced. Examples of all three types of substitution mutation are given in table 4.9.

4.10.4 Sickle cell anaemia

Sickle cell anaemia was the first human disease to be successfully understood at the molecular level, its cause being postulated by Linus Pauling in 1949. Sickle cell anaemia illustrates how the smallest of mutations can significantly influence the phenotype. It is the result of a gene mutation in the gene producing haemoglobin and causes the following sequence of events:

- In the DNA molecule that produces the β-amino acid chain, a single nucleotide base adenine is substituted by the nucleotide base, thymine.
- The normal DNA triplet on the coding strand is hence changed from GAG to GTG.
- As a result, the mRNA produced has the code GUG rather than GAG.
- This mRNA codes for the amino acid valine (GUG) rather than glutamic acid (GAG).
- This minor change produces a molecule of haemoglobin (called haemoglobin-S) that has a 'sticky patch'.
- When the haemoglobin molecules are not carrying oxygen (i.e. at low oxygen concentrations) they tend to adhere to one another by their sticky patches and become insoluble, forming long fibres within the red blood cells.
- These fibres distort the red blood cells, making them inflexible and sickle (crescent) shaped.
- These sickle cells are unable to carry oxygen and may block small capillaries because their diameter is greater than that of capillaries.
- Sufferers of sickle cell anaemia become tired, listless and have a shortened lifespan.

Figure 4.20 illustrates this sequence of events.

As sickle cell anaemia disables and kills individuals, it might be expected that it would have been eliminated by the process of natural selection. However, for reasons that we shall discuss in unit 5.8, the condition is relatively common in some parts of Africa and amongst black populations of African origin.

4.10.5 Mutagens

Mutagens are agents that increase the natural mutation rate (typically around 1 to 2 mutations per 100 000 genes). These agents include:

- **Chemicals** such as dinitrogen oxide and mustard gas that may directly alter the structure of DNA or interfere with transcription. Hydroxylamine, for example, causes cytosine to pair with adenine rather than guanine. Benzopyrene, a constituent of tobacco smoke, is a powerful mutagen that inactivates the tumour-suppressor gene p53 and so leads to cancer (*Essential AS Biology for OCR*, section 14.3.2).
- **High energy radiation**, e.g. α particles, β particles and neutrons as well as short wavelength ionising radiation such as X-rays and ultra violet light. These forms of radiation can disrupt the structure of DNA.

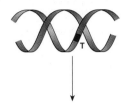

1. The DNA molecule which codes for the β amino acid chain in haemoglobin has a mutation whereby the base thymine replaces adenine on its coding strand

2. The mRNA produced has the triplet codon GUG (for amino acid valine) rather than GAG (for amino acid glutamic acid)

3. The β amino acid chain produced has one glutamic acid molecule replaced by a valine molecule

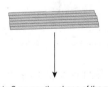

4. The haemoglobin molecule containing the abnormal β chains becomes sticky and forms long fibres when the oxygen level of the blood is low. This haemoglobin is called haemoglobin-S

5. Haemoglobin-S causes the shape of the red bood cell to become crescent (sickle) shaped

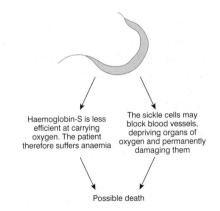

Haemoglobin-S is less efficient at carrying oxygen. The patient therefore suffers anaemia

The sickle cells may block blood vessels, depriving organs of oxygen and permanently damaging them

Possible death

Fig 4.20 *How a single substitution mutation results in sickle cell anaemia*

4.11

Environment and phenotype

Siamese cats have dark fur at the extremities of their bodies as a result of an enzyme involved in melanin production that only functions at lower temperatures

The Arctic fox produces darker pigmentation when the temperature is warmer, giving rise to the grey-blue summer coat. In colder conditions, no pigmentation occurs, giving rise to the white winter coat that camouflages it better against its snowy background

You may recall that in section 4.3.1 we saw how the final appearance of an organism – its phenotype – is the result of the genotype and the effect of the environment upon it. If organisms of identical genotype are exposed to different environmental influences, they show considerable variety. Because environmental influences, e.g. temperature and light intensity, are themselves very various and because they form gradations, they are largely responsible for continuous variation within a population.

4.11.1 How the environment may affect the phenotype

The **alleles** that make up the genotype of an organism provide a blueprint that determines the limits within which the organism will develop. The degree to which an allele is expressed often depends upon the environment. Examples include:

- The **recessive** *ch* allele in Siamese cats and Himalayan rabbits (section 4.7.3) codes for a heat sensitive form of the enzyme tyrosinase. This enzyme is involved in the production of the dark pigment, melanin. The *ch* form of the enzyme does not function at temperatures above 33°C. Over much of the body surface of Siamese cats and Himalayan rabbits the temperature is above 33°C and so the enzyme is inactivated and no melanin is produced during development. The fur in these regions is therefore light in colour. At the extremities such as the tips of the tail, ears, feet and nose, the temperature is usually below 33°C and so the *ch* form of tyrosinase is active and melanin is produced. These regions are therefore much darker in colour.

- A small Californian plant, *Potentilla glandulosa*, has a number of genetic forms, each adapted to growing at different altitudes. Experiments were carried out as follows:
  - plants of *Potentilla* were collected from three altitudes – high, medium and low
  - one plant from each location was split into three cuttings, each of which therefore had an identical genotype
  - one of the cuttings from each location was grown at each altitude (high, medium and low)
  - three separate sets of genetically identical plants were therefore grown in three different environments.

  The results are illustrated in figure 4.21 and show that plants with identical genotypes differ in phenotype (height, number of leaves, overall size and shape) and even survival rate, according to the environment in which they live.

- Arctic foxes have the alleles to make fur pigments and so produce dark coats. These pigments are, however, produced only in warm temperatures. They are therefore not produced as the colder temperatures of winter approach and so the surface hairs are slowly replaced by white ones. By the time the winter snows cover the ground, the Arctic fox is completely white and so better camouflaged and therefore more able to capture its prey.

- The height of humans is determined by the range of alleles for height that each of us inherits from our parents. However, even if our alleles allow us to grow tall, our diet will influence whether we do so. For example, a lack of calcium or poor overall nutrition especially at critical growth periods (early years and adolescence) may prevent maximum bone and body growth and so we fail to realise our full potential height.

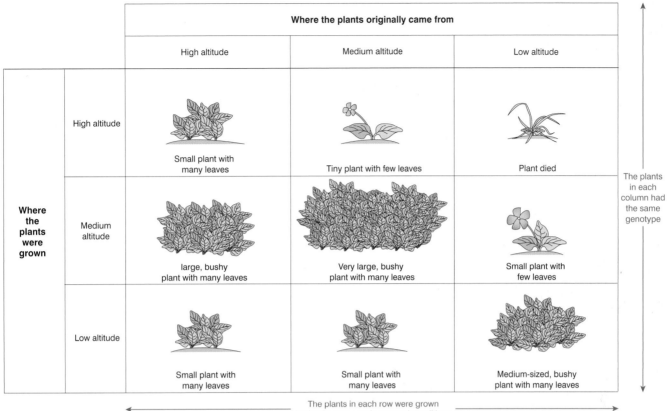

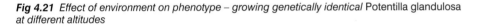

Fig 4.21 *Effect of environment on phenotype – growing genetically identical* Potentilla glandulosa *at different altitudes*

- A set of plants grown in a soil deficient in nitrogen will develop far less **biomass** than another genetically identical set grown in soils with a plentiful supply of nitrogen.

All these examples illustrate how the environment affects the alleles of an organism and so influences its phenotype. The genotype determines the range of possible phenotypes, but the environment often determines where within that range the actual appearance of an organism lies.

SUMMARY TEST 4.11

The phenotype of an organism is the result of the effect of the **(1)** and the organism's **(2)**. For example, in Siamese cats there is a heat sensitive form of the **(3)** called tyrosinase that is involved in the production of the pigment known as **(4)**. The production of this heat sensitive form of tyrosinase is controlled by an **(5)** represented by *ch*. This form of the enzyme is inactive at temperatures **(6)** 33°C. Body temperatures below this normally occur at the **(7)** of the body and so in these regions the pigment is produced and the fur is coloured **(8)**. If genetically identical forms of the plant *Potentilla glandulosa* are grown at different **(9)** their phenotype differs in **(10)** and **(11)** due to the different environments they experience. It is clear therefore that the **(12)** of an organism determines the **(13)** of possible phenotypes, but it is the **(14)** that influences its final appearance.

How can we be sure that the dark extremities of Siamese cats are the result of the temperature at which fur develops, rather than simply being genetically determined? A couple of simple experiments prove the case:

- Some dark fur is removed from the tail of a Siamese cat which is then kept in a warmer than usual environment. The new fur that develops is light in colour.
- Some light fur is removed from the back of a Siamese cat and the shaved area kept at a lower than normal temperature. The new growth of fur is black.

Had fur colour been determined only by genes, with no environmental influence, then in both cases the new fur would have matched the original colour.

4.12

Genes and the environment – control of protein synthesis

We have so far looked at two ways in which the environment may influence the way the **genotype** is expressed in the **phenotype**. In units 4.10 and 4.11 we saw how environmental factors may affect the rate of mutations and thereby affect both genotype and phenotype. In unit 4.12 we looked at how environmental factors such as temperature, altitude and nutrition can influence how the genes of an organism are expressed in the phenotype. There is a third mechanism involving the interaction between the genes and the environment. This is the way in which environmental factors can switch genes on and off. It is nicely illustrated by the way in which the bacterium *Escherichia coli* synthesises certain proteins.

4.12.1 Control of protein synthesis in bacteria

As with all organisms, bacteria such as *E. coli* need to synthesise proteins by the mechanisms described in *Essential AS Biology for OCR* units 5.6 and 5.7. Some of these proteins are needed continually by the cell and so the polypeptides of which they are made are produced continuously. Other proteins are only required in certain circumstances and therefore need not be produced all the time – indeed to do so would be wasteful. Under normal circumstances *E. coli* absorbs and respires glucose as its main respiratory substrate. If, however, it is grown on a medium in which lactose is present it is able to produce two enzymes:

- **lactose permease** – helps the cell to absorb lactose
- **β-galactosidase** – hydrolyses lactose to glucose and galactose.

As lactose is not always available, it would be wasteful of material and energy for *E. coli* to produce these two enzymes continuously. Far better to express (switch on) the genes that code for these enzymes only when they are needed, i.e. when lactose is available. How then is *E. coli* able to do this?

4.12.2 The *lac* operon

The *lac* operon is a length of DNA that is responsible for the production of β-galactosidase and lactose permease. As illustrated in figure 4.22, it is made up of a number of parts:

- **The structural genes** comprise the length of DNA with the bases needed to produce the mRNA that codes for the polypeptides that make up the two enzymes.
- **The operator** is a portion of DNA lying next to the structural genes that effectively switches them on and off.
- **The promoter** is a portion of DNA to which the enzyme RNA polymerase becomes attached in order to begin the process of **transcription** of mRNA from the structural genes (*Essential AS Biology for OCR*, unit 5.6). The promoter is adjacent to the operator – the significance of which will become apparent later. There is another portion of DNA, called the **regulator gene**, involved in the process. This portion of the DNA is not part of the *lac* operon and is situated some distance from it (Fig 4.22).

4.12.3 How the *lac* operon works

The following account of how *E. coli* controls the production of lactose permease and β-galactosidase is illustrated in figure 4.22.

- The regulator gene codes for a protein called the **repressor protein**.

SUMMARY TEST 4.12

One example of how the environment affects the phenotype of organisms is the influence it has in switching genes on and off. The bacterium *E. coli* uses **(1)** as its main **(2)** substrate. If lactose is present in the medium on which *E. coli* is growing, it can absorb it and break it down into **(3)** and **(4)**. It is able to do this using a length of DNA known as the **(5)**, which comprises the **(6)** genes that code for the enzymes involved as well as a portion of DNA called the **(7)** that switches these genes on and off. Another portion of DNA called the **(8)** can bind to the enzyme RNA polymerase that initiates the transcription of **(9)**. The process involves a portion of DNA called the **(10)** gene that lies some distance away producing a protein called the repressor protein. One part of this protein can bind to a part of DNA called the **(11)**, but in doing so the repressor protein covers an adjacent portion of DNA called the promoter. In doing so it blocks an enzyme called **(12)** from binding to this portion of DNA and so prevents the production of mRNA and hence the enzymes involved in using lactose. If lactose is present in the growing medium, however, it binds, to the **(13)** and changes its shape in a way that it can no longer attach to the DNA and block off the promoter. This allows the enzyme that initiates the production of mRNA to bind to the promoter and so ultimately leads to the production of the enzyme called **(14)** that helps *E. coli* absorb lactose and another enzyme called **(15)** that hydrolyses lactose.

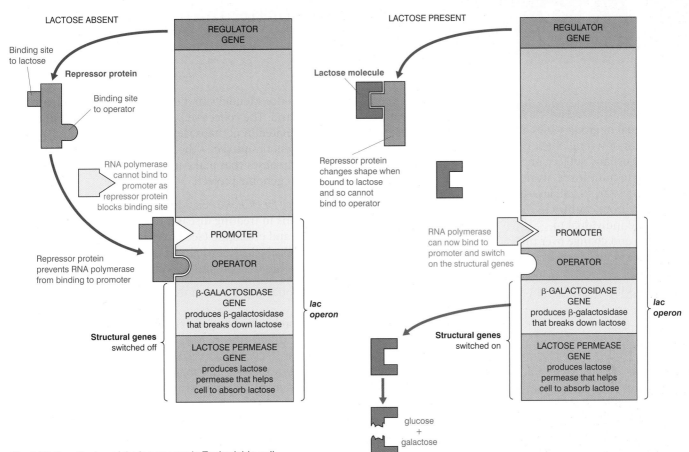

Fig 4.22 *Functioning of the* lac *operon in* Escherichia coli

- The repressor protein has two different binding sites:
  - one that binds to lactose
  - one that binds to the operator.
- If there is no lactose present in the medium on which *E. coli* is growing, the repressor protein will bind to the operator.
- Because the operator and promoter are close together, the repressor protein covers part of the promoter when it binds to the operator. This blocks the site on the promoter to which **RNA polymerase** normally attaches.
- RNA polymerase cannot attach to the promoter and therefore cannot express (switch on) the structural genes that code for the two enzymes.
- mRNA cannot be made on the structural genes and therefore neither β-galactosidase nor lactose permease can be synthesised, i.e. their production stops.
- If lactose is added to the medium on which *E. coli* is growing, it binds to its site on the repressor protein.
- As a result of this binding of lactose, the repressor protein changes shape in such a way that it can no longer use its other binding site to attach to the operator.
- With no repressor protein to block the promoter, RNA polymerase can now attach to the promoter.
- The RNA polymerase is able to initiate the production of mRNA by the structural genes.
- This mRNA acts as a template for the assembly of the polypeptides needed to synthesise β-galactosidase and lactose permease.
- Lactose permease helps *E. coli* to absorb lactose rapidly from the medium and this is hydrolysed by β-galactosidase to glucose and galactose – the glucose being used as a respiratory substrate.

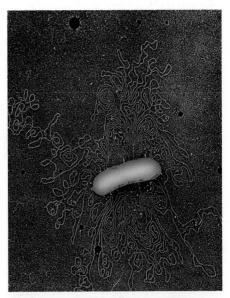

Escherichia coli *treated so that its DNA is ejected from the cell. This DNA is 1.5 mm long – some 1000 times the length of the cell – and part of it forms the* lac *operon*

4.13

The implications of the human genome project

Morals

are individual or group views about what is right or wrong. Such views refer to almost any subject, such as it is wrong to hunt foxes, work on a Sunday, to swear, to tell lies. Morals vary from country to country and individual to individual, and change over time. Most people would now disagree with some of the accepted moral values of a hundred years ago in the UK.

Genetics has come a long way since Mendel's first experiments on pea plants in a small monastery garden in Austria. The collective knowledge of generations of scientific researchers has culminated in perhaps the most significant, and certainly the most ambitious, genetics project – the sequencing of each and every one of the 3.2 billion **nucleotide** bases that make up each human's DNA – otherwise known as the human genome project.

In unit 11.5 of *Essential AS Biology for OCR* we considered the human genome project and its useful applications in treating disease. In this unit we shall look at the many moral, ethical, social and economic (see boxes in margin) implications of this project and the way in which the knowledge it provides is, and could be, used. First to recap on what the human genome project is:

- The largest piece of international collaboration that has ever taken place in biology.
- Begun in 1990, by 2000 the project had sequenced almost all the 3.2 billion base pairs that make up the human genome (i.e. all its genes).
- It indicates that humans have 25 000–30 000 genes, the vast majority of which are shared by other organisms, especially our mammalian relatives.
- Knowledge of the human genome has immense potential in the diagnosis and treatment of disease.

Ethics

is a narrower concept than morals. Ethics are a set of standards that are followed by a particular group of individuals and are designed to regulate their behaviour. They determine what is acceptable and legitimate in pursuing the aims of the group. Ethics vary from society to society and change over time.

4.13.1 What are the implications of the human genome project?

The human genome project has raised many issues, not least the question of who owns the genes that make up human beings. The answer might, at first glance, appear obvious – we each own our own genes. However, the vast majority of these genes are not unique to each individual, but are shared by other humans and indeed other organisms, including bacteria. How can we balance the right of one individual to say how the information on the base sequence of one of their genes is used with the rights of thousands of millions of other humans who possess the same gene and may have a different opinion about how the information should be used? Is a gene the property of an individual, an ethnic group in which it is very prevalent, a researcher who sequenced it, the pharmaceutical company who financed the research or the whole of humanity?

Other dilemmas raised by the information provided by the human genome project include:

Social issues

relate to human society and its organisation. They concern the mutual relationships of human beings, their interdependence and their cooperation for the benefit of all.

- Should insurance companies be allowed to see the results of genetic tests carried out on individuals before they agree to provide life insurance? If they were permitted to, might this discourage some people from taking tests for fear that, if they have a genetic disorder, life insurance companies may increase their premium or refuse cover altogether? Should insurance companies be able to insist that people at risk, i.e. those with a family history of a genetic disorder, take a genetic test? Should they be allowed to insist that we all routinely take a genetic test before they decide on the premium they will charge?
- Should companies who have financed research into a specific gene be allowed to patent the gene and so keep the information for themselves or charge for revealing it to others?
- Would the money being spent on the human genome project and the various new technologies, e.g. DNA chips, that have emerged from it be better spent elsewhere? How do we balance the need to advance medicine and to offer cures for rare genetic diseases with the need to provide clean water to the

Economic issues

relate to the production and distribution of wealth and the application of these to a particular group of individuals, e.g. a community or a business.

millions of people in developing countries who currently lack it and suffer diseases such as cholera as a result?

- Should the information about human DNA that we obtain be used to allow us to select particular genes in our children? Research suggests that intelligence and major personality traits such as aggressiveness and inquisitiveness are considerably influenced by our genes. Should we be allowed to have 'designer babies' that have their sex, physical, personal and behavioural features chosen by their parents in advance? Should we be able to select beneficial genes and eliminate detrimental ones? If so, who decides what constitutes 'beneficial' and 'detrimental'?
- Could information on an individual's DNA be used to discriminate against them, e.g. by employers, who may reject applicants with known genetic diseases? Should employers be able to require applicants to take a genetic test as part of the medical examination that is now commonly required before the offer of a job is made? Should there be legislation to outlaw genetic discrimination?
- How can we ensure that information on human DNA is not used maliciously by unscrupulous individuals for profit or political power?
- How can we ensure that information on racial or ethnic backgrounds revealed by DNA sequencing will not lead to discrimination and prejudice against particular groups?

The central issues are therefore:

- who should have access to genetic information
- what rules should be observed in using that information.

Knowledge of an individual's genetic makeup is perhaps the ultimate invasion of privacy. Keeping records of individual **genotypes** creates major problems of confidentiality, which will need to be confronted. The information that the human genome project will provide will add considerably to our knowledge of life. Used in a proper way, this knowledge can lead to major improvements in food production, health and our environment. In doing so, it can relieve suffering. Used inappropriately, it may have the opposite effect. The challenge is to ensure that the information adds to, rather than detracts from, making the world a better place.

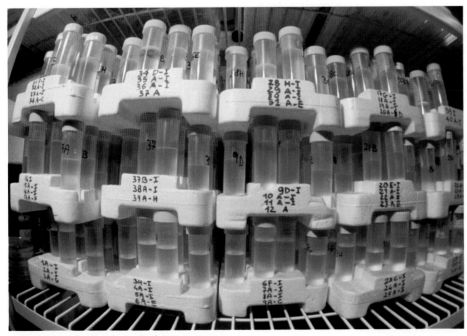

Test tubes containing the entire human genome

EXTENSION
Trouble in store?

Iceland is a relatively small and isolated community of some 270 000 people. Most of its inhabitants can therefore trace back their ancestry to the first people who settled on its shores around 1000 years ago. Tissue has been collected from every one of its inhabitants for several generations and stored with a view to carrying out a complete genetic profile of the whole nation.

Consider what information this could reveal. The relationship of every person to each other can be mapped, the incidence of genetic diseases can be measured. Who should have access to this information and for what purpose? At present the information belongs to a single company that has been set up, with the support of the government. This company's role is to sell any knowledge that comes out of the DNA analysis of this huge tissue bank. Who will share any profits made? Will there be a legal challenge to the ownership of this material from an individual or another company? Will this be a blueprint for similar schemes in other countries? We wait to see.

Iceland – where DNA from every inhabitant has been stored for many generations

5.1.1 The concept of a species

A species is the basic unit of classification. A definition of a species is not easy, but members of a single species have certain things in common:

- **They are capable of breeding** to produce living offspring **which themselves are fertile** and so can successfully produce more offspring. This means that in a species that reproduces sexually, any of the genes of its individuals can, in theory, be combined with any other, i.e. they belong to the same **gene pool**.
- **They have a common ancestry**. In other words they have arisen by adaptation of an existing species.
- **They have very similar genes** and therefore closely resemble one another both biochemically and anatomically.
- **They occupy the same ecological niche**, to the exclusion of other species.

Species are not fixed forever, but change and evolve over time. Within an individual species there can be considerable variation amongst individuals. All dogs, for example, belong to the same species, but artificial selection has led to a variety of different breeds. Nevertheless, a working definition of a species might be 'groups of organisms whose characteristics remain relatively constant, that can be distinguished from other species with whom they do not naturally interbreed'.

5.1.2 Naming species – the binomial system

During the eighteenth century, the Swedish botanist Linnaeus devised both a system of naming organisms and the basics of grouping them that are still used today.

Organisms are identified by two names and hence the system is called the **binomial system**. Its features include:

- It is a universal system based upon Latin names.
- The first name, called the **generic** name, denotes the genus to which the organism belongs. This is equivalent to the surname used to identify people and as such is shared by other close relatives.
- The second name, called the **specific** name, denotes the species to which the organism belongs. This is equivalent to the first (or given) name used to identify organisms although, unlike in people, it is never shared by any other species within the genus.

There are a number of rules that are applied to the use of the binomial system in scientific writing:

- The names are printed in italics or, if hand written, they are underlined to indicate that they are scientific names.
- The first letter of the generic name is in higher case (capitals), but the specific name is not.
- If the specific name is not known, it can be written as *sp.*, e.g. *Felix sp.*
- When referring to all members of a genus, the specific name is written as the plural, *spp.*, e.g. all members of the genus *Amoeba* is written as *Amoeba spp.*
- Once the generic name has been used initially, it can be abbreviated in later text to the first letter, e.g. the creeping buttercup *Ranunculus repens* can be written as *R. repens*.

5.1.3 Grouping species together – the principles of classification

Around 1.8 million different species have been identified and named, and yet this represents only a small proportion of the total thought to exist on Earth. There are probably at least another 5 million species either undiscovered or yet to be named. It makes sense to organise these species into manageable groups, if only to allow better communication

EXTENSION
When is a species not a species?

A horse and a donkey are capable of mating and producing offspring – known as mules. A horse and a donkey are, however, different species and the resulting mules are infertile hybrids, i.e. they can almost never produce offspring when mated with each other. There is some evidence that a few female mules are fertile, although this is exceedingly rare. So rare that the Romans had a saying 'Cum mula peperit' which means 'when a mule foals' and is the equivalent of our modern day 'once in a blue moon'. Why then are mules infertile? It is all down to the number of chromosomes and the first prophase of meiosis. You may remember from unit 4.1 that, during prophase I of meiosis,

chromosomes line up in their pairs across the equator of the cell. These pairs are homologous, i.e. both of the chromosomes are exactly the same in structure and have genes that code for the same characteristics. Now a horse has 64 chromosomes (32 pairs) and a donkey has 62 chromosomes (31 pairs). The gametes of a horse and a donkey therefore have 32 and 31 respectively. On fusion of the gametes of a horse and a donkey, the offspring (the mule) has 63 chromosomes and you cannot exactly match up 63 chromosomes into pairs. However, mitosis can take place and therefore a mule grows and develops normally, but because the chromosomes cannot form homologous pairs at prophase I, meiosis cannot occur. As this is how gametes are formed, a mule cannot produce gametes and is therefore infertile.

between scientists. The grouping of organisms is known as **classification**, while the study of biological classification is called **taxonomy**. There are two basic types of biological classification:

- **Artificial classification** divides organisms according to differences that are useful at the time. Such features may include colour, size, number of legs, leaf shape etc. These are described as **analogous** features where they have the same function but do not have the same evolutionary origins. For example, the wings of butterflies and birds are both used for flight but they originated in different ways.
- **Natural classification** is more widely used in biology and
  - is based upon the evolutionary relationships between organisms and their evolutionary descent (**phylogeny**)
  - classifies species into groups using shared features derived from their ancestors
  - is arranged in a **hierarchy** in which groups are contained within larger groups with no overlap.

Relationships in a natural classification are based upon **homologous** characteristics rather than analogous ones. Homologous characteristics have similar evolutionary origins regardless of their functions in the adult of a species. For example, the wing of a bird, the arm of a human and the front leg of a horse all have the same basic structure and all evolved from a common ancestor and are therefore homologous.

5.1.4 Organising the groups of species – taxonomy

Each group within a natural biological classification is called a **taxon** (plural = **taxa**). Taxonomy is the study of these groups which allows them to be placed in a hierarchical order, known as **taxonomic ranks**, based upon the evolutionary line of descent of the group members. Organisms are placed into one of the five kingdoms (section 5.1.5), within which the largest groups are known as phyla, and organisms in each phylum have a body plan radically different from organisms in any other phylum. Diversity within each phylum allows it to be divided into classes. Each class is divided into orders of organisms that have additional features in common. Each order is divided into families and at this level the differences are less obvious. Each family is divided into genera and each genus (singular) into species. A useful mnemonic for remembering the order of these taxonomic ranks is 'King Prawn Curry Or Fat Greasy Sausages'. The classification of three organisms is given in table 5.1.

5.1.5 The five kingdoms

There are many different schemes for the classification of organisms, each varying in the number of kingdoms they propose. Originally there were considered to be just two – plants and animals. Now five kingdoms are widely recognised: **Prokaryotae**, **Protoctista**, **Fungi**, **Plantae** and **Animalia**.

Table 5.1 *Classification of one organism from each kingdom*

Rank \ Common name	Chlamydia*	Spirogyra	Pin mould	Sweet pea	Tiger
Kingdom	Prokaryotae	Protoctista	Fungi	Plantae	Animalia
Phylum	Eubacteria	Chlorophyta	Zygomycota	Angiospermophyta	Chordata
Class	Rickettsias	Gamophyceae	Zygomycetes	Dicotyledonae	Mammalia
Order	Chlamydiales	Zygnematales	Mucorales	Rosales	Carnivora
Family	Chlamydiaceae	Zygnemataceae	Mucoraceae	Fabaceae	Felidae
Genus	*Chlamydia*	*Spirogyra*	*Mucor*	*Lathyrus*	*Felis*
Species	*pneumoniae*	*ellipsospora*	*mucedo*	*odoratus*	*tigris*

* The classification of bacteria does not strictly follow the usual seven taxonomic ranks and so the nearest equivalent groups have been used in this table.

Colour TEM of the Prokaryote – Chlamydia pneumoniae

LM of the Protoctistan – Spirogyra sp.

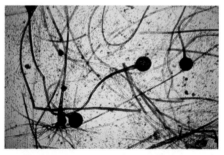

LM of the Fungus – Mucor mucedo *(bread mould)*

The plant – Lathyrus odoratus *(sweet pea)*

The animal – Felix tigris *(tiger)*

Prokaryotae, Protoctista and Fungi

The Prokaryotae, Protoctista and Fungi are three diverse kingdoms of mostly small, often microscopic, organisms.

5.2.1 Prokaryotae

The Prokaryotae are the oldest group of organisms on Earth. Their cellular structure is fundamentally different from that of the other kingdoms (Fig 5.1). All bacteria belong to the Prokaryotae, but it is difficult to sub-divide them, not least because they reproduce rapidly and so quickly evolve into new types. However, two groups are generally recognised:

- The **Archaea** are the oldest inhabitants of the Earth and were probably the first organisms to have evolved – some 3500 million years ago. Similar in appearance to other bacteria, they have fundamentally different biochemistry. They live in some of the least hospitable habitats in the world, such as hot springs and highly acidic pools.
- The **Eubacteria** comprise all the other bacteria, including the cyanobacteria (blue-green bacteria).

The distinguishing features of prokaryotes are:

- the absence of membrane-bounded organelles such as nuclei or mitochondria
- unicellular, although cells may occur in chains or clusters
- ribosomes are smaller (70S type) than in eukaryotic cells
- cell walls are present and made of murein and peptidoglycan (but never **chitin** or cellulose)
- single loop of naked DNA made up of nucleic acids but no **histones**
- no 9 + 2 arrangement of microtubules in **flagella**
- small in size – typically 0.5–5.0 μm in length.

More details about bacteria are provided in *Essential AS Biology for OCR*, unit 1.8.

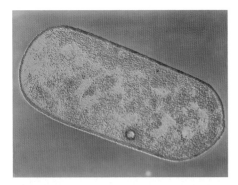

The bacterium – Clostridium perfringens – *that causes food poisoning, blood poisoning and gas gangrene in humans*

SUMMARY TEST 5.2

The Prokaryotae is the oldest group of organisms on Earth and includes the single celled organisms known as (**1**). Prokaryotes are distinguished, amongst other things, by the absence of organelles with (**2**) and having smaller ribosomes of the (**3**) type. Their cell walls are made of peptidoglycan and (**4**). The Protoctista are a very varied group of cells that possess membrane-bounded organelles and are therefore known as (**5**) cells. The Fungi comprise organisms that feed (**6**) as they do not contain (**7**). They are made up of thread-like (**8**) that collectively form a (**9**) and have cell walls made up of (**10**). They store carbohydrate in the form of (**11**).

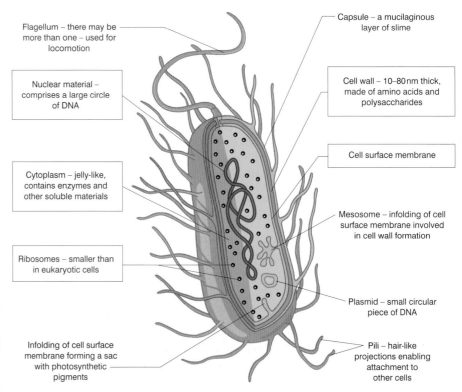

Flagellum – there may be more than one – used for locomotion

Capsule – a mucilaginous layer of slime

Nuclear material – comprises a large circle of DNA

Cell wall – 10–80nm thick, made of amino acids and polysaccharides

Cytoplasm – jelly-like, contains enzymes and other soluble materials

Cell surface membrane

Ribosomes – smaller than in eukaryotic cells

Mesosome – infolding of cell surface membrane involved in cell wall formation

Infolding of cell surface membrane forming a sac with photosynthetic pigments

Plasmid – small circular piece of DNA

Pili – hair-like projections enabling attachment to other cells

Fig 5.1 *Structure of a generalised bacterial cell. Structures in boxes occur in all bacteria.*

5.2.2 Protoctista

The Protoctista are an extremely varied group of organisms with little in common except that they are unicellular or made up of groups of similar cells and they are **eukaryotic**. The group includes:

- **Chlorophyta** – green algae, e.g. *Spirogyra*
- **Phaeophyta** – brown algae, e.g. *Fucus*
- **Rhizopoda** – protoctists with **pseudopodia**, e.g. *Amoeba*
- **Zoomastigina** – protoctists with flagella, e.g. *Trypanosoma*
- **Ciliophora** – protoctists with **cilia**, e.g. *Paramecium*
- **Euglenophyta** – protoctists with flagella but biochemistry different from the zoomastigina, e.g. *Euglena* (Fig 5.2).

The distinguishing features of the Protoctista are:

- eukaryotic cells, i.e. they possess membrane-bounded organelles such as a nucleus and mitochondria
- unicellular or groups of similar cells.

5.2.3 Fungi

The Fungi are a large group of organisms that were once classified as plants but are now allocated to a kingdom in their own right. The group includes:

- **Zygomycota** – pin moulds, e.g. *Mucor*
- **Ascomycota** – *Penicillium* moulds and yeasts, e.g. *Saccharomyces*
- **Basidiomycota** – mushrooms and toadstools, e.g. *Agaricus*

The distinguishing features of the Fungi (Fig 5.3) are:

- eukaryotic organisms
- absence of chlorophyll and therefore do not photosynthesise but feed **heterotrophically** by absorbing their food
- cell walls made of chitin rather than cellulose
- usually made up of thread-like hyphae that collectively form a **mycelium**
- carbohydrate is stored as glycogen
- reproduce sexually and asexually by means of spores that lack a flagellum.

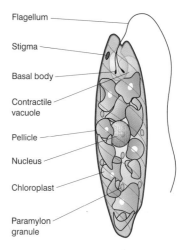

Fig 5.2 Euglena sp. *Belongs to the kingdom Protoctista*

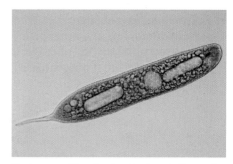

Euglena sp. *The circular structure in the centre is the nucleus and the large cylindrical ones either side of it are large paramylon granules, which store starch made by the numerous chloroplasts that fill much of the rest of the cell. The flagellum can been seen extending from the left of the cell*

Fungal fruiting bodies surround this tree stump, in which the fungal hyphae grow and feed heterotrophically

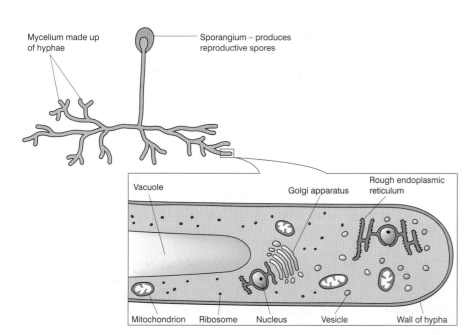

Fig 5.3 *Structure of a fungus e.g.* Mucor sp.

Plants and animals

The Plantae and the Animalia are the most familiar of the five kingdoms. They contain organisms that are multicellular for most of their life cycle.

5.3.1 Plantae

The plant kingdom is a diverse group that ranges in size from liverworts a few millimetres across to giant redwood trees over 120 metres high. The group includes:

- **Bryophyta** – liverworts and mosses, e.g. *Funaria*
- **Filicinophyta** – ferns, e.g. *Dryopteris*
- **Coniferophyta** – coniferous trees, e.g. *Pinus*
- **Angiospermophyta** – flowering plants, e.g. *Ranunculus.*

The distinguishing features of the Plantae are:

- **eukaryotic** organisms
- multicellular organisms
- possess chlorophyll and other pigments and therefore feed **autotrophically** by photosynthesis
- possess cell walls that are composed of cellulose
- carbohydrate is stored as starch

- there is an alternation between a gamete-producing **haploid** generation and a spore-producing **diploid** generation (*Essential AS Biology for OCR*, section 6.3.3).

The structure of a generalised plant cell is illustrated in figure 5.4.

These bluebells and the sycamore, elm, beech, holly and lime trees amongst which they are growing are all flowering plants

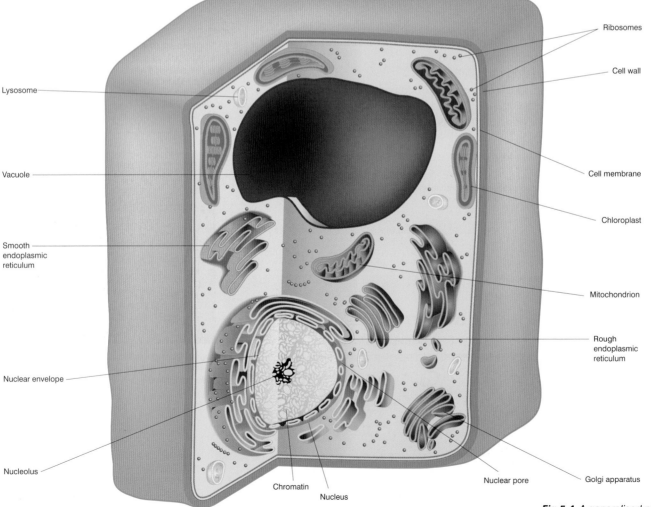

Fig 5.4 A generalised plant cell

5.3.2 Animalia

Animals show the greatest diversity of form of any of the kingdoms. Much of this diversity is a result of their ability to move from place to place, which has led to the evolution of a wide range of different methods of locomotion. The group includes:

- **Cnidaria** – jellyfish and sea anemones, e.g. *Actinia* (sea anemone)
- **Nematoda** – roundworms, e.g. *Ascaris* (roundworm)
- **Platyhelminthes** – flatworms, e.g. *Fasciola* (liver fluke)
- **Annelida** – segmented worms, e.g. *Lumbricus* (earthworm)
- **Mollusca** – limpets, mussels and snails, e.g. *Helix* (snail)
- **Arthropoda** – crabs, spiders and insects, e.g. *Pieris* (cabbage white butterfly)
- **Echinodermata** – sea urchins and starfish, e.g. *Asterias* (starfish)
- **Chordata** – fish, amphibia, reptiles, birds and mammals, e.g. *Rattus* (rat).

The distinguishing features of the Animalia are:

- eukaryotic organisms
- multicellular organisms that do not possess chlorophyll and therefore feed **heterotrophically**
- do not possess cell walls
- carbohydrate is stored as glycogen
- possess a nervous system that allows them to display nervous coordination.

The structure of a generalised animal cell is illustrated in figure 5.5.

This clown fish and the anemone it is hiding in are both animals

The hippopotamus and the wild egret standing on the hippo's head are both Chordate animals

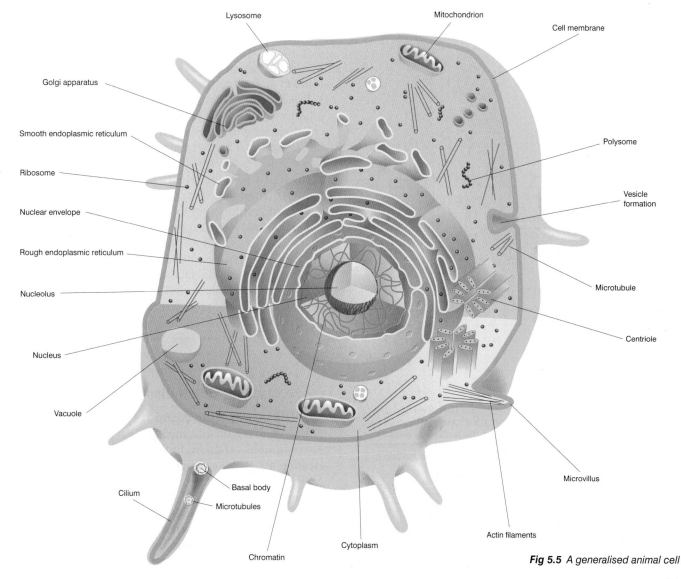

Fig 5.5 *A generalised animal cell*

81

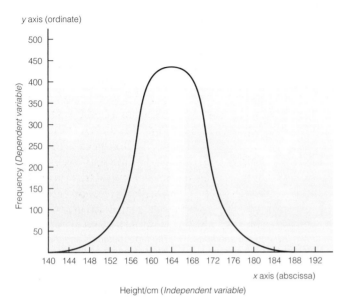

Fig 5.6 *Graph of frequency against height for a sample of humans*

y axis (ordinate)

Frequency (*Dependent variable*)

Height/cm (*Independent variable*)

x axis (abscissa)

TABLE OF PHENOTYPES	♂ GAMETES							
♀ GAMETES	RRR	RRr	RrR	rRR	Rrr	rRr	rrR	rrr
RRR	6	5	5	5	4	4	4	3
RRr	5	4	4	4	3	3	3	2
RrR	5	4	4	4	3	3	3	2
rRR	5	4	4	4	3	3	3	2
Rrr	4	3	3	3	2	2	2	1
rRr	4	3	3	3	2	2	2	1
rrR	4	3	3	3	2	2	2	1
rrr	3	2	2	2	1	1	1	0

NUMBERS OF EACH PHENOTYPE

No. of offspring	1	6	15	20	15	6	1
Colour	6	5	4	3	2	1	0

R = allele for red seed colour
r = allele for white seed colour
The numbers in the squares = the number of dominant red (R) alleles in each offspring

Fig 5.7 *Continuous variation illustrated by seed colour in wheat*

5.4   Variation

Every one of the billions of organisms on planet Earth is unique. Even monozygotic twins, although genetically identical, vary as a result of their different environmental experiences. There are two main types of variation: **continuous variation** and **discontinuous variation**.

5.4.1 Continuous variation

Some characteristics of organisms grade into one another, so forming a continuum known as continuous variation. In humans two examples are height and mass. If we take a large sample of human beings and plot on a graph the number of people at each height we obtain a bell-shaped graph known as a **normal distribution curve** (Fig 5.6).

Characters that display continuous variation are not controlled by a single **gene**, but by many (polygenes). This is called **polygenic inheritance**. A relatively simple example is shown in wheat seeds whose colour is determined by three genes (1, 2, 3) each of which has a dominant red ($R^1R^2R^3$) and a **recessive** white ($r^1r^2r^3$) **allele**. The colour of any seed is determined by the relative number of dominant red alleles and recessive white alleles. $R^1R^1R^2R^2R^3R^3$ produces dark red seeds, whereas $r^1r^1r^2r^2r^3r^3$ produces white ones. Figure 5.7 shows the number and colour range of the seeds that result from a cross between individuals that are **heterozygous** for all three genes ($R^1r^1R^2r^2R^3r^3 \times R^1r^1R^2r^2R^3r^3$). It can be seen that the number of offspring plotted against colour type produces a normal distribution curve. The random assortment of chromosomes during prophase I of **meiosis** ensures that individuals possess a range of alleles from any polygenic complex. Few will get all dominant or all recessive alleles; most will possess a combination of dominant and recessive alleles. Environmental factors have a major role in continuous variation (unit 4.11). For example, individuals who are genetically predetermined to be the same height actually grow to different heights due to variations in environmental factors such as diet. Continuous variation is the product of polygenes and the environment.

5.4.2 Discontinuous variation

Some characteristics in organisms fit into a few distinct forms; there are no intermediate types. This is called discontinuous variation. In the ABO blood grouping system (section 4.7.2), for example, there are four distinct groups: A, B, AB and O (Fig 5.8). A character displaying discontinuous variation is usually controlled by a single gene – in the case of blood groups the immunoglobulin gene (I). Discontinuous variation can be represented on bar charts or pie graphs. Environmental factors have little influence on discontinuous variation.

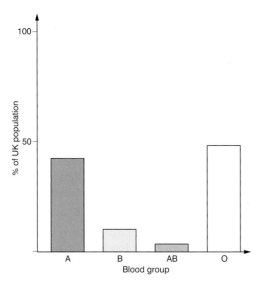

Fig 5.8 *Discontinuous variation illustrated by the percentage of the UK population with blood groups A, B, AB and O*

5.4.3 Causes of variation – genetic differences

Genetic variation is the result of the genotype of each individual, in other words the genes they possess and the forms of allele of each gene that are present. This genetic make-up varies from generation to generation as a result of:

- **Mutations** – a change in quantity or sequence of bases in DNA. There are two basic forms: **gene (point) mutations** and **chromosome mutations** (unit 4.10). While mutations in body (somatic) cells are not passed on to the next generation, those in reproductive tissues

(testes and ovaries in animals and anthers and ovaries in flowering plants) may be inherited.
- **Crossing over** and the consequent formation of recombinants during prophase I of meiosis (unit 4.1) leads to equivalent sections of **chromatids** being exchanged and therefore separates linked genes that would otherwise be inherited together.
- **Independent assortment of homologous chromosomes** at metaphase of meiosis (section 4.2.4) results in daughter cells receiving a mixture of chromosomes in the same way that a card player receives a random combination of cards when a hand is dealt.
- **Random mating between individuals within a species** – which pair of organisms of a species that mate, and hence which two genotypes combine, is largely a matter of chance, although in some animals (especially humans) there may be an element of selection involved.
- **Random fusion of gametes at fertilisation**. When mating takes place, which gamete fuses with which at fertilisation is random.

5.4.4 Causes of variation – environmental influences

Environmental influences affect the way a genotype is expressed and result in different phenotypes (section 4.11.1). Climatic factors (e.g. temperature, rainfall and sunlight) lead to variation, as do pH and amount and type of nutrients. The environment may also influence genetic variation by, for example, affecting the rate of mutation. It may also switch genes on and off. This is best illustrated by the *lac* operon in *Escherichia coli* (unit 4.12).

SUMMARY TEST 5.4

There are two main types of variation in organisms. In continuous variation, the various forms of a characteristic grade into one another to form a continuum. Examples in humans include (**1**) and (**2**). In a large sample of humans, if we plot the number of people at each point within the range of either of these characteristics, we obtain a bell-shaped graph called a (**3**). Continuous variation results from the interaction of many genes rather than a single gene. This is called (**4**) inheritance. Continuous variation is not only the result of a group of genes, but is also affected by (**5**). In discontinuous variation, organisms fit into a number of distinct groups with no intermediate types. It is usually the result of (**6**) gene and an example in humans is (**7**). Discontinuous variation is hardly, if ever, influenced by the environment. Variation has many causes. A change in the quantity of DNA, known as a (**8**), can cause variation, as can crossing over and the consequent formation of (**9**) during the (**10**) stage of meiosis. Further variation results from the (**11**) of homologous chromosomes during the (**12**) stage of meiosis as well as random (**13**) between individuals of a (**14**) and random (**15**).

5.5   Natural selection

Natural selection is the process by which organisms that are better adapted to their environment survive and breed while those less well adapted fail to do so. Those that are adapted and so survive to reproductive age will be the ones that pass on their favourable alleles to the next generation.

5.5.1 Survival of the fittest

Charles Darwin and Alfred Wallace in 1865 independently developed the theory of evolution by natural selection based on the following principles:

- All organisms produce more offspring than can be supported by the supply of food, light, space etc (section 5.6.1).
- Despite the over-production of offspring, most **populations** remain relatively constant in size.
- There must hence be competition between members of a species to be the ones that survive = intraspecific competition (section 3.2.1).
- Within any population of a species there will be a wide variety of genetically different organisms (unit 5.4).
- Some of these individuals will possess **alleles** that make them better able (fitter) to survive and so more likely to breed.
- Only those individuals that do survive and breed will pass on their alleles to the next generation.
- The advantageous alleles that gave these individuals the edge in the struggle to survive and breed are therefore likely to be passed on to the next generation.
- Over many generations, the individuals with beneficial alleles are more likely to survive to breed and therefore increase in number at the expense of the individuals with less favourable alleles.
- The frequency of favourable alleles in the population will increase over time.

Specific examples of how natural selection produces changes within a species include:

- antibiotic resistance in bacteria
- pesticide resistance in insects and mammals
- industrial melanism.

5.5.2 Antibiotic resistance in bacteria

It was not long after the discovery of antibiotics before it was realised that some no longer killed bacteria as effectively as before. It was found that these populations of bacteria had developed resistance, as the result not of a cumulative tolerance to the antibiotic, but rather a chance **mutation** within the bacteria. This mutation resulted in bacteria that could produce an enzyme, penicillinase, which broke down the antibiotic penicillin before it was able to kill them. When penicillin is used thereafter, only the non-resistant forms of the bacteria are killed. There is therefore a selection pressure favouring the resistant form when exposed to penicillin. These penicillin-resistant bacteria therefore gradually predominate in the population. The frequency of the allele for penicillin resistance increases in the population. This type of selection is called directional selection and is described in section 5.7.3.

More significantly, the allele for antibiotic resistance is carried on **plasmids** and these loops of DNA can be transferred from cell to cell by natural as well as artificial means. Resistance can therefore find its way into other bacterial species. Overuse of antibiotics, e.g. for minor infections that present no danger, increases the likelihood of selection of resistant strains over ones that are more susceptible to the antibiotic.

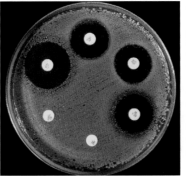

Antibiotic resistance in Escherichia coli. The six white pellets, each possessing a different antibiotic, were placed on a Petri dish with a growing culture of E. coli. *Around four of the pellets there is a lack of bacterial growth (inhibition zone), indicating that the bacterium is sensitive to these antibiotics. The growth of the bacterium around the two other pellets is unaffected, however, indicating that it is resistant to these antibiotics*

5.5.3 Pesticide resistance in insects and mammals

In a similar way to antibiotic resistance in bacteria, insect populations have developed resistance to insecticides such as DDT. Many common insect pests are now resistant to many insecticides through their ability to break down the insecticide with enzymes whose production has arisen as the result of a chance mutation. In the presence of the insecticide, insects with the mutant allele are more likely to survive to breed than the ones with a normal allele. The frequency of the mutant allele in the population therefore increases. This resistance has slowed down progress in controlling both insect pests that harm our crops and ones such as mosquitoes that carry the malarial parasite *Plasmodium*.

Resistance to pesticides in mammals has affected the control of rat populations. A chemical called **warfarin** has been used to kill rats since the 1950s. It is given to rats in the form of food baited with the chemical. Once ingested, warfarin prevents blood clotting, causing haemorrhaging and death of the rats. A warfarin-resistant allele arose in the rat population that allowed them to survive when warfarin was ingested. The continued use of warfarin caused the death of the non-resistant varieties of rats and allowed the allele for resistance to build up in the population as a result of the warfarin-resistant individuals surviving and breeding. Both examples illustrate directional selection (section 5.7.3).

5.5.4 Industrial melanism

Some species of organisms have two or more distinct forms or **morphs**. These different morphs are genetically distinct but exist within the same interbreeding population. This situation is called **polymorphism** ('poly' = many; 'morph' = form). One example is the peppered moth (*Biston betularia*). It existed only in its natural light form until the middle of the nineteenth century. Around this time a melanic (black) variety arose as the result of a mutation. These mutants had undoubtedly occurred before (one existed in a collection made before 1819) but they were highly conspicuous against the light background of lichen-covered trees and rocks on which they normally rest. As a result, the black mutants were subjected to greater predation from insect-eating birds, e.g. robins and hedge sparrows, than were the better camouflaged, normal light forms.

When in 1848 a melanic form of the peppered moth was captured in Manchester, most buildings, walls and trees were blackened by the soot of 50 years of industrial development. The sulphur dioxide in smoke emissions killed the lichens that formerly covered trees and walls. Against this black background the melanic form was less, not more, conspicuous than the light natural form. As a result, the light form was taken by birds more frequently than the melanic form and, by 1895, 98% of Manchester's population of the moth was of the melanic type.

This is an example of selective predation by birds favouring individuals that lie at one extreme or the other of a range of different colour types. As such it illustrates disruptive selection (section 5.7.4). It also shows evolution in action. However, as the two populations overlap and interbreed they are still one species. To become two distinct species, the two populations would need to become reproductively isolated from one another (section 5.9.1).

Industrial melanism in the peppered moth (Biston betularia). Against a natural background (above) the dark melanic form is far more visible and more readily predated on by birds. This natural selection leads to a predominance of the light form in rural areas. In polluted areas, however, the melanic form is better camouflaged and this selective advantage leads to this form predominating

SUMMARY TEST 5.5

The theory of natural selection by survival of the fittest was developed independently by Charles Darwin and **(1)**. It is based on the principles that all organisms produce **(2)** offspring than can be supported by the food, light and space available for them. However the size of most populations is **(3)** as a result of competition between members of each species for the limited resources available. This type of competition is called **(4)**. Within any population there will be many types of **(5)** different individuals. Those individuals with **(6)** that better suit them to the prevailing conditions are more likely to survive and hence more likely to produce **(7)**. As only those that survive can pass their characteristics to the next generation, there is an increased chance that the next generation will have a greater proportion of these advantageous characteristics. Examples of natural selection in practice include **(8)** resistance in bacteria and **(9)** resistance in insects and mammals. For example some bacteria have become resistant to the drug **(10)**, some insects resistant to **(11)** and mammals such as rats resistant to the chemical **(12)**. Another example of natural selection has occurred in the peppered moth. This moth has two forms, a natural light coloured one and a dark coloured one called the **(13)** form. The general term for the situation where a species has two or more distinct forms is **(14)**. Research showed that in areas where there was pollution from soot, the dark form survived better as individuals were **(15)** against the blackened background of buildings and trees and so were less likely to be eaten by birds. In less polluted, rural areas the light form predominated because the dark form was more obvious and so more readily eaten by birds. This overall situation where darker-coloured moths adapted to suit polluted areas is known as **(16)**.

5.6 The roles of over-production and variation in natural selection

The process of evolution by means of natural selection depends upon a number of factors. Two of the most important are that:

- organisms produce more offspring than can be supported by the available supply of food, light, space etc
- there is genetic variety within the **populations** of all species.

5.6.1 Over-production of offspring

Darwin appreciated that all species have the potential to increase their numbers exponentially (Fig 5.9). To illustrate this point he wrote:

> 'Suppose…there are eight pairs of birds, and that only four of them annually…rear only four young, and that these go on rearing their young at the same rate, then at the end of seven years (a short life, excluding violent deaths, for any bird) there will be 2048 birds instead of the original sixteen.'

Darwin realised that, in nature, populations rarely, if ever, increased in size at such a rate. He rightly concluded that the death rate of even the most slow-breeding species must be extremely high. Why and how do organisms reproduce so rapidly with little prospect of all but a tiny proportion of offspring surviving? The reason why reproductive rates are high is because a species cannot control the climate, rate of predation, availability of food, etc. Therefore to ensure a sufficiently large population survives to breed and produce the next generation, each species must produce vast numbers of offspring. This is to compensate for considerable death rates from predation, lack of food (including light in plants) and water, extremes of temperature, natural disasters such as earthquake and fire, disease etc.

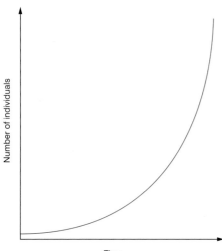

Fig 5.9 *The exponential rise in the population numbers of a species whose growth is left unchecked by environmental factors such as predation, climate, disease etc*

EXTENSION

An example of how genetic variation leads to natural selection – copper tolerance in grasses

Species of grasses such as *Agrostis tenuis* and *Agrostis capillaris* have a variety of different forms with respect to copper tolerance (Fig 5.10). Some varieties are very tolerant and grow readily in soils with a high level of copper **ions**. Other varieties have a very low tolerance and do not survive, even when soil copper levels are very low. The majority of the varieties lie somewhere between these two extremes. The soil around old copper workings is heavily contaminated with copper. If seeds of *Agrostis sp.* are planted in this soil, only those with a high tolerance to copper will survive. These types are therefore the only ones that breed and are hence selected for in preference to the other varieties of *Agrostis sp.* In time, the whole population of the grasses in the copper-contaminated area is of the few very copper-tolerant varieties. Natural selection has shifted the genetic makeup of *Agrostis spp.* towards copper-tolerant varieties. On soils with low levels of copper, there is no selective advantage in being copper-tolerant and so the proportion of these varieties remains low. They nevertheless survive where soil copper levels are low because there is no disadvantage in having tolerance to copper but there is no particular advantage either. Their numbers remain low because copper tolerance shows polygenic inheritance (section 5.4.1) and there is a much lower statistical chance of the predominantly **homozygous** alleles needed for copper tolerance occurring in the population.

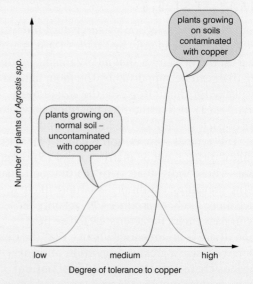

Fig 5.10 *Copper tolerance in* Agrostis spp.

How organisms over-produce depends on the species in question and its means of reproduction. Some examples include:

- A bacterium can divide by binary fission about every 20 minutes when conditions are favourable. A single bacterium could theoretically give rise to 4×10^{21} cells in just 24 hours.
- Some fungi can produce over 500 000 spores each minute at the peak of production. Each spore has the potential to develop a new fungal **mycelium**.
- Higher plants can spread rapidly by **vegetative propagation**, e.g. the production of bulbs, rhizomes, runners etc.
- Flowering plants produce vast amounts of pollen from their anthers. These can fertilise the many ovules in plants of the same species, leading to the production, in some cases, of millions of seeds from a single plant.
- Animals produce vast numbers of sperm, and sometimes large numbers of eggs also. A female oyster, for example, can produce 100 million eggs in a year and the male oyster produces many more times this number of sperm.
- Many organisms, e.g. birds such as blue tits and mammals like the rabbit, produce several clutches/litters every year, each of which comprises several offspring.

The importance of over-production to natural selection lies in the fact that, where there are too many offspring for the available resources, there is competition amongst individuals (**intraspecific competition**) for the limited resources available. The greater the numbers, the greater this competition and the more individuals will die in the struggle to survive. These deaths are, however, not random. Those individuals best suited to prevailing conditions (e.g. better able to hide from or escape predators, better able to obtain light or catch prey, better able to resist disease or find a mate) will be more likely to survive than those less well adapted. These individuals will be more likely to breed and so pass on these favourable characteristics, via their alleles, to the next generation, which will therefore be slightly different from the previous one – i.e. the species will have evolved to be better adapted to the prevailing conditions. This selection process, however, depends on individuals of a species being genetically different from one another.

5.6.2 Variation and natural selection

Variation within a species. Despite the immense variety they show, all dogs, including this Great Dane and Pug dog, all belong to the same species – Canis familiaris

If an organism can survive in the conditions in which it lives, you may wonder why it doesn't produce offspring that are identical to itself. These will, after all, be equally capable of survival in these conditions, whereas variation may produce individuals that are less suited. However, conditions change over time and having a wide range of different individuals in the population means that some will have the combination of genes needed to survive in almost any set of new circumstances. Populations showing little individual variation are vulnerable to new diseases and climate changes. It is also important that a species adapts to changes resulting from the evolution of other species. If, for example, rabbits in a particular region evolve to run faster, foxes and other predators will be less able to catch them and therefore have less food, unless they in turn develop greater speed. A species cannot predict future changes; it does not know whether the climate will become wetter/drier, warmer/colder or how its prey or predator will evolve or what new disease agent may arise. However, the larger a population is, and the more genetically varied the organisms within it, the greater the chance that one or more individuals will have the genetic characteristics that give it an advantage in the struggle for survival. These individuals will therefore be more likely to breed and pass their more suitable characteristics on to future generations. Variation therefore provides the potential for a species to evolve and so adapt to new circumstances.

The influence of variation on natural selection is best summarised by Darwin himself who, nearly a hundred and fifty years ago, wrote:

'How can it be doubted, from the struggle each individual has to obtain subsistence, that any minute variation in structure, habits or instinct, adapting that individual better to the new conditions, would tell upon its vigour and health? In the struggle it would have a better chance of surviving; and those of its offspring which inherited the variation, be it ever so slight, would have a better chance'.

SUMMARY TEST 5.6

The process of natural selection depends upon a species producing more offspring than its environment can support. Over-production of offspring occurs in bacteria because a single bacterium dividing by (1) can, under ideal conditions, produce 4×10^{21} cells in just (2). Fungi can produce up to half a million (3) every minute at the peak of production. Flowering plants make vast quantities of (4) from their anthers and this can fertilise the many (5) and so produce numerous seeds. Many birds and mammals produce several offspring at a time and may have more than one (6) each year. Over-production of offspring leads to (7) competition. As a result only those individuals best suited to the prevailing conditions will survive and therefore are more likely to (8). This process of natural selection can only take place if there is (9) amongst the individuals in the population. If all individuals were identical, no single organism would have a selective advantage over the others.

5.7

How environmental factors act as forces of natural selection

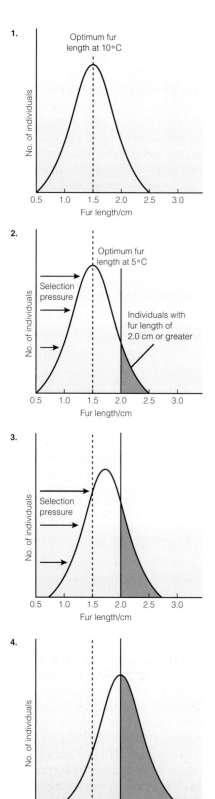

Fig 5.11 *Directional selection*

We saw in unit 5.6 that within a **population** certain individuals are better suited to the existing conditions. These individuals are more likely to survive and pass their **alleles** on to succeeding generations. Selection operates in a number of different ways.

5.7.1 Selection pressure

Every organism is subjected to a process of selection, based upon its suitability for survival under the conditions that exist at the time. The environmental factors that limit the population of a species are called **selection pressures** or **environmental resistances**. These selection pressures include:

- competition for food
- competition for a space in which to live, breed and rear young
- need for light, water, oxygen etc
- climate changes, e.g. temperature, rainfall, wind/water currents
- predation
- disease.

The extent and direction of selection pressures varies from time to time and place to place. These selection pressures determine the frequency of an allele within the gene pool. A **gene pool** is the total of all the alleles of all the genes of all individuals within a particular population at a given time.

There are three main types of selection:

- Selection that preserves the characteristics of a population by favouring average individuals = **stabilising selection**.
- Selection that changes the characteristics of a population by favouring individuals that vary in one direction from the mean of the population = **directional selection**.
- Selection that changes the characteristics of a population by favouring individuals at the extremes rather than those around the mean of the population = **disruptive selection**.

5.7.2 Stabilising selection

Stabilising selection tends to eliminate the extremes of the **phenotype** range within a population and with it the opportunity for evolutionary change. It arises where the environmental conditions are constant. To take the example of fur length in a particular mammalian species. In years when the environmental temperatures are hotter than usual, the individuals with shorter fur length will be at an advantage because they can lose body heat more rapidly. In colder years the opposite is true and those with longer fur length will survive better as they are better insulated. Therefore, if the environment fluctuates from year to year, both extremes will survive because each will have some years when it can thrive at the expense of the other. If, however, the environmental temperature is

In a population of a particular mammal, fur length shows continuous variation.

1. When the average environmental temperature is 10°C, the optimum fur length is 1.5 cm. This then represents the mean fur length of the population.

2. A few individuals in the population already have a fur length of 2.0 cm or greater. If the average environmental temperature falls to 5°C, these individuals are better insulated and so are more likely to survive to breed. There is a selection pressure favouring individuals with longer fur.

3. The selection pressure causes a shift in the mean fur length towards longer fur over a number of generations. The selection pressure continues.

4. Over further generations the shift in the mean fur length continues until it reaches 2.0 cm – the optimum length for the prevailing average environmental temperature of 5°C. The selection pressure now ceases.

constantly 10°C, individuals at the extremes will never be at an advantage and will therefore be selected against in favour of those with average fur length. The mean will remain the same, but there will be fewer individuals at either extreme (Fig 5.12). An actual example of stabilising selection is the body mass of human children at birth. Babies born with a body mass greater or less than the optimum of 3.2 kg have a higher mortality rate.

5.7.3 Directional selection

Within a population there will be a range of individuals in respect of any one character. The continuous variation amongst these individuals forms a normal distribution curve that has a mean that represents the optimum value for the character under the existing conditions. If the environmental conditions change, so will the optimum value needed for survival. Some individuals, either to the left or the right of the mean, will possess a phenotype with the new optimum for the character and so there will be a selection pressure moving the mean to either the left or the right of its original position. Directional selection therefore results in one extreme of a range of variation being selected against in favour of the other extreme. Figure 5.11 (opposite) illustrates a theoretical example of directional selection. A specific example is antibiotic resistance in bacteria (section 5.5.2).

5.7.4 Disruptive selection

Disruptive selection is the opposite of stabilising selection. It favours the two extreme phenotypes at the expense of the intermediate phenotype. Although the least common form of selection, it is the most important in bringing about evolutionary change. Disruptive selection occurs when an environmental factor, such as temperature, takes two or more distinct forms. In our example this might arise if the temperature alternated between 5°C in winter (favouring long fur length) and 15°C in summer (favouring short fur length). This could ultimately lead to two separate species of the mammal – one with long fur and active in winter, the other with short fur and active in summer (Fig 5.13). An actual example is the evolution of the peppered moth, *Biston betularia*, which is described in section 5.5.4.

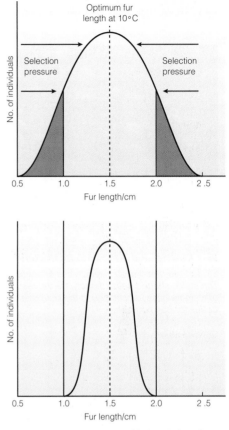

1. Initially there is a wide range of fur length about the mean of 1.5 cm. The fur lengths of less than 1.0 cm or greater than 2.0 cm in individuals are maintained by rapid breeding in years when the average temperature is much warmer or colder than normal.

2. When the average environmental temperature is consistently around 10°C with little annual variation, individuals with very long or very short hair are eliminated from the population over a number of generations.

Fig 5.12 *Stabilising selection*

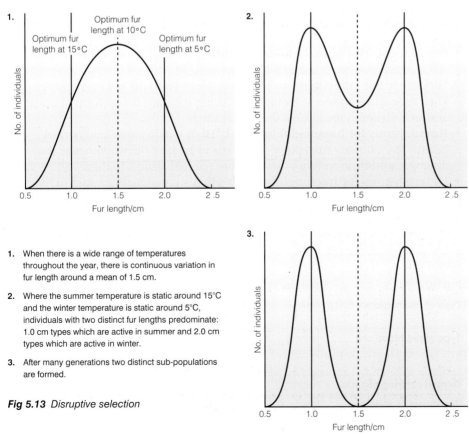

1. When there is a wide range of temperatures throughout the year, there is continuous variation in fur length around a mean of 1.5 cm.

2. Where the summer temperature is static around 15°C and the winter temperature is static around 5°C, individuals with two distinct fur lengths predominate: 1.0 cm types which are active in summer and 2.0 cm types which are active in winter.

3. After many generations two distinct sub-populations are formed.

Fig 5.13 *Disruptive selection*

SUMMARY TEST 5.7

The environmental factors that limit a population are called (1). These factors determine the frequency of an allele within a (2). The type of selection that favours individuals at the extremes rather than those around the mean of a population is called (3) selection. Selection that favours average individuals is called (4) selection and where individuals that vary in one direction are favoured, it is called (5) selection.

Allelic frequencies and the processes affecting them

SEM of red blood cells in sickle cell anaemia. The sickle shaped cells (darker) are the result of a single base substitution in the DNA that codes for haemoglobin

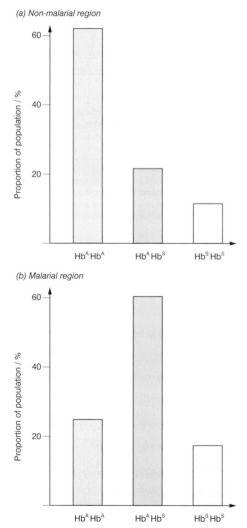

(a) Non-malarial region

(b) Malarial region

Fig 5.14 Distribution of the sickle cell allele in a non-malarial and a malarial population

In theory, any sexually mature individual in a **population** is capable of breeding with any other. This means that the **alleles** of any individual organism may be combined with the alleles of any other. All the alleles of all the genes of all the individuals in a population at any one time is known as the **gene pool**. The number of times an allele occurs within the gene pool is referred to as the **allelic frequency**. The allelic frequency is affected by **selection** and, as we saw in section 5.7.1, selection is affected by environmental factors. Environmental changes therefore affect the probability of an allele surviving in a population and hence the number of times it occurs within the gene pool. It must be emphasised that environmental factors do **not** affect the probability of a **particular** mutant allele arising, they simply affect the frequency of a mutant allele that is already present in the gene pool. It should also be remembered, however, that some environmental factors may influence the overall **mutation** rate (section 4.10.5), but that this is a **general** and **random** process rather than one that affects a specific allele in a specific way. To illustrate the effect of an environmental factor on the frequency of an allele, we shall look at the condition in humans known as sickle cell anaemia.

5.8.1 Sickle cell anaemia

We saw in section 4.10.4 that sickle cell anaemia is the result of a gene mutation in which a single base substitution in DNA causes the wrong amino acid to be incorporated into two polypeptides in **haemoglobin** molecules. The result is red blood cells with a sickle (crescent) shape. Sickle cell anaemia is the result of a single **gene** for the β-polypeptide chain of haemoglobin which has two co-dominant (section 4.7.1) alleles, Hb^A (normal) and Hb^S (sickled). The malarial parasite, *Plasmodium*, is unable to exist in red blood cells with Hb^S. Table 5.2 shows the three possible genotype combinations of these two alleles and the corresponding phenotypes. The selection pressures on each genotype differ as follows:

- **Homozygous for haemoglobin-S (Hb^SHb^S)** – individuals suffer from sickle cell anaemia and are considerably disadvantaged without medical attention. They rarely live long enough to pass their genes on to the next generation. Their anaemia is so severe it outweighs being resistant to one form of malaria and so individuals are always selected against.
- **Homozygous for haemoglobin-A (Hb^AHb^A)** – individuals lead normal healthy lives, but are susceptible to malaria in areas of the world where the disease is **endemic** and they are therefore selected against in these regions only.
- **Heterozygous for haemoglobin (Hb^AHb^S)** – individuals are said to have **sickle cell trait**, but are not badly affected except when the oxygen concentration of their blood is low, e.g. in exercising muscles, when the

Table 5.2 Comparison of different genotypes of the gene for haemoglobin-A

GENOTYPE	Hb^AHb^A	Hb^AHb^S	Hb^SHb^S
PHENOTYPE	**Normal**	**Sickle cell trait**	**Sickle cell anaemia**
Type of haemoglobin	Normal	50% normal and 50% mutant	Mutant
Type of red blood cell	Normal	Usually normal, but sickle shaped at low oxygen concentrations	Sickle shaped
Oxygen carrying capacity	Normal	Reduced (mild anaemia)	Poor (severe anaemia)
Resistance to malaria	None	Moderate	High

haemoglobin crystallises and makes the red blood cells sickle shaped and less able to carry oxygen. Sufferers may therefore become tired more easily, but in general the condition is symptomless. They do, however, have resistance to malaria and this advantage outweighs the disadvantage of tiredness in areas of the world where malaria occurs. This situation is called **heterozygote superiority**. Heterozygous individuals are therefore selected against in areas without malaria, but selected for in areas where malaria is common.

To summarise, in parts of the world where malaria is prevalent, the heterozygous state (Hb^AHb^S) will be selected for at the expense of both homozygous states. This is a form of stabilising selection (section 5.7.2). In areas where malaria does not occur, the homozygous state for haemoglobin-A (Hb^AHb^A) is selected for – a form of directional selection (section 5.7.3). The homozygous recessive state for haemoglobin-S (Hb^SHb^S) is so debilitating that it is always selected against. (Figure 5.14 shows the proportion of these three genotypes in malarial and non-malarial regions.) Homozygous recessive individuals remain in the population because a recessive allele is always present in each heterozygous individual of the population. When two heterozygous individuals produce offspring, there is a one in four chance that one will be a homozygous recessive (Hb^SHb^S). Because a greater proportion of the population in a malarial region are heterozygous than in a non-malarial region, it follows that the frequency of the sickle cell allele (Hb^S) is greater in areas where malaria is present than in ones where it is absent (Fig 5.15).

SUMMARY TEST 5.8

The total number of all individual alleles of all the genes in a population is called the **(1)** and the number of times an allele occurs within a population is called the **(2)**. The occurrence of an allele in a population is affected by environmental factors through the process of **(3)**. An example of such an environmental factor occurs in the condition known as sickle cell anaemia that results from a single base in DNA being **(4)** by another base. As a result, affected individuals have **(5)** cells that are sickle (crescent) shaped. The gene for haemoglobin A has two distinct alleles, Hb^A and Hb^S, that are **(6)**. Individuals with sickle cell anaemia have the genotype **(7)** and are so disadvantaged that they rarely survive long enough to breed. Individuals with normal haemoglobin lead normal lives but are susceptible to malaria. Heterozygous individuals are affected when the **(8)** concentration of their blood is low, because this causes their haemoglobin to **(9)**, making it more difficult for them to transport oxygen. These individuals are, however, more resistant to malaria, which puts them at an advantage over both homozygous states in areas where this disease is common. This is an example of **(10)** selection. In areas where malaria is absent, individuals with normal haemoglobin are selected in favour of those with the other two genotypes – an example of **(11)** selection.

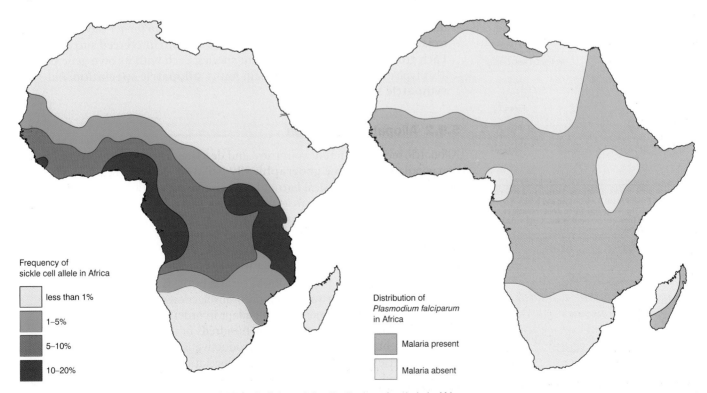

Frequency of sickle cell allele in Africa

- less than 1%
- 1–5%
- 5–10%
- 10–20%

Distribution of *Plasmodium falciparum* in Africa

- Malaria present
- Malaria absent

Fig 5.15 *Comparison of the frequency of the sickle cell allele and the distribution of malaria in Africa*

Isolation mechanisms in the evolution of new species

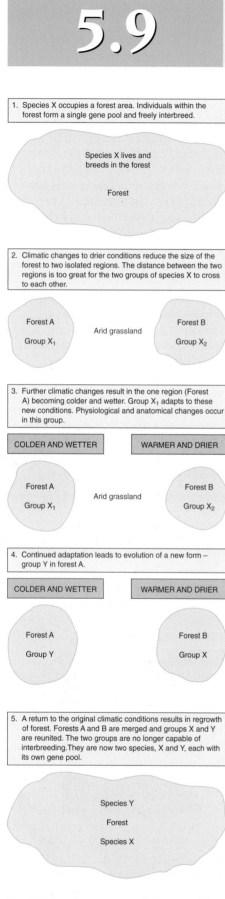

1. Species X occupies a forest area. Individuals within the forest form a single gene pool and freely interbreed.

Species X lives and breeds in the forest

Forest

2. Climatic changes to drier conditions reduce the size of the forest to two isolated regions. The distance between the two regions is too great for the two groups of species X to cross to each other.

Forest A

Group X₁

Arid grassland

Forest B

Group X₂

3. Further climatic changes result in the one region (Forest A) becoming colder and wetter. Group X₁ adapts to these new conditions. Physiological and anatomical changes occur in this group.

COLDER AND WETTER

WARMER AND DRIER

Forest A

Group X₁

Arid grassland

Forest B

Group X₂

4. Continued adaptation leads to evolution of a new form – group Y in forest A.

COLDER AND WETTER

WARMER AND DRIER

Forest A

Group Y

Forest B

Group X

5. A return to the original climatic conditions results in regrowth of forest. Forests A and B are merged and groups X and Y are reunited. The two groups are no longer capable of interbreeding. They are now two species, X and Y, each with its own gene pool.

Species Y

Forest

Species X

Fig 5.16 *Speciation as a result of geographical isolation*

Speciation is the evolution of new species from existing ones. A **species** is a group of individuals that have a common ancestry and so share similar **genes** and are capable of breeding with one another to produce fertile offspring (section 5.1.1). In other words, members of a species are **reproductively isolated**.

It is through the process of speciation that evolutionary change has taken place over millions of years. This has resulted in great diversity of forms amongst organisms, past and present.

5.9.1 How new species are formed

New species can arise in two different ways:

- **Cross fertilisation between individuals of two different species** that leads to the formation of a hybrid. This is thought to have occurred in the production of modern wheat plants from a chance hybridisation of emmer wheat and goat grass followed by chromosome doubling (**polyploidy**).

- **Reproductive isolation followed by genetic change due to natural selection**. Within a population of any species there are groups of individuals that breed with one another. These breeding sub-units are called **demes**. Although individuals tend to breed only with others in the same deme, they are nevertheless capable of breeding with individuals in other demes. In other words, the population has a single **gene pool**. Suppose, however, that the demes become isolated in some way and, due to differing selection pressures, each deme becomes genetically different as it adapts to the different environmental influences it is subjected to. This is known as **adaptive radiation** and results in changes to the **allele** frequencies in each population and in the various **phenotypes** present. As a result of these genetic differences it may be that, even if the species were no longer physically isolated from one another, they would be unable to interbreed successfully. Each group would now be a different species, each with its own gene pool. This type of speciation has two main forms, **allopatric speciation** and **sympatric speciation**.

5.9.2 Allopatric speciation

Allopatric means 'different countries' and describes the form of speciation when two populations become **geographically isolated**. Geographical isolation may be the result of any physical barrier between two populations which prevents them interbreeding. Such barriers include oceans, rivers, mountain ranges and deserts. What proves a barrier to one species may be no problem to another. While an ocean may isolate populations of hedgehogs, it can be traversed by many birds and for marine fish it is their very means of getting from place to place. A tiny stream may be a barrier to snails, whereas the whole of the Pacific Ocean fails to separate populations of certain birds. If environmental conditions either side of the barrier vary, then natural selection will influence the two populations differently and each will adapt in order to survive in their local conditions. These changes take many hundreds or even thousands of generations, but ultimately lead to reproductive isolation and the formation of separate species. Figure 5.16 shows how speciation might occur when two populations of a forest-living species become geographically isolated by a region of arid grassland.

5.9.3 Sympatric speciation

Sympatric means 'same country' and describes the form of speciation that results from populations living together becoming reproductively isolated. There are various forms of isolation that lead to sympatric speciation and these are divided into two groups:

- **Pre-mating (prezygotic) mechanisms** – occur before mating takes place and prevent the exchange of gametes. They are more efficient than post-mating mechanisms in bringing about natural selection. One example occurs in frogs, where each of four types has a different breeding season (Fig 5.17), effectively making interbreeding between different varieties so unlikely that in time they will form four different species.

- **Post-mating (postzygotic) mechanisms** – occur after mating has taken place and in some way prevent the development of zygotes into offspring.

Table 5.3 summarises all forms of reproductive isolating mechanisms.

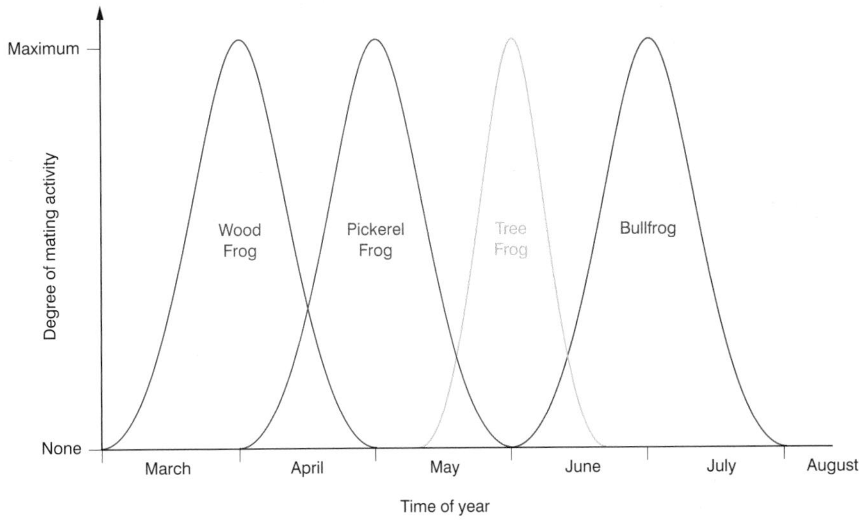

Fig 5.17 Seasonal reproductive isolation as illustrated by four varieties of frog

SUMMARY TEST 5.9

The evolution of new species from existing ones is known as **(1)**. A species is a population of organisms that is **(2)** isolated from other populations. New species can arise when cross fertilisation occurs between two different species to form a **(3)** that can reproduce to form individuals with more than two sets of chromosomes – a state called **(4)**. New species may also arise when a breeding sub-unit, called a **(5)**, of a population becomes isolated in some way. The isolated sub-unit may become genetically different as it adapts to different environmental conditions. This process is called **(6)** and results in changes to **(7)** and phenotypes of the two populations. In time the two populations may become so changed that they are unable to interbreed, at which point they have become different **(8)**. The variety of species formation is of two main types: **(9)** speciation occurs when two populations become geographically isolated, e.g. by rivers, oceans or mountain ranges. Where the two populations become reproductively isolated it is known as **(10)** speciation. Isolation may occur before mating and is called **(11)** isolation, or after mating. An example of the latter occurs when a horse (diploid number = 64) is crossed with a **(12)** (diploid number = 62), the resultant offspring called a **(13)** has 63 chromosomes. As this odd number of chromosomes cannot pair up during **(14)**, this animal is sterile. The condition is known as **(15)** sterility.

Table 5.3 Summary of the forms of reproductive isolating mechanisms

Time of isolation	Type of variation	Explanation of isolation
Pre-mating (prezygotic)	Geographical	Populations are isolated by physical barriers such as oceans, mountain ranges, rivers etc
	Ecological	Populations inhabit different habitats within the same area and so individuals rarely meet
	Temporal	The breeding seasons of each population do not coincide and so they do not interbreed. Figure 5.17 illustrates this in relation to 4 types of frog
	Behavioural	Mating is often preceded by courtship, which is stimulated by the colour or markings of the opposite sex, the call or particular actions of a mate. Any variations in these patterns may prevent mating, e.g. if a female stickleback does not respond appropriately to the actions of the male, he ceases to court her
	Mechanical	Anatomical differences may prevent mating occurring, e.g. it may be physically impossible for the penis to enter the vagina in mammals
Post-mating but prezygotic	Gametic	The gametes may be prevented from meeting due to genetic or biochemical incompatibility. For instance, some pollen grains fail to germinate or grow when they land on a stigma of different genetic makeup. Some sperm are destroyed by chemicals in the female reproductive tract
Post-mating (postzygotic)	Hybrid sterility	Hybrids formed from the fusion of gametes from different species are often sterile because they cannot produce gametes. For example, in a cross between a horse (2n = 64) and a donkey (2n = 62) the resultant mule has 63 chromosomes. It is impossible for these chromosomes to pair up during meiosis and so no gametes are formed and the mule is sterile (unit 5.1 – extension)
	Hybrid inviability	Despite fertilisation taking place, further development does not occur or fatal abnormalities arise in early growth. As the offspring do not reach sexual maturity, breeding does not occur
	Hybrid breakdown	The first generation of hybrids is fertile but the second generation fails to develop or, if it does, it is sterile

93

Adaptation of organisms to their environment

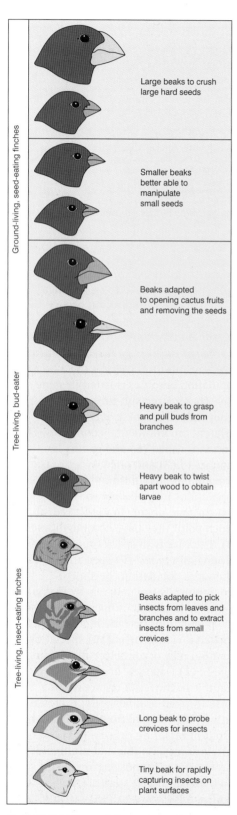

Fig 5.18 *Adaptive radiation amongst the thirteen species of Galapagos (Darwin's) finches*

An organism is considered to be adapted to a particular environment if it survives and reproduces better than other organisms in that environment. Adaptation is thus a relative term that compares performance both within and between species.

5.10.1 Adaptation and speciation

Adaptation and speciation are often related. As species adapt to different environments, they will develop differences that may lead to reproductive isolation and therefore speciation. For example, the male *Anolis* lizards of the Caribbean court females by extending a colourful flap of skin under their throat called a dewlap. There is considerable variation in the colour of these dewlaps. Some are easier to see in open **habitats**, others in shaded areas. As lizards occupy new habitats, there is selection pressure favouring the dewlaps that are most conspicuous, e.g. light coloured ones in a dark shaded forest. This adaptive change in dewlap colour means that the male may only be attractive to females stimulated by lighter dewlaps and not to ones attracted by darker dewlaps, i.e. they have become reproductively isolated and hence form a separate species.

5.10.2 Adaptive radiation – Darwin's finches

While visiting the Galapagos Islands during his voyage on HMS Beagle, Darwin was struck by the range of different beaks displayed by the 13 species of finches found there and in particular how each was adapted to obtaining different food. It is generally accepted that this variety of beaks arose as a result of what is called **adaptive radiation**. This process occurred as follows:

- The Galapagos Islands are geographically isolated, being some 1000 km from Ecuador, the nearest country on the South American mainland.
- By some means, e.g. blown by gales, or carried on a boat or vegetation, some seed-eating finches made the improbable journey from the mainland to one of the volcanic Galapagos Islands.
- This single ancestral species found few competitors on this sparsely colonised island, and so flourished.
- As with all species, **mutations** arose, leading to natural selection favouring those individuals that were better suited to some of the many **ecological niches** available on the island. In particular, changes in beak shape allowed them to exploit new food sources.
- The adaptations to these niches meant that these finches now differed from the ancestral ones on the mainland.
- Some finches found their way to other islands in the Galapagos, despite the island groups being some distance apart and hence geographically isolated.
- Again, these new arrivals flourished because there was little competition.
- Mutations again led to increased variety and natural selection favoured those changes of beak that allowed some types to use new and different varieties of food.
- The geographical isolation of the islands from the mainland, and from each other, meant that the finches on each island group were reproductively isolated and so, in time, became separate species. Even where they returned to former islands or the mainland, they could not breed successfully with their predecessors.
- Even on a single island group, the adaptations to different niches led to reproductive isolation and speciation.

The range of beak adaptations to suit different food sources among Galapagos finches is shown in figure 5.18.

5.10.3 Other examples of structural adaptations to different environments

As heat is lost and gained through the body surface it follows that, the larger the body surface area compared with the body volume, the faster will be the rate of exchange. In general, animals in cold environments have a smaller surface area to volume ratio than their relatives living in warmer climates. Mammals are **endotherms**; they gain their heat from the metabolic activities taking place inside their bodies in order to maintain a more or less constant body temperature. Those living in cold climates, such as an Arctic fox, have a smaller body surface area to volume ratio than their relations, like the fennec fox, that live in warm conditions. This is largely achieved through the size of their ears – Arctic foxes have very short external ears that reduce heat loss. Fennec foxes, by contrast, have very large external ears, enabling them to lose heat, especially during and after exertion (see photos).

For plants, the ability to withstand a shortage of water is very important. Plants transpire and so lose water continuously. If water is in short supply they must reduce **transpiration** if they are to survive. Structural adaptations to reduce transpiration are known as **xeromorphic** features and include:

- a thick waxy **cuticle** on leaves
- leaves that roll and trap moist air within the leaf
- hairy leaves that trap moist air next to the surface
- **stomata** in grooves or pits that reduce the diffusion gradient
- leaves reduced in size that give a small surface area to volume ratio
- leaves absent and photosynthesis carried out by stems as these have fewer stomata
- succulent leaves and stems that store water
- extensive root systems that collect water quickly when it is available.

5.10.4 Examples of physiological adaptations to different environments

Desert living animals need to survive water shortage. In the case of the kangaroo rat, a desert rodent, the kidney shows a range of physiological adaptations designed to conserve water by producing concentrated urine. It oxidises fat rather than carbohydrate, which yields almost twice as much water, but it is still crucial to keep water losses to a minimum. Kangaroo rats reduce evaporation from the lungs, do not sweat and produce very dry faeces, as well as reducing water loss when removing waste products through the kidney. They produce urine that is four times more concentrated than that of humans (24% urea as opposed to a maximum of 6% in humans) and seventeen times more concentrated than their own blood. This is achieved by having an extremely long loop of Henlé (section 6.5.1) that is important in creating a **counter-current system** involved in the reabsorption of water back into the blood stream. Reabsorption of water is aided by the unusually high levels of ADH (section 6.6.1) in the blood.

One physiological adaptation of plants to the high temperatures of the tropics is a modified form of photosynthesis involving the use of phosphoenolpyruvate (PEP) as the carbon dioxide acceptor rather than the more usual ribulose bisphosphate (section 2.5.1). This results in the formation of a 4-carbon compound, oxaloacetate, and hence the plants using this pathway are referred to as **C_4 plants**. The advantages of this pathway to plants living in hot and occasionally dry environments are:

- High carbon dioxide concentrations can be maintained in specialised bundle sheath cells in the plant. These act as a reserve supply of carbon dioxide. This is especially important at the hottest periods of the day, when the carbon dioxide concentration in the atmosphere is very low due to the large amount of photosynthesis that is taking place.
- They can continue to photosynthesise for long periods with their stomata closed. This reduces water loss and a potentially harmful process called photorespiration.
- C_4 plants need only half as much water for photosynthesis as C_3 plants.

Arctic fox (top), living in a colder environment, has much shorter ears than the fennec fox (below) that lives in a warmer climate

Artificial selection

Artificial selection, also known as **selective breeding**, entails identifying individuals with the desired characteristics and using them to parent the next generation. Offspring that do not exhibit the desired characters are culled, or at least prevented from breeding. In this way the **gene pool** is deliberately restricted to a number of desired genes and the diversity of individuals within the **population** is reduced. Over many generations, this leads to a population all of which possess the desired qualities. Some differences between artificial selection and the evolutionary process (natural selection) are given in table 5.4.

Table 5.4 *Differences between artificial selection and the evolutionary process (natural selection)*

Artificial selection	Natural selection
Selection pressure exerted by humans	Selection pressure exerted by environmental factors
Genetic diversity is lowered	Genetic diversity remains high
Does not lead to new species arising	May lead to new species arising
Inbreeding is common, leading to loss of vigour in offspring	Outbreeding is common, leading to hybrid vigour
Proportion of heterozygotes in the population is reduced	Proportion of heterozygotes in the population remains high
Genetic isolation mechanisms do not operate	Genetic isolation mechanisms operate

5.11.1 Carrying out selective breeding

There are two main methods of carrying out selective breeding:

- **Inbreeding** is used to retain, as far as possible, a desirable characteristic that has arisen by chance **mutation**. By breeding the individual with close relatives, the chances of the offspring showing the desired character are greater. There are harmful effects with inbreeding. For example, there is loss of vigour, with the population being weakened by a lack of diversity and reduced fertility. There is also an increased danger of a harmful recessive allele expressing itself, because there is a greater risk of a **homozygous recessive** individual arising. As a result, inbreeding is not carried out indefinitely and outside genes have to be introduced from time to time to make the population stronger and healthier.
- **Outbreeding** involves the breeding of unrelated individuals. This may be used to try to combine two different desirable characters each possessed by separate individuals, for example by crossing a crop plant that gives an excellent yield with one resistant to disease in the expectation of a plant with a high yield and disease resistance. It frequently produces tougher individuals with a better chance of survival. This is called **hybrid vigour**.

5.11.2 Selective breeding in cattle

Selection of modern-day cattle for milk production (dairy herds) will normally include consideration of the following factors:

- volume of milk produced each day
- length of milking (lactation) period
- protein and fat content of milk
- type of udder, e.g. degree of support, length, shape and angle of teats (important for use of milking machine)
- amount and type of feed required
- disease resistance, e.g. to mastitis
- temperament.

The selective breeding process entails:

- Selecting a suitable cow and bull by consulting the pedigree records of each and through progeny testing (section 5.11.3).
- Collection of sperm from the selected bull and storing by freezing.
- Detection of when the cow is in **oestrus** by observing changes in her behaviour, e.g. increasing restlessness, mounting other cows and being mounted by them, feeding less.
- Artificially inseminating the defrosted semen into the cow (section 5.11.4).
- Checking that fertilisation has occurred and that the cow is in calf.

Domesticated milking cow

Wild cow (Bos sp.)

An alternative to artificial insemination is the use of embryo transplantation (see extension).

5.11.3 Progeny testing

Progeny testing involves the maintenance of detailed data on all the offspring (progeny) of a particular organism. In the case of dairy cattle this might include growth rate of the calves, body size, amount of body fat, milk yield, quality of milk, length of lactation period, lifespan and veterinary history. The data produced are extremely useful in selecting the correct animal for any particular set of desired characters, based upon the offspring it has already produced.

EXTENSION

Artificial insemination and embryo transplantation

Artificial insemination of cattle

Artificial insemination (AI) is the collection of semen and its introduction into the vagina or uterus by artificial means. In the UK, around 80% of insemination in cattle is by artificial means. It has a number of advantages over natural insemination:

- Specific characteristics required in the offspring can be selected.
- Semen can be used from a bull with certain desired characteristics even though it is hundreds, even thousands, of kilometres away.
- Semen can be frozen and transported easily as well as be kept for years, often long after the death of the donor bull.
- The costs of keeping bulls are reduced or eliminated altogether.
- The rate of conception is greater.

- The risk of contracting a sexually transmitted disease is reduced.

One disadvantage of artificial insemination is that the semen of one male can be used to inseminate many hundreds of females and there is therefore less genetic diversity amongst offspring than where natural processes are used.

Artificial insemination is used in cattle as follows:

- A suitable bull is stimulated to ejaculate into the vagina of a 'false' cow, using suitable smells to attract the bull.
- The semen is collected, checked in a laboratory and, depending on the concentration of sperm, may be diluted.
- The semen is stored in liquid nitrogen at −196°C.
- When needed, the sperm is defrosted and inserted into a receptive cow's vagina around 6–8 hours before oestrus, using a plastic pipette.

Embryo transplantation involves fertilising ova in the laboratory before implanting the developing embryos into the uterus of the natural or a surrogate mother. There are two basic methods of embryo transplantation in cattle:

- Ova are removed from cows at the abattoir, grown for 5 days and then fertilised, *in vitro*, with semen from a bull with the desired characteristics. After 5–6 days of growth in the laboratory, the embryos are frozen and stored ready for transplantation into a suitable cow.
- A cow is treated with follicle stimulating hormone (FSH), causing her to release a large number of ova. These are fertilised by artificial insemination and allowed to implant in the uterus. After about 6 days they are 'flushed' out through the vagina and transferred to a culture medium before being implanted into receptive cows, either through the vagina or surgically.

SUMMARY TEST 5.11

Artificial selection is also known as **(1)** and differs from natural selection in that genetic diversity is **(2)** and the proportion of **(3)** in the population is reduced. The two main methods of carrying out artificial selection are **(4)** and **(5)**. The process can be used with dairy herds to increase milk production and begins with the selection of a suitable bull and cow by consulting the **(6)** records of each and the checking of data on the offspring each have produced – a process called **(7)**. Semen is then collected from the chosen bull and inserted into the **(8)** of the chosen cow by a technique known as **(9)**. Alternatively, ova may be removed from the cow and fertilised in the laboratory before being returned to the donor cow. This process is known as **(10)**.

part SIX

Control, coordination and homeostasis

Coordination and homeostasis

The physical exertion involved in these lions catching their warthog prey requires highly efficient coordination of many of their body systems

Homeostasis allows animals such as these penguins in the Antarctic (above) and these camels in the desert (below) to survive in extreme environments

As species of organisms evolved from simple, single-celled organisms into complex, multicellular ones, the cells of which they were composed evolved to perform a specialist function. With specialisation in one function came the loss of the ability to perform others. This division of labour, whereby different groups of cells each carried out their own function, made the cells dependent upon one another. Cells specialising in reproduction, for example, depend on other cells to obtain oxygen for their respiration, yet others to provide glucose and others to remove their waste products. These different functional systems must be coordinated if they are to perform efficiently. No bodily system can work in isolation, but all must be integrated in a coordinated fashion.

There are two forms of coordination in most multicellular animals: nervous and endocrine. The nervous system permits rapid communication between specific parts of an organism in much the same way as a telephone system allows rapid communication between two specific individuals in human society. The endocrine system usually provides a slower, less specific form of communication and can be likened to a nationwide mailshot with its slower, more general message to all parts that is responded to only by those individuals that are sensitive to it. Both systems need to work together. Along with increased complexity of multicellular organisms came the development of an internal environment. This internal environment is made up of extracellular fluids that bathe each cell, supplying nutrients and removing wastes. By maintaining this fluid at levels which suit the cells, the cells are protected from the changes that affect the external environment and thereby give the organism a degree of independence.

6.1.1 What is homeostasis?

Homeostasis is the maintenance of a constant state. More specifically, it refers to the internal environment of organisms and involves maintaining the chemical make-up, volume and other features of blood and tissue fluid within narrow limits, sometimes called **normal ranges**. Homeostasis ensures that the cells of the body are in an environment that meets their needs and allows them to function normally despite external changes. This does not mean that there are no changes – on the contrary, there are continuous fluctuations brought about by variations in internal and external conditions. These changes, however, occur around a **set point**. Homeostasis is the ability to return to that set point and so maintain organisms in a balanced equilibrium.

6.1.2 The importance of homeostasis

Homeostasis is essential for the proper functioning of organisms because:

- The enzymes that control the biochemical reactions within cells, and other proteins such as channel proteins, are sensitive to changes in pH and temperature (*Essential AS Biology for OCR* unit3.2). Any change to these factors reduces the efficiency of enzymes or may even prevent them working altogether, e.g. may **denature** them.
- Changes to the water potential of the blood and tissue fluids may cause cells to shrink and expand (even to bursting point) due to water leaving or entering by **osmosis**. In both instances the cells cannot operate normally.

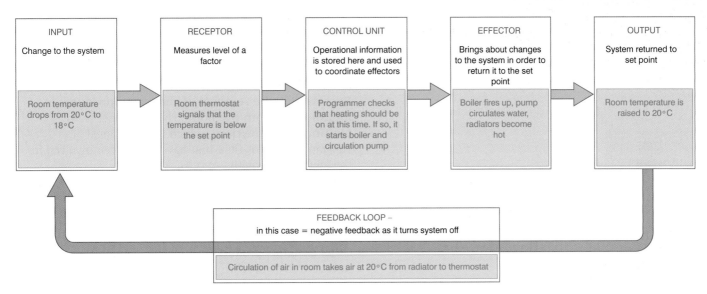

Fig 6.1 *Components of a typical control system*

- Biochemical reactions in organisms are in a state of dynamic equilibrium between the forward and reverse reactions. Changes to the environment of cells can upset this equilibrium to the detriment of the organism.
- Organisms with the ability to maintain a constant internal environment are more independent of the external environment. They have a wider geographical range and therefore have a greater chance of finding food, shelter, etc. Mammals, for example, with their ability to maintain a constant temperature, are found in most habitats from the hot arid deserts to the cold, frozen poles.

6.1.3 Control mechanisms and feedback

The control of any self-regulating system involves a series of stages:

- **set point** – the desired level at which the system operates. This is monitored by a
- **receptor** that detects any deviation from the set point and informs the
- **controller** that coordinates information from various sources and sends instructions to an appropriate
- **effector** that brings about the necessary change needed to return the system to the set point. This return to normality creates a
- **feedback loop** that informs the receptor of the changes to the system brought about by the effector.

Figure 6.1 illustrates the relationship between these stages using the everyday example of controlling a central heating system.

Most systems, including biological ones, use **negative feedback**, i.e. the information fed back turns the system off. We shall see examples of negative feedback in the following units.

Positive feedback occurs when a deviation from the set point causes changes that result in an even greater deviation from the normal. Examples are rare, but include:

- In **neurones**, a stimulus causes a small influx of sodium ions (section 6.10.2). This influx increases the permeability of the neurone to sodium, more ions enter, causing a further increase in permeability and even more rapid entry of ions. In this way, a small stimulus can bring about a large and rapid response.
- Oxytocin causes contractions of the uterus at childbirth. The contractions stimulate the release of more oxytocin, causing even more contractions. The increasing frequency of contractions leads to the birth of the baby.

6.1.4 Coordination of control mechanisms

Systems normally have many receptors and effectors. It is important to ensure that the information provided by receptors is analysed by the control centre before action is taken. Receiving information from a number of sources allows a better degree of control. For example, temperature receptors in the skin may signal that the skin itself is cold and that body temperature should be raised. However, information from the hypothalamus in the brain may indicate that blood temperature is already above normal. This situation could arise during strenuous exercise when blood temperature rises but sweating cools the skin. By analysing the information from all the detectors, the brain can decide the best course of action – in this case not to raise the body temperature further. In the same way, the control centre must coordinate the action of the effectors so that they operate harmoniously. For example, sweating would be less effective in cooling the body if it were not accompanied by vasodilation.

Excretion and kidney structure

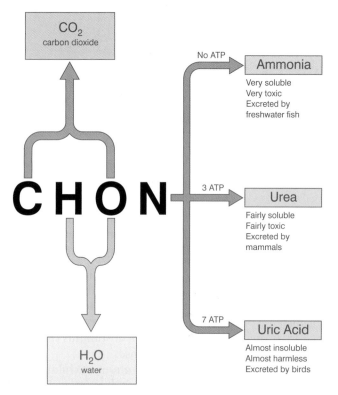

Fig 6.2 Waste products formed from the four main elements in organic compounds

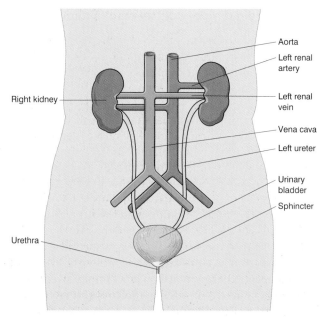

Fig 6.3 Position of the kidneys in humans

Excretion is the removal of the waste products of metabolism from the body. This is distinct from **elimination (egestion)**, which is the removal of substances such as fibre that have never been involved in the metabolic activities of cells.

6.2.1 Excretory substances

An adult human produces about 500 dm^3 of carbon dioxide and 400 cm^3 of water each day as a result of respiration. Other excretory products include bile pigments and mineral salts as well as the nitrogenous excretory products – ammonia, urea and uric acid.

- **Ammonia (NH_3)** is the easiest product to form from the amino groups (NH_2) produced when amino acids are oxidised. Its production requires no **ATP** and it is very soluble in water and so is easily dissolved and washed out of the body. It is, however, extremely poisonous – 800 times more so than carbon dioxide. Only organisms such as freshwater fish with access to copious volumes of water are therefore able to use ammonia as their nitrogenous excretory product.

- **Urea – $CO(NH_2)_2$** – although still moderately toxic, is 400 times less so than ammonia, allowing it to be stored temporarily. It is fairly soluble, although less so than ammonia. It requires three ATP molecules to produce it from two molecules of ammonia and one of carbon dioxide. Urea is used as the nitrogenous excretory product of organisms that have some access to water, but not in large volumes, e.g. animals living on land, such as mammals. Urea is produced in the liver from excess amino acids in three stages:
  - Amino groups (NH_2) are removed from the amino acids in a process called **deamination** and made into ammonia.
  - The remainder of the amino acid can be respired to give ATP.
  - The ammonia is converted to urea by the addition of carbon dioxide in a pathway called the **ornithine cycle**.

- **Uric acid** is almost insoluble in water and cannot diffuse into cells, making it hardly poisonous at all. However, it takes seven ATP molecules to produce it. As almost no water is needed for its removal, it is used by organisms living in very dry conditions. As it is low in mass when stored it is also used by flying organisms. Animals like birds and reptiles that lay eggs have an additional reason for using it – to remove their nitrogenous waste. As the young develop within the egg, their wastes cannot be removed and so anything more toxic than uric acid would kill them.

Figure 6.2 summarises how these waste products are formed from the main elements in organic compounds.

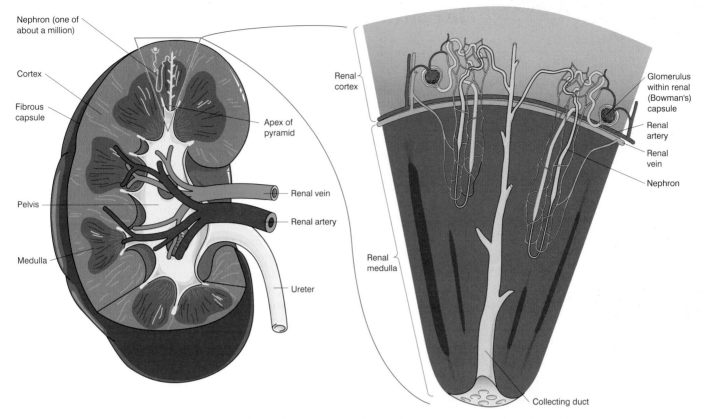

Fig 6.4 *Detailed structure of mammalian kidney (LS) showing the position of two of the million or more nephrons in each kidney*

6.2.2 Structure of the mammalian kidney

In mammals there are two kidneys found at the back of the abdominal cavity, one on each side of the spinal cord (Fig 6.3). In humans each kidney is around 11 cm long, 6 cm wide and 2.5 cm thick and is usually surrounded by fat that gives it some physical protection. Weighing only 150 g each, they filter your blood plasma every 22 minutes of your life. A section through the kidney (Fig 6.4) shows it is made up of the

- **fibrous capsule** – an outer membrane that protects the kidney
- **cortex** – a lighter coloured outer region made up of **renal (Bowman's) capsules**, convoluted tubules and blood vessels
- **medulla** – a darker coloured inner region made up of **loops of Henlé**, collecting ducts and blood vessels
- **renal pelvis** – a funnel-shaped cavity that collects urine into the ureter
- **ureter** – a tube that carries urine to the bladder
- **renal artery** – supplies the kidney with blood from the heart via the aorta
- **renal vein** – returns blood to the heart via the vena cava.

A microscopic examination of the cortex and medulla reveals around one million tiny tubular structures in each kidney. These are the basic structural and functional units of the kidney – the **nephrons**.

SUMMARY TEST 6.2

Excretion is the removal of metabolic waste products from the body, whereas the removal of non-metabolic material such as roughage is known as (**1**). Respiration in humans produces around 400 cm³ of (**2**) and 500 dm³ of (**3**) that need to be removed from the body. Other excretory products include mineral salts, bile pigments and nitrogenous wastes, of which there are three forms. Ammonia is the (**4**) soluble of the three and is formed from (**5**) groups when protein is oxidised. Urea is less toxic than ammonia and needs less (**6**) but more (**7**) to remove it from the body. Urea is made by removing amino groups from amino acids and converting them to ammonia – a process called (**8**). The ammonia is then converted to urea by the addition of (**9**) in a pathway called the (**10**) cycle. The nitrogenous waste known as (**11**) is almost insoluble in water and hardly toxic at all. It is used by animals such as (**12**) and (**13**) because it can be stored within eggs without harming the developing young. The mammalian kidney is surrounded by a protective (**14**) and in cross section is seen to be made up of a lighter coloured outer region called the (**15**) and a darker inner region called the (**16**). These regions are made up of around a million tubular structures called (**17**). Blood is brought to the kidney by the vessel called the (**18**), and urine leaves it via a tube called the (**19**).

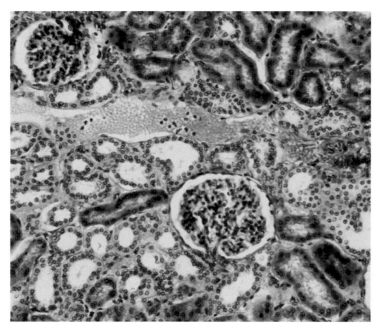

Cortex of human kidney (TS). Glomeruli are seen as regions of small cells surrounded by a clear space

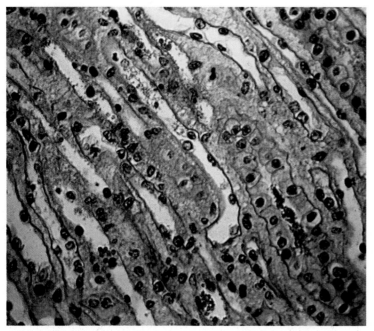

Medulla of human kidney (LS) showing loops of Henlé (white tubes). Around them are blood capillaries containing red blood cells

The nephron is the functional unit of the kidney. It is a narrow tube up to 14 mm long, closed at one end, with two twisted regions separated by a long hairpin loop. Each nephron is made up of a:

- **Renal (Bowman's) capsule** – the closed end at the start of the nephron. It is cup-shaped and contains within it a mass of blood capillaries known as the glomerulus. Its inner layer is made up of specialised cells called **podocytes**.
- **Proximal (first) convoluted tubule** – a series of loops surrounded by blood capillaries. Its walls are made of cuboidal epithelial cells with microvilli.
- **Loop of Henlé** – a long, hairpin loop that extends from the cortex into the medulla of the kidney and back again. It is surrounded by blood capillaries.
- **Distal (second) convoluted tubule** – a series of loops surrounded by blood capillaries. Its walls are made of cuboidal epithelial cells, but it is surrounded by fewer capillaries than the proximal tubule.
- **Collecting duct** – a tube into which a number of distal convoluted tubules empty. It is lined by cuboidal epithelial cells and becomes increasingly wide as it empties into the renal pelvis.

Associated with each nephron are a number of blood vessels (Fig 6.5), namely:

- **afferent arteriole** – a tiny vessel that ultimately arises from the renal artery and supplies the nephron with blood. The afferent arteriole enters the renal capsule of the nephron where it forms the
- **glomerulus** – a many-branched tuft of capillaries from which fluid is forced out of the blood. The glomerular capillaries recombine to form the
- **efferent arteriole** – a tiny vessel that leaves the renal capsule. It has a smaller diameter than the afferent arteriole and so causes an increase in blood pressure within the glomerulus. The efferent arteriole carries blood away from the renal capsule and later branches to form the
- **peritubular capillaries** – a concentrated network of capillaries that surrounds the proximal convoluted tubule, the loop of Henlé and the distal convoluted tubule and from where they reabsorb mineral salts, glucose and water. The peritubular capillaries merge together into venules (tiny veins) that in turn merge together to form the renal vein.

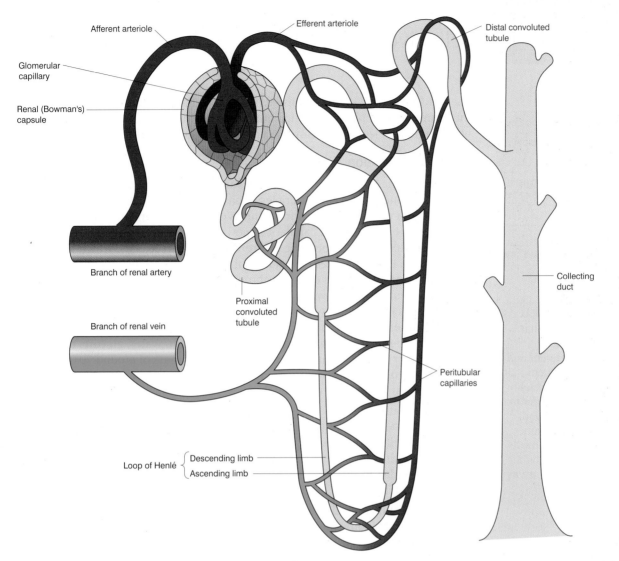

Fig 6.5 *Regions of the nephron and associated blood vessels*

SUMMARY TEST 6.3

The nephron is the structural unit of the kidney. It comprises a cup-shaped structure called the **(1)** that contains a knot of blood vessels called the **(2)** which receives its blood from a vessel called the **(3)** arteriole. The inner wall of this cup-shaped structure is lined with specialised cells called **(4)**, and from it extends the first, or **(5)**, convoluted tubule whose walls are lined with **(6)** epithelial cells that have **(7)** to increase their surface area. The next region of the nephron is a hairpin loop called the **(8)**, which then leads onto the second, or **(9)**, convoluted tubule. This in turn leads onto the **(10)**, which empties into the renal pelvis. Around much of the nephron is a dense network of blood vessels called the **(11)** capillaries.

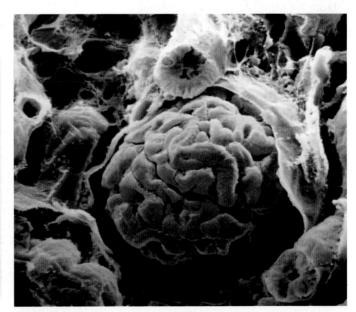

The glomerulus at the centre of this photograph is surrounded by the renal capsule, seen as a white-brown membrane at centre right. Part of the proximal convoluted tubule is seen, coloured blue

103

Kidney functions – ultrafiltration and selective reabsorption

Table 6.1 *The functions of the kidneys*

- Regulating the composition of the blood by:
  - Maintaining the water volume constant
  - Removing wastes such as urea
  - Maintaining the concentration of mineral ions and other substances constant
- Regulating blood pressure
- Maintaining the body's calcium level
- Stimulating the production of red blood cells

'Where there's muck there's brass'

This is an old Yorkshire saying that may help you avoid a common confusion over the terms afferent and efferent. For 'muck' read 'effluent'; for 'brass' read 'affluence'. Ask yourself which of the two you would prefer to come **towards** you and which you would prefer to go **away** from you. Afferent ('affluence') arterioles move blood **towards** the glomerulus, while efferent ('effluent') move blood **away** from the glomerulus.

EXTENSION
The glomerulus – a unique capillary bed

In mammals, the glomerulus is the only capillary bed in which an arteriole (the afferent arteriole) supplies it with blood and an arteriole (the efferent arteriole) also drains blood away. In all other mammalian capillary beds it is a venule that drains away the blood. Why then do we not make life simpler and call the efferent arteriole a venule? The reason is that the efferent arteriole later divides up into a second capillary bed – the peritubular capillaries – and these are drained by a venule. In any case, the structure of the wall is that of an arteriole and not a venule. The glomerular capillaries need to merge into an efferent arteriole because this increases the hydrostatic pressure within the glomerulus and allows ultrafiltration to occur.

The functions of the kidney are listed in table 6.1. The main one, that of regulating the composition of blood, is carried out by the nephrons in a series of stages – ultrafiltration, selective reabsorption and the reabsorption of water and minerals.

6.4.1 Ultrafiltration

Blood enters the kidney through the renal artery, which branches frequently to give around one million tiny arterioles, each of which enters a **renal (Bowman's) capsule** of a nephron. This is called the **afferent arteriole** and it divides to give a complex of capillaries known as the **glomerulus**. The glomerular capillaries later merge to form the **efferent arteriole** (see box), which then sub-divides again into capillaries (the peritubular capillaries), which wind their way around the various tubules of the nephron before combining to form the renal vein (see extension). The walls of the glomerular capillaries are made up of endothelial cells with pores between them. As the diameter of the afferent arteriole is greater than that of the efferent arteriole, there is a build up of hydrostatic pressure within the glomerulus. As a result, water, glucose, mineral ions and other substances up to a relative molecular mass of around 70 000 are squeezed out of the capillary into the **filtrate**. The movement of this filtrate out of the glomerular filtrate is resisted by the

- capillary epithelium
- basement membrane of the epithelial layer of the renal (Bowman's) capsule
- epithelial cells of the renal (Bowman's) capsule
- the hydrostatic pressure of the fluid in the renal capsule space – the **intracapsular pressure**
- the low water potential of the blood in the glomerulus.

This total resistance would be sufficient to prevent filtrate leaving the glomerular capillaries, but for some ingenious modifications to reduce this barrier to the flow of filtrate:

- The inner layer of the renal (Bowman's) capsule is made up of highly specialised cells called **podocytes**. These cells, which are illustrated in figure 6.6, are lifted off the surface membrane on little 'feet' ('podo' = feet). This allows filtrate to pass beneath them and through gaps between their branches. Filtrate passes between these cells rather than through them.
- The endothelium of the glomerular capillaries has spaces up to 100 nm wide between its cells (Fig 6.6). Again, fluid can therefore pass between, rather than through, these cells.

As a result, the hydrostatic pressure of the blood in the glomerulus is sufficient to overcome the resistance and so filtrate passes from the blood into the renal capsule. This is known as the **effective filtration pressure**. The filtrate has much the same composition as blood plasma, with the exception of the plasma proteins which are too large to pass across the basement membrane. Many of the substances in the 125 cm^3 of filtrate passing out of blood each minute are extremely useful to the body and need to be reabsorbed.

6.4.2 Selective reabsorption

In the proximal convoluted tubule nearly 85% of the filtrate is reabsorbed back into the blood. Why then, you may ask, allow it to leave the blood in the first place? Ultrafiltration operates on the basis of size of molecule: all below around 70 000 relative molecular mass are removed. Some are wastes, but most are useful. It would be difficult to select which was which in the renal capsule and so all are removed and only the useful ones are later taken back. The process may be

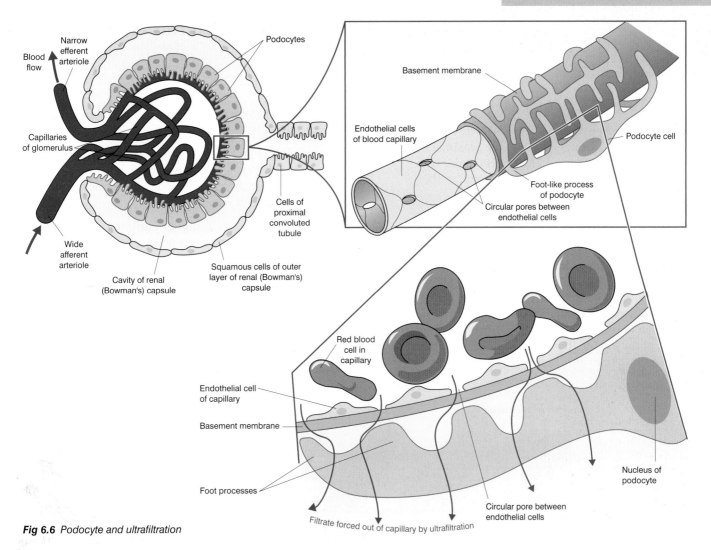

Fig 6.6 *Podocyte and ultrafiltration*

likened to clearing out a drawer or box with a jumbled mixture of essential and unwanted items. It is often easier to empty out all the contents and then systematically put back what is needed (leaving the rest to be disposed of), rather than trying to pick through the jumble, selecting the unwanted items.

The proximal convoluted tubule reabsorbs substances into the blood in a number of ways:

- Diffusion and **facilitated diffusion** are used to reabsorb mineral ions, glucose and amino acids into the epithelial cells of the convoluted tubules. This is speeded up by the larger surface area provided by the microvilli (Fig 6.7).

- **Active transport** is used to transport glucose and amino acids out of the epithelial cells into the space around them, from where they are diffused into the blood capillaries. The many mitochondria in the epithelial cells provide the energy for this active transport (Fig 6.7).

- **Endocytosis** is used to take up large molecules, such as some proteins, into the epithelial cells.

- **Osmosis** is used to absorb water. Sodium ions are actively transported into the tissue fluid between the epithelial cell and the capillary. This creates a lower water potential and water therefore follows by osmosis.

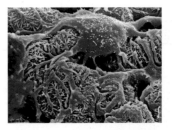

SEM of podocyte cells (purple) in a human kidney

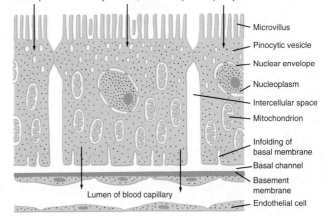

Fig 6.7 *Details of cells from the wall of the proximal convoluted tubule*

105

About 180 dm³ of water enters the nephrons each day. Of this volume, only about 1 dm³ leaves the body as urine. 85% of the reabsorption of water occurs in the proximal convoluted tubule (section 6.4.2). The remainder is reabsorbed from the collecting duct as a result of the functioning of the loop of Henlé.

6.5.1 The loop of Henlé

The loop of Henlé is a hairpin-shaped tubule that extends into the medulla of the kidney. It is responsible for reabsorbing water from the collecting duct, thereby concentrating the urine so that it has a lower **water potential** (is hypertonic) than the blood. The concentration of the urine produced is directly related to the length of the loop of Henlé. It is short in mammals whose **habitats** are in or by water (e.g. beavers) and long

in those whose habitats are arid regions (e.g. kangaroo rat). The loop of Henlé has two regions:

- The descending limb, which is narrow, with thin walls that are highly permeable to water.
- The ascending limb, which is wider, with thick walls that are impermeable to water.

The loop of Henlé acts as a counter-current multiplier. To understand how this works it is necessary to consider the following sequence of events in conjunction with figure 6.8, to which the numbers refer.

1. Sodium and chloride ions are actively pumped out of the ascending limb of the loop of Henlé using ATP provided by the many mitochondria in the cells of its wall.

2. This creates a low water potential (high ion concentration) in the region of the medulla between the

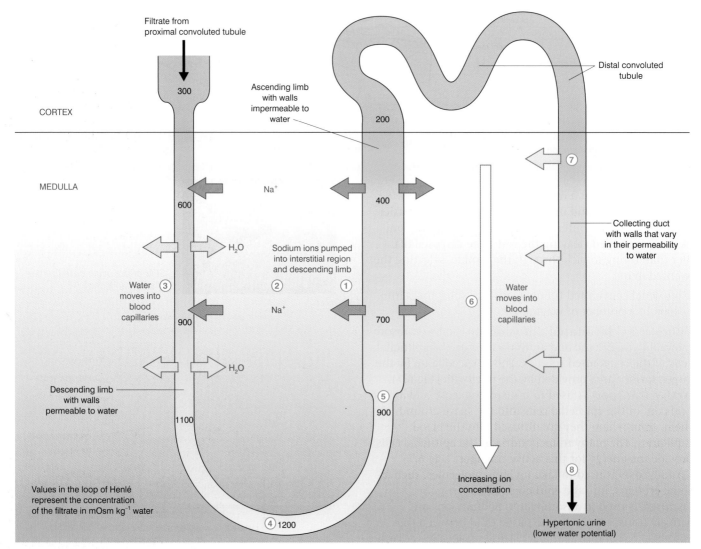

Fig 6.8 *Counter-current multiplier of the loop of Henlé*

two limbs (called the interstitial region). In normal circumstances water would pass out of the ascending limb by osmosis. However, the thick walls are almost impermeable to water and so very little, if any, escapes.

3. The walls of the descending limb are, however, very permeable to water and so it passes out of the filtrate, by osmosis, into the interstitial space. This water enters the blood capillaries in this region by osmosis and is carried away.

4. The filtrate progressively loses water in this way as it moves down the descending limb lowering its water potential. It reaches its minimum water potential at the tip of the hairpin.

5. At the base of the ascending limb, sodium and chloride ions diffuse out of the filtrate and as it moves up the ascending limb these ions are also actively pumped out (see point **1** above) and therefore the filtrate develops a progressively higher water potential.

6. In the interstitial space between the ascending limb and the collecting duct there is a gradient of water potential with the highest water potential (lowest concentration of ions) in the cortex and an increasingly lower water potential (higher concentration of ions) the further into the medulla one goes.

7. The collecting duct is permeable to water and so, as the filtrate moves down it, water passes out of it by osmosis. This water passes by osmosis into the blood vessels that occupy this space, and is carried away.

8. As water passes out of the filtrate its water potential is lowered. However, the water potential is also lowered in the interstitial space and so water continues to move out by osmosis down the whole length of the collecting duct. The counter-current multiplier (section 6.5.3) ensures that there is always a water potential gradient drawing water out of the tubule.

The water that passes out of the collecting duct by osmosis does so through water channels. The hormone ADH (section 6.6.1) can alter the number of these channels and so control water loss. By the time the filtrate, now called urine, leaves the collecting duct on its way to the bladder, it has lost most of its water and so it has a lower water potential (is more concentrated) than the blood.

6.5.2 The distal (second) convoluted tubule

The cells that make up the walls of the distal (second) convoluted tubule have microvilli and many mitochondria that allow them to reabsorb material rapidly from the filtrate, by either diffusion or **active transport**. The main role of the distal tubule is to make final adjustments to the water and salts that are reabsorbed and to control the pH of the blood by selecting which ions to reabsorb. To achieve this, the permeability of its walls becomes altered under the influence of various hormones (unit 6.6). A summary of the processes taking place in the **nephron** is given in figure 6.9.

6.5.3 Counter-current multiplier

When two liquids flow in opposite directions past one another, the exchange of substances (or heat) between them is greater than if they flowed in the same direction next to each other. In the case of the loop of Henlé, the counter-current flow means that the filtrate in the collecting duct with a lower water potential meets interstitial fluid that has an even lower water potential. This means that, although the water potential gradient between the collecting duct and interstitial fluid is small, it exists for the whole length of the collecting duct. There is therefore a steady flow of water into the interstitial fluid, so that around 80% of the water enters the interstitial fluid and hence the blood. If the two flows were in the same direction (parallel) less of the water would enter the blood.

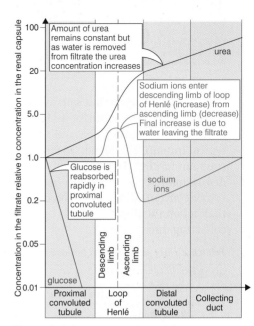

Fig 6.9 *Relative concentrations of three substances in the filtrate as it passes along a nephron. NB Scale is not linear*

SUMMARY TEST 6.5

The loop of Henlé is shaped like a **(1)** and extends into the **(2)** of the kidney. Although its role is to reabsorb water from the collecting duct, most water is actually reabsorbed into the blood from the **(3)**. The loop of Henlé has a descending and an ascending limb. The **(4)** limb has thinner walls. Of the two limbs, the **(5)** one is much more permeable to water. The loop of Henlé operates by pumping sodium and chloride ions out of the **(6)** limb, thereby creating a **(7)** water potential in the interstitial region. As a result water is drawn out of the descending limb by **(8)** and passes into the blood capillaries by the same process. There is a gradient of water potential in the filtrate in the loop of Henlé so that water potential is at its **(9)** at the tip of the loop. The arrangement of the loop of Henlé means that the filtrate flows in opposite directions in its two limbs. This ensures that more water is reabsorbed than if the flow was in the same direction. This arrangement is referred to as **(10)**. The distal convoluted tubule makes final adjustments to salt and water reabsorption and controls the **(11)** of the blood. To aid this reabsorption, the cells in its wall have both **(12)** and **(13)**.

6.6

Control of water and solute concentration of the blood

The amount of water and salts we take in varies from day to day, as does the quantity we lose. Table 6.2 shows the daily balance between loss and gain of salts and water for a typical human. The blood, however, needs to have a constant level of water and salts to avoid osmotic disruption to cells. The **homeostatic** control of water and solute concentrations in the blood is achieved by hormones that act on the distal (second) convoluted tubule and the collecting duct.

Table 6.2 Daily water and salt balance in a typical human

WATER

Volume of water / cm³day⁻¹			
Water gain		**Water loss**	
Diet	2300	Urine	1500
Metabolism, e.g. respiration	200	Expired air	400
		Evaporation from skin	350
		Faeces	150
		Sweat	100
TOTAL	2500	TOTAL	2500

SALT

Mass of salt / gday⁻¹			
Salt gain		**Salt loss**	
Diet	10.50	Urine	10.00
		Faeces	0.25
		Sweat	0.25
TOTAL	10.50	TOTAL	10.50

6.6.1 Regulation of the water potential of the blood

The **water potential** of the blood is determined by the balance of water and salts within it. A rise in solute concentration lowers its water potential. This may be caused by:

- too little water being consumed
- much sweating occurring
- large amounts of salt being taken in.

The body responds to this fall in water potential as follows:

- Cells called **osmoreceptors** in the **hypothalamus** of the brain detect the fall in water potential.
- It is thought that, when the water potential of the blood is low, water is lost from these osmoreceptor cells by osmosis.
- Due to this water loss the osmoreceptor cells shrink, a change that stimulates the neurosecretory cells in the hypothalamus to produce a hormone called **antidiuretic hormone (ADH)**.
- ADH passes along the neurosecretory cells to the posterior **pituitary gland**, from where it is secreted into the capillaries.

The naming of anitdiuretic hormone

The name antidiuretic hormone (ADH) may, at first, seem unusual. However, it describes its function precisely. **Diuresis** is the production of large volumes of dilute urine. It is a symptom of a disease called **diabetes insipidus** (so called because the urine from sufferers did not taste sweet!). The disease was successfully treated with pituitary extract. Therefore it was suggested that a hormone existed that was given the name 'antidiuretic hormone'. As the effect of ADH is to increase the permeability of collecting ducts so that more water is reabsorbed into the blood, it causes the production of small volumes of concentrated urine.

This is the opposite of diuresis – hence the name **anti**diuretic hormone.

- ADH passes in the blood to the kidney, where it increases the permeability to water of the cell surface membrane of the cells that make up the walls of the distal (second) convoluted tubule and the collecting duct.
- Receptors on the cell surface membrane of these cells pick up ADH molecules, thereby activating an enzyme within the cell.
- The activation of this enzyme causes vesicles within the cell to move to, and fuse with, its cell surface membrane.
- These vesicles contain pieces of membrane that have numerous water channels and so when they fuse with the membrane the number of water channels is considerably increased, making the cell surface membrane much more permeable to water.
- ADH also increases the permeability of the collecting duct to urea, which therefore passes out, further decreasing the water potential of the fluid around the duct.
- The combined effect is that more water leaves the collecting duct by osmosis and re-enters the blood.
- As the reabsorbed water came from the blood in the first place, this will not, in itself, increase the water potential of the blood, but merely prevent it getting worse. Therefore the osmoreceptors also stimulate the thirst centre of the brain, to encourage the individual to seek out and drink more water.
- The osmoreceptors in the hypothalamus detect the rise in water potential and stop sending impulses to the pituitary gland.
- The pituitary gland reduces the release of ADH and the permeability of the collecting ducts to water and urea is therefore reduced to its former state.

This is an example of homeostasis and the principle of negative feedback (section 6.1.3).

A fall in the solute concentration of the blood raises its water potential. This may be caused by:

- large volumes of water being consumed
- salts used in metabolism or excreted not being replaced in the diet.

The body responds to this rise in water potential as follows:

- The osmoreceptors in the hypothalamus detect the rise in water potential and stimulate the pituitary gland to reduce its release of ADH.
- ADH, via the blood, decreases the permeability of the collecting ducts to water and urea.
- Less water is drawn back into the blood from the collecting duct.
- More dilute urine is produced and the water potential of the blood decreases.
- When the water potential of the blood has returned to normal, the osmoreceptors in the hypothalamus cause the pituitary to raise its ADH release back to normal (= negative feedback).

These events are summarised in figure 6.10.

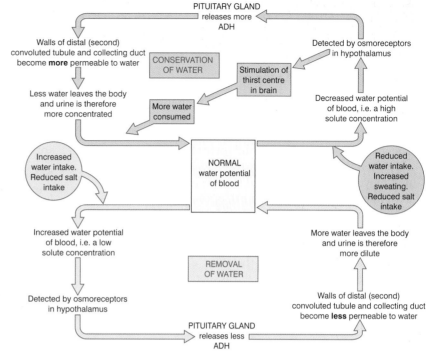

Fig 6.10 *Regulation of water potential of the blood by antidiuretic hormone (ADH)*

EXTENSION

Control of the water budget in desert mammals

Small mammals such as kangaroo rats and gerbils, which live in a hot, arid desert environment have to be specially adapted to maintain their water balance. In the kangaroo rat, these adaptations enable them to survive for long periods without drinking water, because they:

- Avoid the heat and conserve water by spending long periods of time in underground burrows where the air is cooler and the humidity higher.
- Have extremely long loops of Henlé, enabling them to produce urine four times more concentrated than in humans because almost all the water is reabsorbed from the nephron.

- Oxidise fat rather than carbohydrate, as fat produces twice as much metabolic water.
- Do not sweat, but depend on behavioural mechanisms to keep cool.
- Produce very dry faeces.

Table 6.3 shows the daily water balance for a kangaroo rat. Compare this with the one for a human in table 6.2.

Table 6.3 *Daily water balance in a kangaroo rat*

Volume of water / cm³day⁻¹			
Water gain		**Water loss**	
Diet	6.0	Expired air	44.0
Metabolism	54.0	Urine	13.5
		Faeces	2.5
TOTAL	60.0	TOTAL	60.0

SUMMARY TEST 6.6

A human takes in around (1) cm³ of water each day, of which (2) cm³ comes from the diet, with the remainder being produced in metabolic processes such as (3). More than half this water is lost from the body as (4). The same typical human needs around 10.5 g of salt in the diet, of which 10 g is lost in the urine and 0.25 g in faeces. The remainder is lost in (5). Despite daily fluctuations in water and salt intake, the water potential of the blood remains relatively constant as a result of (6) control achieved by hormones that act on the (7) and collecting duct. If too little water or too much salt is consumed, or if (8) is excessive, the water potential of the blood will (9). In response to this, osmoreceptors in the (10) of the brain detect the change and produce antidiuretic hormone (ADH) that passes to the (11) gland from where it is secreted. ADH passes via the blood to the kidney where it increases the (12) of the distal convoluted tubule and collecting duct to water and (13). As a result more water is reabsorbed and enters the blood. The osmoreceptors also stimulate a thirst response and so more water is drunk and the water potential of the blood therefore (14). When the water potential returns to normal, the osmoreceptors detect this and ADH production is reduced to normal – an example of the principle of (15).

Nervous communication and neurones

6.7.1 Stimulus and response

The ability to react to **stimuli** is a basic characteristic of all living organisms. The stimuli may arise internally or externally and they lead to a **response** from the organism. The ability to respond to stimuli increases the chances of survival for an organism. For example, to be able to detect and move away from harmful stimuli such as predators, extremes of temperature and pH, or to detect and move towards a source of food clearly aid survival. Those organisms that survive have a greater chance of raising offspring and of passing their **alleles** to the next generation. There is always, therefore, a **selection** pressure favouring organisms with better responses. A single-celled organism responds directly to environmental changes, by moving its whole body towards a favourable stimulus or away from an unfavourable one. This simple response is called a **taxis**. Sometimes when the stimulus is less directional, the organism simply moves faster and changes direction more often when the environmental conditions are unsuitable for it – behaviour designed to bring it back into favourable conditions. This is known as a **kinesis**.

Stimuli are received by **receptors** and the response is carried out by **effectors**. Receptors and effectors are often some distance apart and a form of communication is therefore needed between them if the organism is to respond effectively. This communication may be relatively slow via the endocrine system, which uses hormones (unit 6.15), or rapid via the nervous system, which uses **neurones** (nerve cells). Further differences between the endocrine and nervous system are given in table 6.4.

Table 6.4 *Comparison of endocrine and nervous systems*

Endocrine system	Nervous system
Communication is by chemicals called hormones	Communication is by nerve impulses
Transmission is by the blood system	Transmission is by nerve fibres
Relative strength of stimulus affects concentration of hormone	Relative strength of stimulus affects frequency of nerve impulses
Transmission is usually relatively slow	Transmission is very rapid
Hormones travel to all parts of the body, but only target organs respond	Nerve impulses travel to specific parts of the body
Effects are widespread	Effects are localised
Response is slow	Response is rapid
Response is often long lasting	Response is short lived
Effect may be permanent and irreversible	Effect is temporary and reversible

As animal species became more complex and the number of receptors and effectors increased, it became more efficient to link each receptor and effector to a central 'switchboard'. This is the **central nervous system**, consisting of the brain and spinal cord. The inter-relationships of all these various components are shown in figure 6.11.

6.7.2 The structure of neurones

Neurones (nerve cells) are specialised cells adapted to rapidly carry electrochemical changes called nerve impulses from one part of the body to another. Mammalian neurones are made up of:

- **A cell body** that contains a nucleus and large amounts of rough endoplasmic reticulum grouped to form **Nissl's granules**. These are associated with the production of proteins and **neurotransmitters**.
- **Dendrons** – small extensions of the cell body that subdivide into smaller branched fibres called dendrites that carry nerve impulses towards the cell body.
- **Axon** – a single long fibre that carries nerve impulses away from the cell body.

Many axons are surrounded by **Schwann cells**, which protect and provide insulation, act as phagocytes to remove cell debris and play a part in peripheral nerve regeneration. These Schwann cells wrap themselves around the axon many times, so that layers of their membranes build up around the axon. These membranes are rich in a lipid known as **myelin** and so form a covering to the axon called the **myelin sheath**. The space between adjacent Schwann cells lacks myelin, forming gaps 2–3 μm long, called **nodes of Ranvier**, which occur every 1–3 mm in humans. Neurones with a myelin sheath are called **myelinated neurones** and transmit nerve impulses faster than neurones without the myelin sheath (unmyelinated neurones) (section 6.12.1). The structure of a typical neurone is illustrated in figure 6.12. Neurones can be classified according to their function:

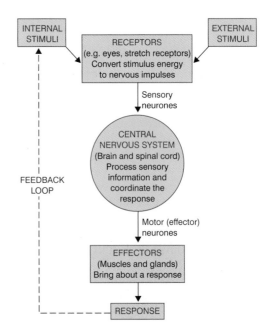

Fig 6.11 *Inter-relationships of components of the nervous system*

- **Sensory neurones** transmit nerve impulses from a receptor to a relay or motor neurone. They have one dendron that brings the impulse towards the cell body and one axon that carries it away from the cell body.
- **Relay neurones (intermediate neurones)** transmit impulses between neurones, e.g. from sensory to motor neurones. They have numerous short processes.
- **Motor neurones (effector neurones)** transmit nerve impulses from a relay or sensory neurone to an effector such as a gland or a muscle. They have a long axon and many short dendrites.

The three different types of neurone are illustrated in figure 6.13.

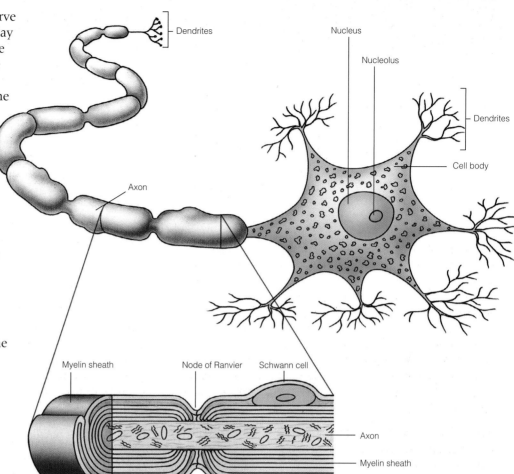

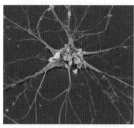

SEM of neurone with cell body at its centre and dendrites radiating from it

Fig 6.12 *Motor (effector) neurone*

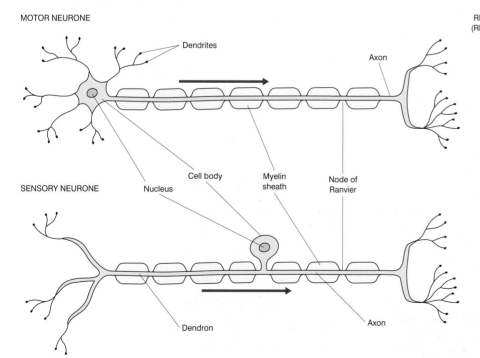

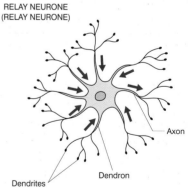

Direction of impulse
(from dendrites to axon)

Fig 6.13 *Types of neurone*

The central nervous system receives sensory information from its internal and external environment through a variety of sense cells and organs called **receptors**, each type responding to a different type of stimulus. **Sensory reception** is the function of these sense organs, whereas **sensory perception** involves making sense of the information from the receptors. This is largely a function of the brain. The concept of stimulus and response is covered in section 6.7.1. In this unit we shall look at how Pacinian corpuscles act as pressure receptors and rods and cones act as light receptors.

6.8.1 Principles of sensory reception as illustrated by the Pacinian corpuscle

Pacinian corpuscles respond to changes in mechanical pressure and are therefore a type of **mechanoreceptor**. They not only occur deep in the dermis of the skin, but also in joints, ligaments and **tendons**, where they allow the organism to know which joints are changing direction. They are most abundant on the fingers, soles of the feet and external genitalia. The **dendrite** of a single sensory neurone is at the centre of layers of connective tissue, each separated by a gel, giving it the appearance of an onion when cut vertically (Fig 6.14). As with all sensory receptors, Pacinian corpuscles:

- **Are specific to a single type of stimulus** – in this case to mechanical pressure only.
- **Act as transducers** – they convert the energy of the stimulus into a **receptor potential** (a small potential difference across the dendrite of the sensory neurone) – in the case of the Pacinian corpuscle, pressure causes it to flatten therefore stretching the receptor membrane (= **deformation**). This opens the sodium channels in the membrane, allowing sodium ions to move in and set up local circuits (Fig 6.15).
- **Produce a generator potential** – in the case of the Pacinian corpuscle, the generator potential and the receptor potential are the same because the sensory cell and the **sensory neurone** are one and the same thing. Such

SUMMARY TEST 6.8

Receptors are cells and organs that respond to different stimuli. Making sense of the information provided by sensory receptors is called sensory **(1)**. Pacinian corpuscles respond to the stimulus of **(2)**, converting the energy of the stimulus into a **(3)** potential – as such they act as **(4)**. The stimulus alters the membrane of the Pacinian corpuscle in a manner that allows **(5)** ions to move in and produce a **(6)** potential. If this potential equals or exceeds a threshold level, then an **(7)** is produced, which is the same regardless of how much the threshold level is exceeded. This is known as an **(8)** response.

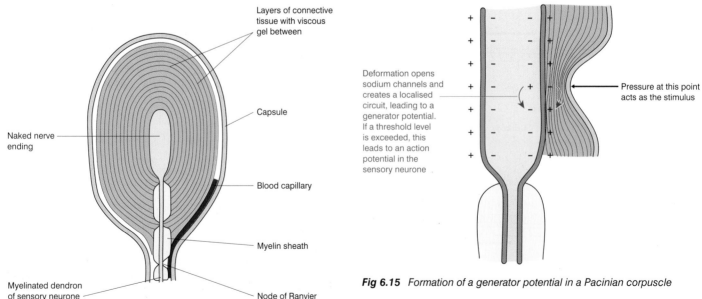

Layers of connective tissue with viscous gel between

Capsule

Naked nerve ending

Blood capillary

Myelin sheath

Myelinated dendron of sensory neurone

Node of Ranvier

Deformation opens sodium channels and creates a localised circuit, leading to a generator potential. If a threshold level is exceeded, this leads to an action potential in the sensory neurone

Pressure at this point acts as the stimulus

Fig 6.14 *Structure of a Pacinian corpuscle*

Fig 6.15 *Formation of a generator potential in a Pacinian corpuscle*

receptors are called **primary receptors**. In more complex sensory organs, sensory cells are separate from the sensory neurones and so their receptor potentials are transmitted to the sensory neurones, where they set up a generator potential. Such receptors are called **secondary receptors**.

- **Give an all or nothing response** – the greater the intensity of the stimulus, the greater the size of the generator potential. If the generator potential reaches or exceeds the set **threshold level**, an action potential is generated in the sensory neurone of that one cell. Anything less than the threshold level and no action potential is generated. Anything more than the threshold level, the same action potential is generated, regardless of by how much the level is exceeded.

- **Become adapted** – if exposed to a steady stimulus over a period of time, there is a slow decline in the generator potentials produced and so action potentials in the sensory neurone become less frequent and eventually cease. This is **adaptation** and prevents the nervous system becoming overloaded with unimportant information, e.g. our Pacinian corpuscles cease to respond to pressure from the clothes we wear.

Rods and cones as light receptors

Rods and cones are **photoreceptor** cells found in the retina of the mammalian eye. The structure of a single rod cell is illustrated in figure 6.16. Both rods and cones are secondary receptors (section 6.8.1). There are around 6 million cones, often with their own separate sensory neurone, in each human eye. The rods are more numerous, with 120 million in each eye, but up to 150 of them may share a single sensory neurone. As they share sensory neurones they cannot discriminate very well, i.e. they have low **visual acuity**. Rods cannot distinguish different wavelengths of light and therefore produce images only in black and white. Cones, by contrast, need much higher light intensities to respond, but have high visual acuity and detect colour.

Transduction in rod cells

Although a rod cell is used in this account, the basic mechanism of **transduction** is the same in rods and cones. Each rod cell possesses up to a thousand vesicles in its outer segment. These contain the photosensitive pigment called **rhodopsin**, which is made up of the protein **opsin** and a derivative of vitamin A, called **retinal**.

The process of transduction in the rod cell is as follows:

- Light reaching a rod cell changes one isomer of retinal into another.
- This causes the rhodopsin to split into opsin and retinal – a process called **bleaching**.
- The splitting causes a chain of reactions that make the cell surface membrane of the rod cell less permeable to sodium ions.
- As sodium ions cannot now easily diffuse back into the rod cell, but continue to be actively pumped out of it, they accumulate outside, making this positive relative to the inside.
- This redistribution of sodium creates **hyperpolarisation**, which acts as the generator potential.

- If the threshold level is reached or exceeded by this change, then an action potential will be generated in the sensory neurone, which is connected to the brain via the optic nerve.
- Mitochondria found in the inner segment of the rod cell, generate ATP, which provides the energy necessary to recombine retinal and opsin into rhodopsin.

The process in a cone cell is very similar except that the pigment here is **iodopsin**. This is less sensitive to light and so a greater light intensity is required for it to breakdown and so create an action potential in the sensory neurone.

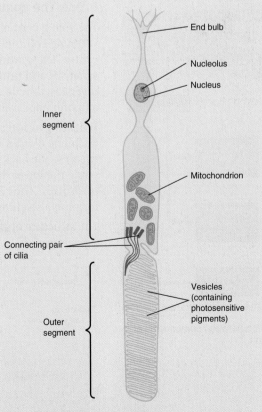

Fig 6.16 *Structure of a single rod cell*

End bulb

Nucleolus

Nucleus

Inner segment

Mitochondrion

Connecting pair of cilia

Vesicles (containing photosensitive pigments)

Outer segment

The reflex arc

The simplest type of nervous response is a **reflex arc**. Before considering how a spinal reflex works, it is helpful to understand how the millions of **neurones** in a mammalian body are organised, and the structure of the spinal cord.

6.9.1 Nervous organisation

The nervous system has two major divisions: the **central nervous system** (CNS), which is made up of the brain and spinal cord, and the **peripheral nervous system** (PNS), which is made up of pairs of nerves that originate from either the brain or the spinal cord.

The peripheral nervous system is divided into:

- **The sensory (afferent) nervous system**, which carries nerve impulses towards the central nervous system.
- **The motor (efferent) nervous system**, which carries nerve impulses away from the central nervous system.

The motor nervous system can be further sub-divided into:

- **The somatic nervous system**, which carries nerve impulses to skeletal muscles and is under voluntary control.
- **The autonomic nervous system**, which carries nerve impulses to glands, **smooth muscle** and **cardiac muscle** and is not under voluntary control, i.e. it is involuntary.

A summary of nervous organisation is given in figure 6.17 and the way its components interact is illustrated in figure 6.18.

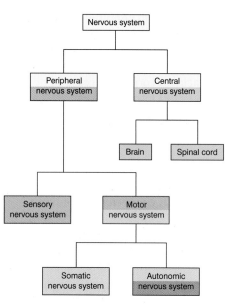

Fig 6.17 Nervous organisation

6.9.2 The spinal cord

The spinal cord is a column of nervous tissue running along the back within the vertebral column for protection. There is a small canal, the spinal canal, at its centre. The central region, called **grey matter**, comprises neurone cell bodies, synapses and unmyelinated relay neurones. Around the grey matter are many myelinated neurones running along the spinal cord. The **myelin** gives this region a lighter appearance and it is therefore known as **white matter**.

Emerging at intervals along the spinal cord are 31 pairs of nerves (in humans). Each one divides into two soon after leaving the spinal cord. The upper division (nearest the back) is called the **dorsal root**, and contains **sensory neurones**, while the lower division is called the **ventral root**, and contains **motor neurones**. The cell bodies of sensory neurones occur within the dorsal root, forming a swelling called the **dorsal root ganglion**.

The structure of the spinal cord is shown in figure 6.19.

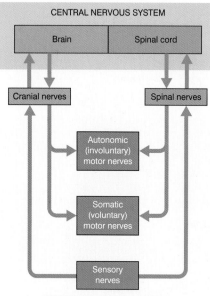

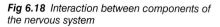

Fig 6.18 Interaction between components of the nervous system

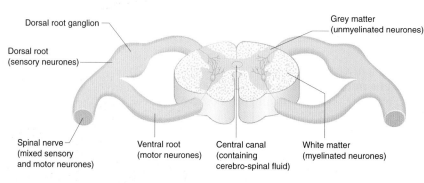

Fig 6.19 TS through the spinal cord

6.9.3 A spinal reflex

An involuntary response that follows a sensory stimulus is called a **reflex**. The pathway of neurones involved in a reflex is known as a **reflex arc**. The simplest forms of reflex arc, such as the knee jerk reflex, involve only a sensory and a motor neurone. More complex ones, such as the withdrawal reflex, also involve a relay neurone. If a reflex involves the spinal cord but not the brain it is known as a **spinal reflex**. The main stages of a spinal reflex arc such as withdrawing the hand from a hot object are:

- **stimulus** – heat from the hot object
- **receptor** – temperature receptors in the skin of the back of the hand. If the threshold value of the temperature receptor is exceeded, a **generator potential** is established
- **sensory neurone** – the generator potential leads to an **action potential** passing along the sensory neurone to the spinal cord
- **relay (intermediate) neurone** – links the sensory neurone via **synapses** to the motor neurone within the grey matter of the spinal cord
- **motor (effector) neurone** – carries an action potential away from the spinal cord to the biceps muscle in the forearm
- **effector** – the biceps muscle of the forearm is stimulated to contract

- **response** – the hand is raised away from the hot object.

These events are illustrated in figure 6.20.

6.9.4 Adaptive value of reflex arcs

Any action that confers an advantage for survival is said to have an **adaptive value**. Reflexes are involuntary – the actions they control do not need to be 'considered', because there is only one obvious course of action, e.g. remove the hand from the hot object. The adaptive value of reflex actions include:

- Being involuntary, they do not need the decision-making powers of the brain, leaving it free to carry out more complex responses. In this way the brain is not overloaded with situations in which the response is always the same. Some impulses are nevertheless sent to the brain, so that it is informed of what is happening and can over-ride the reflex if necessary.
- They protect the body from dangerous stimuli. They are effective from birth as they do not have to be learned.
- They are fast, because the neurone pathway is short with very few, typically one or two, synapses (which are the slowest link in a neurone pathway). This is important in withdrawal reflexes.

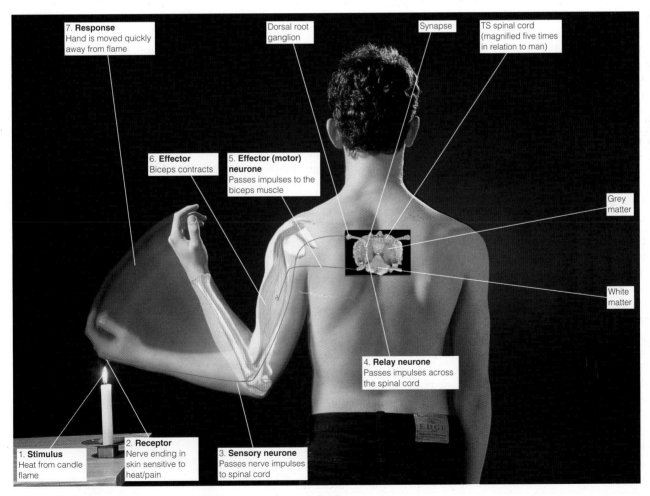

Fig 6.20 *Reflex arc involved in the withdrawal from an unpleasant stimulus*

The nerve impulse

A nerve impulse may be defined as a self-propagating wave of electrical disturbance that travels along the surface of the **neurone** cell surface membrane. It is not, however, an electrical current, but a temporary reversal of the electrical potential difference across the neurone membrane. This reversal is between a state called the **resting potential** and another called the **action potential**.

6.10.1 Resting potential

The movement of ions such as sodium ions (Na$^+$) and potassium ions (K$^+$) across the neurone membrane is controlled in a number of ways:

- The **phospholipid** bilayer of the cell surface membrane is impermeable to sodium ions (Na$^+$) and potassium ions (K$^+$).
- Protein molecules span this phospholipid bilayer. These **intrinsic proteins**, as they are called, have channels known as ion channels through them (*Essential AS Biology for OCR*, section 4.1.2). Some of these channels have 'gates' that can be opened or closed to allow sodium or potassium ions through at one time, but prevent their movement on other occasions. There are different gates for sodium and potassium. Some channels, however, remain open all the time and therefore allow unhindered diffusion of sodium and potassium.
- Some intrinsic proteins **actively transport** potassium ions into the cell and sodium ions out of it. This is called the **sodium–potassium pump (cation pump)**.

As a result of these various controls, the inside of a neurone is negatively charged relative to the outside. This is known as the **resting potential** and is in the range 50–90 millivolts (mV), but is usually 65 mV. In this condition the neurone is said to be **polarised**. The establishment of this potential difference is due to the following events:

- Negatively charged organic ions do not pass across the membrane and so remain trapped inside the neurone.
- Sodium ions are actively transported **out of** the neurone by sodium–potassium pumps (specialised carrier proteins).
- Potassium ions are actively transported **into** the neurone by sodium–potassium pumps (specialised carrier proteins).
- The active transport of sodium is faster than that of potassium, so that three sodium ions move out for every two potassium ions that move in.
- Although both sodium and potassium ions are positive, the increased movement outward of the sodium compared with the potassium inward leads to more positive ions in the tissue fluid outside the neurone than in the cytoplasm of the **axon**
- Both ions naturally begin to diffuse back in the opposite way from which they came, because there is a large concentration gradient of each between the inside and the outside of the neurone.
- However, most of the gates in the channels that allow potassium ions through are open, while most of the gates in the channels allowing sodium ions through are closed.
- The result is that the membrane is 100 times more permeable to potassium ions, which therefore diffuse back out of the neurone faster than the sodium ones diffuse back in. This further increases the potential difference between the negative inside and the positive outside of the neurone.
- Apart from the chemical gradient that causes the movement of the potassium and sodium ions, there is also an electrical gradient. As more and more potassium ions diffuse out of the neurone, so the outside becomes more and more positive. Further outward movement of potassium ions is therefore made difficult because, being positively charged, they are attracted back into the neurone by its overall negative state and repelled from moving outwards by the overall positive state of the tissue fluid.
- An equilibrium is established whereby there is no net movement of ions and which is a balance between the chemical and electrical gradients.

These events are summarised in figure 6.21.

6.10.2 The action potential

When a stimulus arrives at a receptor or nerve ending, its energy causes a temporary reversal of the charges on the neurone cell surface membrane. As a result, the negative charge of 65 mV inside the membrane becomes a positive charge of around +40 mV. This is known as the **action**

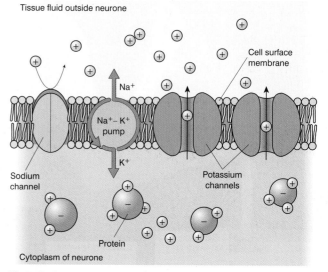

Fig 6.21 *Distribution of ions at resting potential*

potential, and in this condition the membrane is said to be **depolarised**. This depolarisation occurs because channels in the axon membrane change shape, and hence open or close, depending on the voltage across the membrane. They are therefore called **voltage-gated** channels. The sequence of events is described below and the numbers relate to the stages illustrated in figure 6.22:

1. At resting potential some potassium voltage-gated channels are open but the sodium voltage-gated channels are closed.
2. The energy of the stimulus causes the sodium voltage-gated channels in the neurone cell surface membrane to open and therefore sodium ions diffuse in through the channels along their electrochemical gradient. Being positively charged, they begin a reversal in the potential difference across the membrane.
3. As sodium ions enter, so more sodium channels open, causing an even greater influx of sodium ions. This is an example of positive feedback (section 6.1.3).
4. Once the action potential of around +40 mV has been established, the voltage gates on sodium channels close (so further influx of sodium is prevented) and the voltage gates on the potassium channels begin to open.
5. With some potassium voltage-gated channels now open, the electrical gradient that was preventing further outward movement of potassium ions (section 6.10.1) is now reversed, causing more potassium channels to open. This means that yet more potassium ions diffuse out, causing repolarisation of the neurone.

6. The outward movement of these potassium ions causes the temporary overshoot of the electrical gradient, with the inside of the neurone being more negative (relative to the outside) than usual. This is called **hyperpolarisation**. The gates on the potassium channels now close and the activities of the sodium–potassium (cation) pumps cause sodium ions to be pumped out and potassium ions in, once again. The resting potential of 65 mV is re-established and the neurone is said to be **repolarised**.

The terms **action** potential and **resting** potential can be misleading, because the movement of sodium ions inwards during the action potential is purely due to diffusion – a passive process – and the resting potential is maintained by active transport – an active process. The term action potential simply means that the neurone membrane is transmitting a nerve impulse, whereas resting potential means that it is not.

SUMMARY TEST 6.10

A nerve impulse is the result of a temporary reversal of **(1)** potential difference across the neurone membrane. At resting potential the potential difference is in the range **(2)** millivolts but is usually around **(3)** millivolts. In this condition the neurone is said to be **(4)** with the outside being **(5)** charged relative to the inside. During an action potential, the charges are reversed with a potential difference of **(6)** millivolts and the membrane is said to be **(7)**.

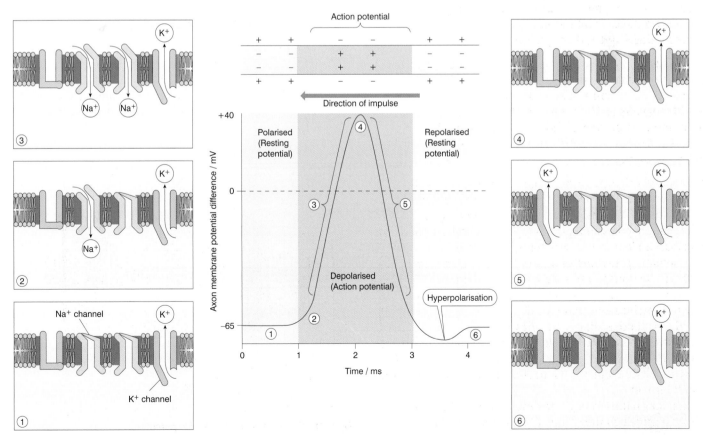

Fig 6.22 The action potential

Once it has been created, an **action potential** 'moves' rapidly along a **neurone**. The size of the action potential remains the same from one end of the neurone to the other. Strictly speaking, nothing physically 'moves' from place to place along the **axon** of the neurone, but rather the reversal of electrical charge is reproduced at different points along the axon membrane. As one region of the axon produces an action potential and becomes **depolarised**, it acts as a stimulus for the depolarisation of the next region of the axon. In this manner, action potentials are regenerated along each small region of the axon membrane. In the meantime, the previous region of the membrane returns to its **resting potential**, i.e. it is repolarised.

The process can be likened to the 'Mexican wave' that frequently takes place in a crowded stadium during a sporting event. Although the wave of people standing up and raising their hands (action potential) moves around the stadium, the people themselves do not move from seat to seat with the wave. They do not physically pass around the stadium until they return to their original seat. Rather, their individual action of standing and raising their hands is reproduced by the person to one side of them, in the same way that they were stimulated to stand and wave by the person on the other side of them. For this reason, the 'movement' of the impulse is more accurately termed **propagation**.

6.11.1 Propagation of the nerve impulse in an unmyelinated nerve

It is easier to understand how a nerve impulse is propagated in a myelinated nerve if we first look at how it is propagated in an unmyelinated one. The process is described and illustrated in figure 6.23 (opposite).

6.11.2 Propagation of a nerve impulse in a myelinated neurone

In myelinated neurones, the fatty sheath of myelin around the axon acts as an electrical insulator, preventing action potentials from forming. At intervals of 1–3 mm there are breaks in this insulatory myelin, called **nodes of Ranvier** (section 6.7.2). Action potentials can occur at these points. The localised circuits therefore arise between adjacent nodes of Ranvier and the action potentials in effect 'jump' from node to node in a process known as **saltatory conduction** (Latin 'saltare' = to jump) (Fig 6.24, below). This results in an action potential passing along a myelinated neurone faster than an unmyelinated one (section 6.12.1). In our Mexican wave analogy, this is equivalent to a whole block of spectators leaping up simultaneously, followed by the next block and so on. Instead of the wave passing around the stadium in hundreds of small stages, it passes around in 20 or so large ones and is consequently more rapid.

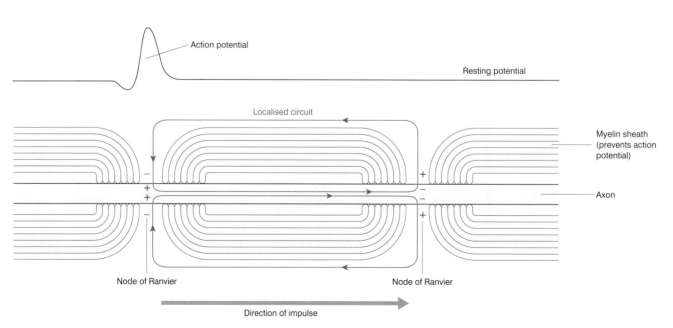

Fig 6.24 *Propagation of an impulse along a myelinated neurone. Action potentials are produced only at nodes of Ranvier. Depolarisation therefore skips from node to node – saltatory conduction*

☐ Polarised

▨ Depolarised

☐ Repolarised

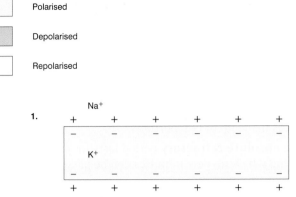

1. At resting potential (section 6.10.1) the concentration of sodium ions outside the axon membrane is high relative to the inside, whereas that of the potassium ions is high inside the membrane relative to the outside. The overall concentration of positive ions is, however, greater on the outside, making this positive compared with the inside. The axon membrane is polarised. In our Mexican wave analogy, this is equivalent to the whole stadium being seated, i.e. at rest.

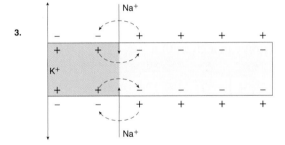

2. A stimulus causes a sudden influx of sodium ions and hence a reversal of charge on the axon membrane. This is the action potential (section 6.10.2) and the membrane is depolarised. In our analogy, a prompt leads a vertical line of people to stand and wave their arms, i.e. they are stimulated into action.

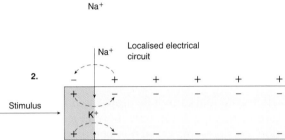

3. The localised electrical circuits established by the influx of sodium ions cause the opening of sodium voltage-gated channels (section 6.10.2) a little further along the axon. The resulting influx of sodium ions in this region causes depolarisation. Behind this new region of depolarisation, the sodium voltage-gated channels close and the potassium ones open. Potassium ions begin to leave the axon along their electrochemical gradient. The sight of the person next to them standing and waving prompts the person in the adjacent seat to stand and wave. A new vertical line of people stands and waves, while the original line of people begin to sit down again.

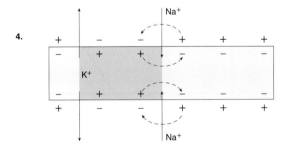

4. The action potential (depolarisation) is propagated in the same way further along the neurone. The outward movement of the potassium ions has continued to the extent that the axon membrane behind the action potential has returned to its original charged state (positive outside, negative inside), i.e. it has been repolarised. The second line of people standing and waving prompts the third line of people to do the same. Meanwhile, the first line have now resumed their original positions, i.e. they are re-seated.

5. Repolarisation of the neurone allows sodium ions to be actively transported out, once again returning the neurone to its resting potential in readiness for a new stimulus if it comes. The people who have just sat down settle back in their seats and readjust themselves in readiness to repeat the process should they be prompted to do so again.

Fig 6.23 Propagation of an impulse along an unmyelinated nerve

Once an **action potential** has been set up, it moves rapidly from one end of the **neurone** to the other without any decrease in amplitude. In other words, the final action potential at the end of the **axon** is as large as the first action potential. A number of factors, however, affect the speed at which the action potential passes along the axon. Depending upon these factors, an action potential may travel at as little as 0.5 m in a second or as much as 120 m in the same time. Table 6.5 gives some examples of transmission speeds in different axons.

Table 6.5 *Transmission speeds of different axons*

Axon	Myelin	Axon diameter / μm	Transmission speed / ms⁻¹
Human motor axon to leg muscle	Yes	20	120
Human sensory axon from skin pressure receptor	Yes	10	50
Squid giant axon	No	500	25
Human motor axon to internal organ	No	1	2

6.12.1 Factors affecting the transmission of action potentials

- **The myelin sheath** – we saw in section 6.11.2 that the myelin sheath acts as an electrical insulator, preventing an action potential forming in the part of the axon covered in myelin. It does, however, jump from **node of Ranvier** to node of Ranvier (**saltatory conduction**), thereby speeding transmission from 30 ms⁻¹ in a unmyelinated neurone to 90 ms⁻¹ in a similar myelinated one.
- **The diameter of the axon** – the greater the diameter of an axon, the faster the speed of transmission. This is due to less leakage of ions from a large axon (leakage makes membrane potentials harder to maintain).
- **Temperature** – affects the rate of diffusion of ions and therefore the higher the temperature the faster the nerve impulse. Above a certain temperature, the cell surface membrane proteins are **denatured** and impulses fail to be conducted at all. Temperature is clearly an important factor in response times in **ectothermic** animals, in which body temperature varies in accordance with the environment.
- **The refractory period** – we shall look at this in more detail in the next section.

6.12.2 The refractory period

Once an action potential has been created in any region of a neurone, there is a period afterwards when inward movement of sodium ions is prevented because the sodium

voltage-gated channels are closed. During this time it is not possible for a further action potential to be generated. This is known as the **refractory period**. The refractory period is made up of two portions:

- **The absolute refractory** period lasts for about 1 ms, during which no new impulses can be passed, however intense the stimulus.
- **The relative refractory** period lasts around 5 ms, during which a new impulse may be propagated provided the stimulus exceeds the normal threshold value (section 6.12.3). The degree to which it needs to exceed the threshold value diminishes over the period (Fig 6.25).

The refractory period serves two purposes:

- The action potential cannot be propagated in the region that is refractory, i.e. it can only move in a forward direction. This prevents the action potential from spreading out in both directions, which it would otherwise do.
- Because a new action potential cannot be formed immediately behind the first one, it ensures that action potentials are separated from one another and therefore limits the number of action potentials that can pass along a neurone in a given time.

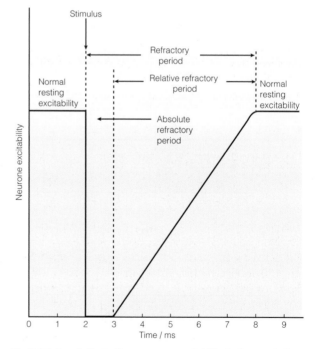

Fig 6.25 *Graph illustrating neurone excitability before and after a nerve impulse*

6.12.3 All or nothing response

Nerve impulses are described as **all or nothing** responses. There is a certain level of stimulus, called the **threshold value**, which triggers an impulse. Below the threshold value no impulse is generated; above the threshold value an impulse is generated. The action potential, however, is the same regardless of how much the stimulus is above the threshold value. How then can an organism determine the size of a stimulus? This is achieved in two ways:

• by the number of impulses passing in a given time. This is known as **frequency coding**. The larger the stimulus, the more impulses that are generated in a given time (Fig 6.26).
• by having different neurones with different threshold values. The brain interprets the number and type of neurones that pass impulses as a result of a given stimulus and thereby determines its size.

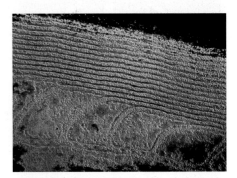

TEM of layers of myelin that form a sheath around nerve axons

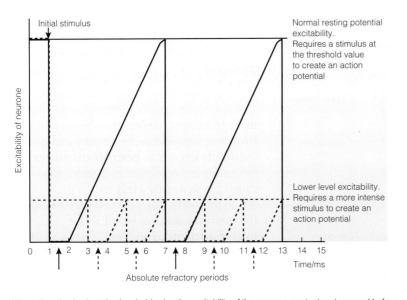

Where the stimulus is at the threshold value the excitability of the neurone must return to normal before a new action potential can be formed. In the time interval shown, this allows just two action potentials to pass, i.e. a low frequency of impulses. Where the stimulus exceeds the threshold value, a new action potential can be created before neurone excitability returns to normal. In the time interval shown, this allows six action potentials to pass, i.e. a high frequency of impulses.

Fig 6.26 *Determination of impulse frequency*

EXTENSION
Multiple sclerosis

Multiple sclerosis (MS) causes progressive damage to the nervous system. It usually affects young adults, causing weak limbs, 'pins and needles', numbness and blurred vision. In some people the condition is unrelenting, leading to severe physical disability. It affects around 80 000 people in the UK and some 400 000 in the USA. In multiple sclerosis there is gradual degradation of the **myelin** sheath that surrounds most nerve **axons**. These areas of the axon, known as **plaques**, are approximately 2–10 mm in length and leave the axon demyelinated and unable to conduct impulses in the usual manner. Scar tissue develops in these areas – a process known as **sclerosis**, from which the disease gets its name. While the exact cause of MS is unknown, it is generally accepted that it is an autoimmune disease in which the body's own blood immune system reacts to self **antigens** as if they were non-self antigens. It is not clear what triggers this response, but several factors are involved, including sex (it is more common in females), genetics and environmental factors.

SUMMARY TEST 6.12

The speed at which an action potential passes along an axon may vary from as little as **(1)** metres s^{-1} to as much as **(2)** metres s^{-1}. Various factors influence this speed of transmission. For example, it is **(3)** if the diameter of the axon is smaller, and it is slower if the temperature is **(4)**, because the rate of **(5)** of ions is slower. The presence of a myelin sheath **(6)** the rate of transmission of an action potential because the action potential jumps from one node of **(7)** to the next in a process called **(8)**. Once an action potential has passed along an axon, the sodium **(9)** remain closed, preventing any inward movement of sodium ions. There is hence a period of about 1 ms, called the **(10)** refractory period, during which no new action potential can be passed. This is followed by a period called the **(11)** refractory period, during which a new action potential will pass only if the normal **(12)** is exceeded.

Structure and functions of synapses

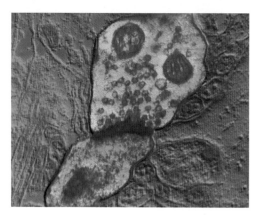

TEM of synapse. The synaptic cleft between the two neurones (centre) appears deep red. The cell above the cleft has many small vesicles (red-yellow spheres) containing neurotransmitter, whereas the two larger spheres above the vesicles are mitochondria

A synapse is the point where the **axon** of one **neurone** connects with the **dendrite** of another or with an effector. They are important in linking different neurones together and therefore coordinating activities. The human brain has 10^{11} (100 000 000 000) neurones and a thousand times more (10^{14}) synapses.

6.13.1 Structure of a chemical synapse

There are two types of synapse – electrical and chemical. Chemical synapses are the most common type and transmit impulses from one neurone to the next by means of chemicals known as **neurotransmitters**. Neurones are separated by a small gap called the **synaptic cleft** which is 20–30 nm wide. The neurone that releases the neurotransmitter is called the **presynaptic neurone** and it has a swollen portion of axon, the **synaptic knob**, at its end. This possesses many mitochondria, large amounts of endoplasmic reticulum and **synaptic vesicles** containing the neurotransmitter which, once released from the vesicles by exocytosis, diffuses across to the postsynaptic neurone, which possesses **receptor molecules** on its membrane to receive it. The structure of a chemical synapse is illustrated in figure 6.27. Details of how nerve impulses are transmitted across synapses are given in unit 6.14.

6.13.2 Functions of synapses

Synapses perform a number of important functions:

- **Transmit information between neurones** – synapses convey impulses from one neurone to the next and it is from this basic function that all the others arise.
- **Are unidirectional** – synapses can only pass impulses in one direction, because only the presynaptic neurone has vesicles containing the neurotransmitter. Any action potential arriving at the postsynaptic neurone would simply cease at this point. In this way synapses act like valves.

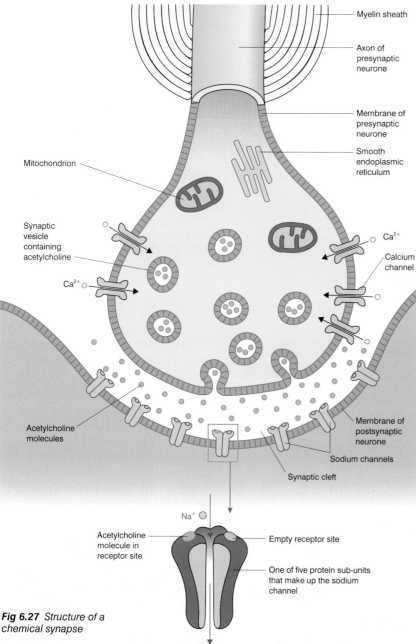

Myelin sheath

Axon of presynaptic neurone

Membrane of presynaptic neurone

Smooth endoplasmic reticulum

Mitochondrion

Synaptic vesicle containing acetylcholine

Ca^{2+}

Ca^{2+}

Calcium channel

Acetylcholine molecules

Membrane of postsynaptic neurone

Sodium channels

Synaptic cleft

Na^+

Acetylcholine molecule in receptor site

Empty receptor site

One of five protein sub-units that make up the sodium channel

Fig 6.27 *Structure of a chemical synapse*

- **Act as junctions** – allowing nerve impulses to diverge and converge. In divergence a single impulse along one neurone can be conveyed to a number of different neurones at a synapse (Fig 6.28a). This allows a single stimulus to create a number of simultaneous responses. In convergence, a number of impulses can be combined into a single impulse (Fig 6.28b). This occurs in the retina of the eye, for example.
- **Filter out low level stimuli** such as the drone of traffic or machinery. The stimulus produces low frequency impulses that cause the release of only small amounts of neurotransmitter at the synapse. This is insufficient to create a new impulse in the postsynaptic neurone and so there is no response. The absence of a response is rarely, if ever, harmful.
- **Summation** – low frequency impulses that produce insufficient amounts of neurotransmitter to trigger a new action potential in the postsynaptic neurone, can be made to do so by a process called **summation**. This entails a build-up of neurotransmitter in the synapse by one of two methods:
  - where a number of different presynaptic neurones together release enough neurotransmitter to trigger a new action potential
  - where a single presynaptic neurone releases neurotransmitter many times over a short period. If the total amount of neurotransmitter exceeds the **threshold value** of the postsynaptic neurone, then a new action potential is triggered.
- **Prevent overstimulation and fatigue** – where a stimulus is powerful and prolonged, the high frequency of impulses in the presynaptic neurone leads to the release of considerable amounts of neurotransmitter. In these circumstances the release of neurotransmitter ceases, along with any response to the stimulus. The synapse is said to be **fatigued**. The purpose of such a response is to prevent overstimulation, which might otherwise damage an effector.
- **Involved in memory and learning** – it is thought that synapses have a role in the brain in allowing organisms to recall events and learn to recognise individuals.

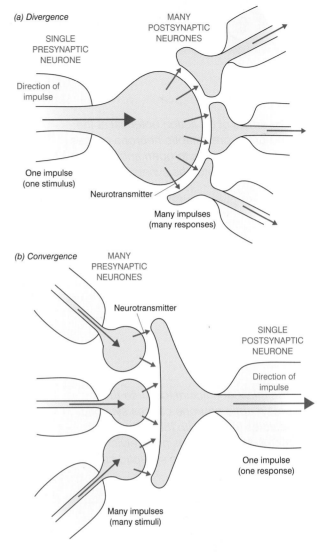

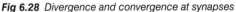

Fig 6.28 *Divergence and convergence at synapses*

SUMMARY TEST 6.13

Synapses connect the axon of one neurone with the **(1)** of another. The two parts are separated by a gap called the synaptic **(2)** that is around **(3)** nm wide. One neurone, called the **(4)** neurone, releases a chemical messenger known generally as a **(5)**, of which acetylcholine is an example. These messengers are stored within small containers called **(6)** and, once released, diffuse across to receptor molecules on the **(7)** neurone. Synapses perform a number of functions, all of which derive from their ability to transmit impulses between one neurone and the next. They are **(8)**, as they only allow impulses to pass in one direction across them. Synapses also act as **(9)**, because they allow nerve impulses to diverge and converge. They can also allow low frequency impulses to build up sufficient messenger substance over time that they trigger a new impulse in the postsynaptic neurone – a process called **(10)**. Synapses also have an important role in the brain, where it is thought they are involved in **(11)** and **(12)**.

Synaptic transmission

In the following sequence of diagrams (Fig 6.29), only relevant structures are shown in each figure.

1. *The arrival of an action potential at the end of the presynaptic neurone causes calcium channels to open and calcium ions (Ca^{2+}) enter the synaptic knob.*

Presynaptic neurone

Action potential

Ca^{2+}

Ca^{2+}

Synaptic vesicle containing acetylcholine

Calcium channel open

Sodium channel closed

Postsynaptic neurone

2. *The influx of calcium ions into the presynaptic neurone causes synaptic vesicles to fuse with the presynaptic membrane, so releasing acetylcholine by exocytosis into the synaptic cleft.*

Vesicle fuses with membrane

Acetylcholine released into the synaptic cleft

Sodium channel closed

Empty receptor site

Sodium channel closed

3. *Acetylcholine molecules fuse with receptor sites on two of the five protein sub-units that make up each sodium channel. This causes the sodium channels to open, allowing sodium ions (Na$^+$) to diffuse in rapidly along a concentration gradient.*

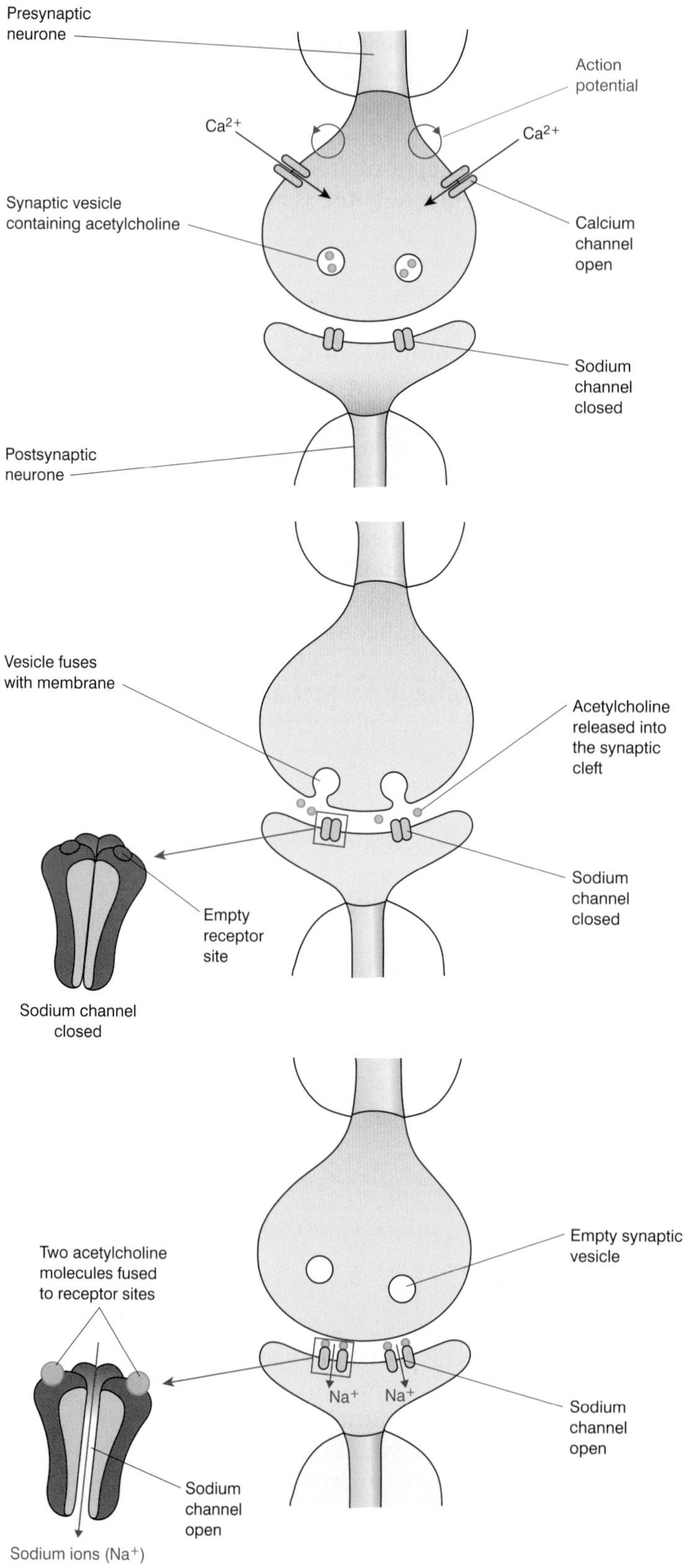

Two acetylcholine molecules fused to receptor sites

Empty synaptic vesicle

Na$^+$ Na$^+$

Sodium channel open

Sodium channel open

Sodium ions (Na$^+$)

Fig 6.29 *Mechanism of transmission across a cholinergic synapse*

4. *The influx of sodium ions generates a new action potential in the postsynaptic neurone. This is called the* **excitatory postsynaptic potential (EPSP).**

New action potential

5. *Acetylcholinesterase hydrolyses acetylcholine into choline and ethanoic acid (acetyl), which diffuse back across the synaptic cleft into the presynaptic neurone (=* **recycling***).*

Acetylcholinesterase

6. *ATP released by mitochondria is used to recombine choline and ethanoic acid into acetycholine. This is stored in synaptic vesicles for future use. Sodium channels close in the absence of acetylcholine in the receptor sites.*

Mitochondrion produces ATP

ATP recombines choline and ethanoic acid

ATP

Acetylcholine returns to synaptic vesicle

Sodium channel closed

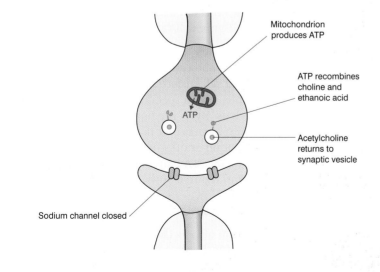

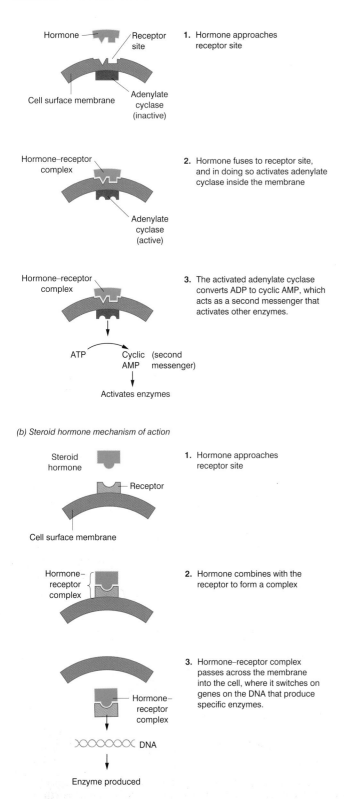

Fig 6.30 *Mechanisms of hormone action*

(a) Use of second messenger, e.g. protein and polypeptide hormones such as adrenaline

1. Hormone approaches receptor site

2. Hormone fuses to receptor site, and in doing so activates adenylate cyclase inside the membrane

3. The activated adenylate cyclase converts ADP to cyclic AMP, which acts as a second messenger that activates other enzymes.

(b) Steroid hormone mechanism of action

1. Hormone approaches receptor site

2. Hormone combines with the receptor to form a complex

3. Hormone–receptor complex passes across the membrane into the cell, where it switches on genes on the DNA that produce specific enzymes.

We saw in section 6.7.1 that animals possess two principal coordinating systems – the nervous system that communicates rapidly, and the endocrine system that usually does so more slowly. Both systems interact in order to maintain the constancy of the internal environment while being responsive to a varying external environment. Both systems also use chemical messengers – the endocrine system exclusively so, and the nervous system through the use of **neurotransmitters** in chemical synapses. It is worth noting that **adrenaline** may act both as a hormone and a neurotransmitter.

6.15.1 Hormones

A hormone is a regulating chemical produced by an endocrine gland (section 6.15.2) and is carried in the blood to the cells, tissues or organ on which it acts – known as the **target cell (organ)** – that have complementary receptors on their cell membranes. Hormones may differ chemically from one another, but they share many common characteristics. They are:

- effective in very small quantities, but often have widespread and permanent effects
- normally relatively small molecules
- often proteins or polypeptides, although some are **steroids**
- transported by the blood system
- produced by endocrine glands.

There are two mechanisms of hormone action:

- **Protein and peptide hormones** (e.g. insulin, glucagon, adrenaline) bind to receptors on the cell surface membrane. The hormone–receptor complex so produced causes a series of chemical changes within the cell and produces a specific response. The mechanism for the action of adrenaline is illustrated in figure 6.30(a).

- **Steroid hormones** (e.g. oestrogen and testosterone) are soluble in lipids and can therefore pass across the **phospholipid** cell surface membrane. Once inside, the hormone binds with a specific receptor protein that carries it into the nucleus. Here, the hormone–receptor complex combines with a particular portion of DNA (a **gene**), which it switches either on or off, thereby affecting protein (enzyme) synthesis. The mechanism for the action of a steroid hormone is illustrated in figure 6.30(b).

6.15.2 Endocrine glands

A gland is a group of cells that produce a particular substance or substances by a mechanism known as **secretion**. Glands can be divided into two groups:

- **Exocrine** glands transport their secretions to the site of action by special ducts. Many digestive secretions such as saliva and pancreatic juice are produced by exocrine glands.

- **Endocrine** glands are ductless glands that secrete hormones directly into the blood.

Endocrine glands may be discrete organs such as the thyroid gland, or groups of cells within other organs, such as the **islets of Langerhans** in the pancreas. Endocrine glands are found throughout the body and figure 6.31 shows the location of the main ones in humans.

6.15.3 The pancreas

The pancreas is a large, pale coloured gland that is situated in the upper abdomen, behind the stomach. It is both an exocrine and an endocrine gland.

- As an **exocrine gland** it produces the digestive secretion called pancreatic juice that passes along the pancreatic duct and into the small intestine. Among other substances, pancreatic juice contains the digestive enzymes protease, amylase and lipase.
- As an **endocrine gland** the pancreas produces the hormones **insulin** and **glucagon**, which pass directly into the blood capillaries that pass through it.

When examined microscopically, the pancreas is made up largely of exocrine cells arranged radially around tiny ducts. These cells produce pancreatic juice, which is secreted into these ducts. Scattered throughout the pancreas, like small islands in the sea of exocrine cells, are the groups of endocrine cells known as **islets of Langerhans**. These cells appear different in structure from the exocrine cells and, upon close examination, are seen to be of two types:

- the larger **α cells** that produce the hormone glucagon
- the smaller **β cells** that produce the hormone insulin.

Figure 6.32 illustrates the cellular structure of part of the pancreas. Both types of cells are rich in secretory vesicles and their role in controlling blood sugar levels is the topic of our next unit.

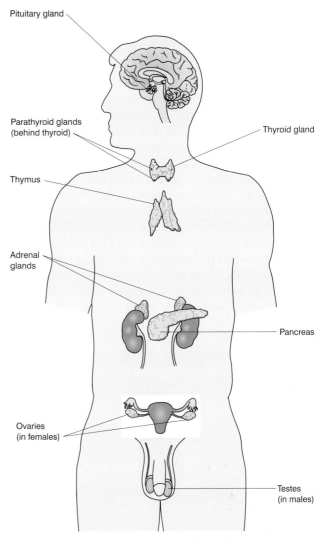

Fig 6.31 *Location of major endocrine glands in humans*

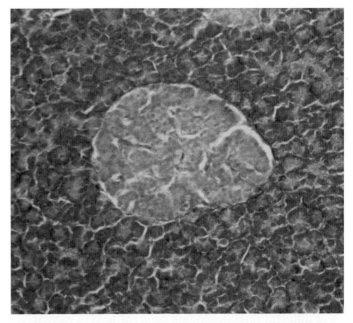

LM of the pancreas showing an islet of Langerhans (centre) containing α cells (red) and β cells (purple). The meshworks of blue and white in the islet are blood capillaries. Around the islet are the exocrine pancreatic cells

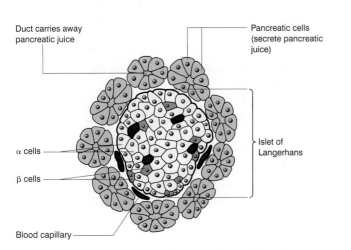

Fig 6.32 *Section through the pancreas showing an islet of Langerhans*

127

6.16 Regulation of blood glucose

Glucose is the main substrate for respiration, providing the source of energy for almost all organisms. It is broken down during glycolysis (unit 1.3) and, if oxygen is present, the Krebs cycle (unit 1.4) and electron transport system (unit 1.5), to provide ATP – the energy currency of cells (unit 1.2). It is therefore essential that the blood of mammals contains a constant supply of glucose for respiration. This level must be kept relatively constant. If it falls too low, cells will be deprived of energy and die – brain cells are especially sensitive in this respect because they can only respire glucose. If the level rises too high, it lowers the water potential of the blood and creates osmotic problems that can cause dehydration and be equally dangerous. Homeostatic control (unit 6.1) of blood glucose is therefore essential.

Terminology

To help understand some terms in this unit it is worth remembering that:

'gluco' / 'glyco'	= glucose
'glycogen'	= glycogen
'neo'	= new
'lysis'	= splitting
'genesis'	= birth / origin

Therefore:

glycogen – o – lysis	= splitting of glycogen
gluco – neo – genesis	= formation of new glucose

6.16.1 Blood glucose and variations in its level

The normal level of blood glucose is 90 mg in each 100 cm³ of blood. There are three sources of blood glucose:

- **Directly from the diet** as glucose from the breakdown of other carbohydrates such as starch, maltose, lactose and sucrose.
- **Breakdown of glycogen (glycogenolysis)** from the stores in the liver and muscle cells. A normal liver contains 75–100 g of glycogen, made by converting excess glucose from the diet in a process called glycogenesis.
- **Gluconeogenesis** is the production of new glucose, i.e. from sources other than carbohydrate. The liver, for example, can make glucose from glycerol and amino acids.

As animals do not eat continuously and their diet varies, their intake of glucose fluctuates. Likewise, glucose is used up at different rates depending upon the level of mental and physical activity. It is against these changes in supply and demand that three main hormones, insulin, glucagon

and **adrenaline** operate to maintain a constant blood glucose level.

6.16.2 Insulin and the β cells of the pancreas

We saw in section 6.15.3 that in the pancreas there are groups of special cells known as the islets of Langerhans. These cells are of two types: larger alpha (α) cells and smaller beta (β) cells. The β cells respond to a rise in blood glucose level by secreting the hormone **insulin** directly into the blood. Insulin is a globular protein made up of 51 amino acids.

Almost all body cells (red blood cells being a notable exception) have **glycoprotein** receptors on their membranes that bind with insulin molecules. Once combined with the receptors, insulin increases membrane permeability and enzyme action so that the blood glucose level is lowered in one or more of the following ways:

- Cellular respiratory rate is increased, using up more glucose and increasing its uptake by cells.
- The rate of conversion of glucose into glycogen (glycogenesis) is increased in the cells of the liver and muscles.
- The rate of conversion of glucose to fat in **adipose tissue** is increased.
- The rate of absorption of glucose into cells increases, especially in muscle cells.

The effect of these processes is to remove glucose from the blood and so return its level to normal. This lowering of the blood glucose level causes the β cells to reduce their secretion of insulin (= **negative feedback**).

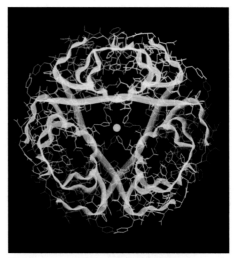

Molecular graphic of an insulin molecule. Insulin is made up of 51 amino acids arranged in two chains (shown here as yellow and green ribbons) held together by disulphide bridges

6.16.3 Glucagon and the α cells of the pancreas

The α cells of the islets of Langerhans respond to a fall in blood glucose by secreting the hormone glucagon directly into the blood. Only the cells of the liver have receptors that bind to glucagon, so only liver cells respond, by activating the enzyme phosphorylase, which converts glycogen to glucose, and by increasing the conversion of amino acids and glycerol into glucose (= **gluconeogenesis**).

The overall effect is therefore to increase the amount of glucose in the blood and return it to its normal level. This raising of the blood glucose level causes the α cells to reduce the secretion of glucagon (= negative feedback).

6.16.4 Adrenaline and other hormones regulating the blood glucose level

There are at least four other hormones besides glucagon that can increase blood glucose level. The best known of these is **adrenaline**. At times of excitement or stress, adrenaline is produced by the adrenal glands that lie above the kidneys. It causes the breakdown of glycogen in the liver, thereby raising the blood glucose level. Should the glycogen supply in the liver become exhausted, the adrenal glands produce the hormone **cortisol**, which causes the liver to convert amino acids and glycerol into glucose.

6.16.5 Hormone interaction in regulating blood sugar

The two hormones, insulin and glucagon, act in opposite directions. Insulin lowers blood glucose levels, whereas glucagon increases it. The two hormones are said to act **antagonistically**. The system is self-regulating in that it is the level of glucose in the blood that determines the quantity of insulin and glucagon produced. In this way the interaction of these two hormones allows highly sensitive

control of the blood glucose level. The level of glucose is, however, not constant, but fluctuates around a set point. This is because of the way negative feedback mechanisms work. Only when the blood glucose level falls below the set point is insulin secretion reduced (negative feedback), leading to a rise in blood glucose. In the same way, only when the level exceeds the set point is glucagon secretion reduced (negative feedback), causing a fall in the blood glucose level. The control of blood glucose level is summarised in figure 6.33.

SUMMARY TEST 6.16

Glucose is the main respiratory substrate in organisms. It is converted, by respiration, into **(1)** – the universal energy currency of cells. It is important that blood glucose levels are maintained at **(2)** mg in each 100 cm³ of blood by **(3)**, because if they fall too low cells are deprived of energy, and **(4)** cells are especially sensitive in this regard. If it rises too high **(5)** problems occur that may cause dehydration. Blood glucose is formed directly from **(6)** in the diet or from the breakdown of **(7)**, which is stored in the cells of the liver and **(8)**. The liver can also increase blood glucose levels by making glucose from other sources such as glycerol and **(9)** in a process known as **(10)**. Blood glucose is used up when it is absorbed into cells, converted into fat or **(11)** for storage or is used up during **(12)** by cells. To maintain a constant level of blood glucose the pancreas acts as an **(13)** gland in producing two hormones from clusters of cells within it called **(14)**. The β cells are **(15)** in size and produce the hormone **(16)**, which causes the blood glucose level to **(17)**. The α cells produce the hormone **(18)**, which has the opposite effect. The two hormones are therefore said to act **(19)**. Another hormone called **(20)** can also raise blood sugar levels.

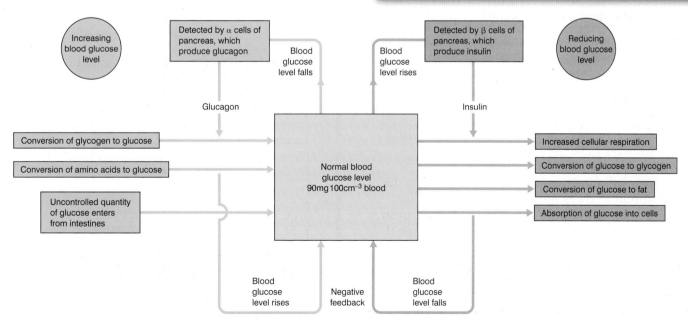

Fig 6.33 *Summary of regulation of blood glucose*

Diabetes is a chronic disease in which the patient is unable to metabolise carbohydrate, especially glucose, properly. There are over 100 million people worldwide with diabetes, 1.4 million of whom are in the UK. In addition, a further 1 million people in the UK are thought to have the disease but are currently unaware of the fact. There are two distinct forms of diabetes:

- **Diabetes insipidus** is rare and results from a deficiency of antidiuretic hormone (ADH), which controls urine production (section 6.6.1).
- **Diabetes mellitus** or 'sugar diabetes' is much more common and has two types depending on the cause.

Symptoms of diabetes mellitus

- a high blood glucose level
- presence of glucose in the urine
- increased thirst and hunger
- need to urinate excessively
- genital itching or regular episodes of thrush
- tiredness
- weight loss
- blurred vision.

6.17.1 Diabetes mellitus

Diabetes mellitus is a metabolic disorder in which there is an inability to control blood glucose levels due to a lack of the hormone **insulin** or a loss of responsiveness to it (Fig 6.34).

There are two forms of diabetes mellitus:

- **Type I (insulin dependent)** is due to the body being unable to produce insulin. It normally begins in childhood and is therefore also called juvenile-onset diabetes. It may be the result of an **autoimmune response** whereby the body's immune system attacks its own cells – in this case the β cells of the **islets of Langerhans**. Type I diabetes develops quickly, usually over a few weeks, and the symptoms (see box) are normally obvious.
- **Type II (insulin independent)** is normally due to the **glycoprotein** receptors on the body cells losing their responsiveness to insulin. It may, however, be due to an inadequate supply of insulin from the pancreas. Type II diabetes usually arises in people over the age of 40 years and used to be known as mature-onset diabetes. There are, however, some recent cases of obesity and poor diet leading to Type II diabetes in adolescents. It develops slowly, and the symptoms are normally less severe and may go unnoticed or be put down to 'overwork' or 'old

age'. People who are overweight are particularly likely to develop Type II diabetes. Over 75% of people with diabetes have Type II.

6.17.2 Treatment of diabetes mellitus

Although diabetes cannot be cured, it can be treated very successfully. Treatment varies depending on the type of diabetes mellitus.

- **Type I diabetes** is treated by injections of insulin. It cannot be taken by mouth because, being a protein, it would be digested in the alimentary canal. It is therefore injected, typically either twice or four times a day. The dose of insulin must exactly match that required for the glucose intake. Too much insulin and the patient will experience hypoglycaemia, a condition of low blood glucose level which can result in unconsciousness. To ensure the correct dose, blood glucose levels are monitored using **biosensors**. By injecting insulin and managing their carbohydrate intake and exercise carefully, diabetics can lead normal lives.

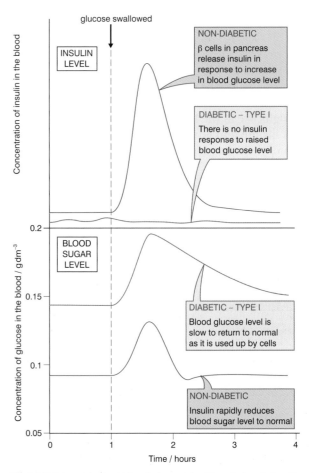

Fig 6.34 *Comparison of blood glucose and insulin levels in a Type I diabetic and a non-diabetic individual after each swallowed a glucose solution*

- **Type II diabetes** is treated by controlling the intake of carbohydrate in the diet and matching this to the amount of exercise taken. This may, in some cases, be supplemented by injections of insulin, or by use of drugs like sulphonylureas, which stimulate insulin production. Other drugs slow down the rate at which the body absorbs glucose from the intestine.

6.17.3 Genetically engineered insulin

Until relatively recently, insulin for use by diabetics was extracted from the pancreases of animals such as cows and pigs. Through the use of **gene technology** *(Essential AS Biology for OCR, unit 5.8)* it is now possible to produce insulin using genetically engineered bacteria by:

- isolating the insulin mRNA from human tissue
- using reverse transcriptase to produce complementary DNA (cDNA)
- multiplying the cDNA using the **polymerase chain reaction**
- inserting the cDNA into a **vector**, e.g. bacterial plasmid, and transferring it to host cells, e.g. the *Escherichia coli* bacterium
- culturing of host cells with the human insulin gene; they therefore produce insulin
- separating and purifying the insulin for clinical use.

A diabetic individual injecting insulin

Genetically engineered insulin has a number of advantages over that extracted from animals when it comes to treating diabetes:

- It is more effective because it is an **exact** copy of human insulin, whereas animal insulin has slight differences.
- It is more rapid in its action because it is identical to human insulin.
- There is no immune response, whereas animal insulin, with its slight differences, can sometimes stimulate an immune reaction.
- There is no risk of infection being transferred with the insulin. Animal insulin can transfer certain diseases.
- Some patients develop tolerance to animal insulin and become less sensitive to it, requiring them to have increasingly large doses to achieve the same effect. This, as yet, is less of a problem with genetically engineered insulin.
- It is cheaper to produce than extracting and purifying animal insulin.
- Animals are not involved in its production. While the animals from which insulin was extracted were killed primarily for food (insulin being purely a by-product), many vegetarians were unhappy using an animal product in this way.

> **The people most at risk of developing Type II diabetes are those:**
> - with a family history of diabetes
> - aged between 40 and 75 years
> - of Asian or African-Caribbean origin
> - who are very overweight
> - who have given birth to a large baby.

SUMMARY TEST 6.17

Diabetes mellitus, also known as **(1)** diabetes, occurs when the body is unable to control blood glucose levels. Its symptoms include a blood glucose level that is **(2)** than normal, increased **(3)** and **(4)**, tiredness and the need to **(5)** excessively. There are two forms of diabetes mellitus. Type I is also called **(6)** or **(7)** diabetes and may result from the body's white blood cells attacking the **(8)** cells found in the **(9)** of the pancreas. This form of self-attack is known as an **(10)** response. Type I normally affects young people and the symptoms develop quickly and are obvious. It is treated by injections of insulin. Insulin cannot be taken by mouth because it is a **(11)** and would therefore be digested. The dose is important, because if too much insulin is injected the blood glucose level could fall below normal – a condition called **(12)**. Type II diabetes is also called **(13)** or **(14)** diabetes and is caused by the **(15)** receptors on the body cells failing to respond to insulin or the pancreas producing too little insulin. It usually arises slowly in people over 40 years of age. More than **(16)** % of diabetes is Type II diabetes. It is treated by controlling the intake of **(17)** and exercise. Genetically engineered insulin is preferable to that extracted from animals because it is an **(18)** copy of human insulin and so is more **(19)** in its action and does not induce an **(20)** response. There is no risk of **(21)** being transferred, it is **(22)** to produce and there is less risk of **(23)** to insulin developing. As animals are not involved in its production, it is more acceptable to vegetarians.

6.18 Plant growth regulators – gibberellins

Plant responses to light

Photosynthesis
Light of wavelengths in the region of 430 nm (blue) and 660 nm (red) is needed for photosynthesis (unit 2.4). Provided other factors are not limiting, more light produces more growth. However, in the absence of light, shoots elongate rapidly and the stem becomes **etiolated**.

Phototropism
Shoots bend towards a directional light source (i.e. they are positively phototropic). Roots either grow away from directional light (negatively phototropic) or are not affected by it. Leaves of dicotyledonous plants position themselves at right angles to light.

Chlorophyll synthesis
Light is needed to make chlorophyll. In the dark, plants become yellow due to a lack of chlorophyll pigment (= **chlorotic**). Without chlorophyll, plants cannot photosynthesise and so growth ceases once food reserves are used up.

Germination
Some seeds, e.g. certain varieties of lettuce, need light in order to germinate.

Photoperiodism
The growth and development of flowers are affected by the length of the day (or more accurately the length of uninterrupted darkness) and the wavelength of light.

Effects of gibberellins on plant growth

Unlike animals, plants have no nervous system; nevertheless, to survive, plants must respond to changes in both their external and internal environments. For example, plants must respond to:

- **light** – stems grow towards it, as it is needed for photosynthesis and other essential processes (see box)
- **gravity** – plants need to be firmly anchored in the soil. Roots are sensitive to gravity and grow in the direction of its pull
- **water** – almost all plant roots bend towards moisture in order to absorb it for use in photosynthesis and other metabolic processes
- **chemicals** – pollen tubes grow towards chemicals produced at the micropyle of an ovule in order for fertilisation to occur
- **touch** – the shoots of plants such as beans or the tendrils of peas grow spirally around supports when they touch them. This allows them to reach above their competitors to obtain more light.

Plants communicate by means of plant hormones or, more correctly, **plant growth regulators**. The latter term is more explanatory because:

- they exert their influence by affecting growth
- unlike animal hormones, they are not made in particular organs but rather by cells located throughout the plant
- unlike animal hormones, some plant growth regulators, e.g. ethene, affect the tissues that release them rather than act on some distant target organ.

6.18.1 Plant growth regulators

Plant growth regulators are produced in small quantities and either affect the tissues that make them directly, or are transported by diffusion, active transport or by mass flow in phloem or xylem to other regions where they have their effects. As plant growth regulators are produced in such tiny amounts, it is often difficult to determine precisely where they are produced or indeed where exactly they have their effects. To make matters more confusing, the effects of plant growth regulators are different depending on their concentration and the tissues they act on. A concentration of **auxin** of around 10 parts per million, for example, will increase the growth of shoots by 200% but decrease that of roots by 100%. In addition, plant growth regulators interact with each other in a number of ways, two main ones being:

- **Synergism** – occurs where two or more plant growth regulators act together to reinforce an effect. The overall influence on growth is therefore greater than the sum of the effect of each of the individual regulators, e.g. auxins and **gibberellins** work together to increase cell elongation.
- **Antagonism** – occurs where two or more plant growth regulators have opposing actions and so diminish each other's effects, e.g. gibberellins break dormancy in seeds, whereas **abscisic acid** induces dormancy.

There are five groups of plant growth regulators generally recognised – auxins, gibberellins, **cytokinins**, abscisic acid and **ethene**.

132

6.18.2 Role of gibberellins in stem elongation

Gibberellins are a group of over 90 plant growth regulators found not only in flowering plants but also in fungi, algae and some bacteria. They are thought to be made in developing seeds and apical portions of stems and roots. One gibberellin, called GA_1 (gibberellic acid one), increases the length of stems and so increases the height of plants. If the gibberellin GA_1 is added to certain genetic dwarf varieties of plants, the plants grow to normal size. This is probably because in these, and other plants, height is controlled by a gene with two alleles:

- a dominant **allele** that controls the production of an enzyme needed for the activation of the gibberellin – GA_1. Plants with at least one dominant allele therefore grow to normal height
- a **recessive** allele that does not code for the enzyme involved in GA_1 activation. Plants with both alleles of the recessive form therefore do not activate GA_1 and therefore they develop into dwarf varieties.

These dwarf varieties therefore require an external supply of GA_1 to make them grow to normal size.

6.18.3 Role of gibberellins in the germination of barley seeds

Once plant seeds are formed they often remain dormant for some period of time before they germinate. This allows them to overcome adverse conditions such as the cold temperatures of winter and allows time for them to be dispersed to new regions by wind or animals. This dormancy is, in part, due to the very low water content – between 5 and 10% – of most seeds. What then breaks dormancy and starts the process of germination? To answer this question, we need first to look at the structure of a typical endospermous seed such as wheat or barley. These seeds are made up of:

- **pericarp and testa** – an outer tough, protective layer made up of the testa (seed coat) and pericarp (fruit coat) fused together
- **aleurone layer** – a protein-rich layer just beneath the testa
- **endosperm** – a large region of stored starch that provides an energy source for the growing embryo
- **scutellum** – a modified form of the single cotyledon (seed leaf) of the seed
- **embryo** – the result of **mitotic** division of the zygote, this will develop into the new plant.

These structures are shown in figure 6.35.

The process of germination typically requires the presence of water, oxygen and a favourable temperature and occurs as follows (the numbers refer to those on the summary of the process in figure 6.35):

1. Water softens the testa–pericarp covering and enters the rest of the seed.

2. The water stimulates the embryo to produce gibberellin.
3. The gibberellin diffuses into the aleurone layer, where it induces **transcription** of the genes producing α-amylase and other enzymes that are manufactured from its protein store.
4. The α-amylase and other enzymes diffuse into the endosperm.
5. α-amylase **hydrolyses** the starch in the endosperm into maltose, which in turn is hydrolysed by maltase to glucose.
6. The glucose diffuses, via the scutellum, into the embryo where it is used to provide the ATP (from respiratory breakdown) and raw material (e.g. cellulose) needed for growth.

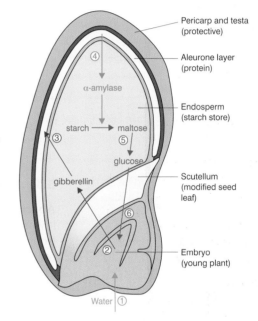

Fig 6.35 *Structure of a barley seed and the role of gibberellin in its germination*

SUMMARY TEST 6.18

Plants need to respond to both internal and external stimuli such as light which they require in photosynthesis and to make (**1**). Other external stimuli include chemicals, water, (**2**) and (**3**). To enable plants to respond to these stimuli, they produce plant growth regulators such as gibberellins that increase the length of (**4**) when a plant possesses a (**5**) allele that controls the production of an (**6**) needed to activate gibberellin. Gibberellins also promote germination in seeds such as wheat and barley. Germination occurs when water softens the (**7**) that protect the seed and stimulates the (**8**) to produce gibberellin, which then diffuses to the (**9**) layer, causing it to make enzymes. One such enzyme is (**10**), which diffuses into the (**11**) and hydrolyses (**12**) into maltose. The maltose is in turn hydrolysed into (**13**), which diffuses into the embryo where it is (**14**) to release energy and built up into substances such as (**15**).

6.19

Plant growth regulators – auxins and abscisic acid

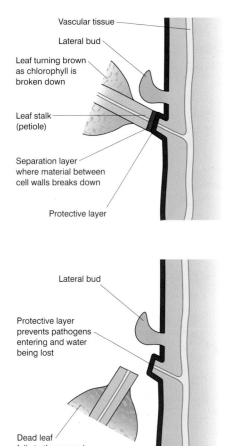

Vascular tissue

Lateral bud

Leaf turning brown as chlorophyll is broken down

Leaf stalk (petiole)

Separation layer where material between cell walls breaks down

Protective layer

Lateral bud

Protective layer prevents pathogens entering and water being lost

Dead leaf falls to the ground

Fig 6.36 *Leaf abscission in a woody plant*

6.19.1 Role of auxins in apical dominance

Auxins are a group of chemicals synthesised in the tips of shoots and roots. The most common form is **indole-3-acetic acid (IAA)**. The effects of auxins include promoting cell elongation, stimulating cell division, preventing leaf fall and maintaining apical dominance. Apical dominance occurs when the bud at the tip **(apical bud)** of a shoot inhibits the growth of side shoots (lateral buds) further down the stem. The apical bud is thought to achieve this by producing auxin in high enough concentrations to inhibit growth of the buds lower down the stem. Apical dominance can be demonstrated experimentally in young seedlings as follows:

- If the plants remain intact, the stem grows from the apical bud and the lateral buds do not develop.
- If the apical bud is removed, the lateral buds grow vigorously because the source of auxin, the apical bud, has been removed.
- If auxin solution is applied to the cut end of the stem immediately the apical bud is removed, the lateral buds do not grow.

The actual mechanism of apical dominance is unclear, and it seems that other regulators such as abscisic acid and **cytokinins** may be involved.

6.19.2 Role of abscisic acid in leaf fall

Abscisic acid (ABA) is a plant growth regulator that derived its name because it was initially thought to be responsible for abscission (leaves or fruits falling from plants) (Fig 6.36). It is made in the chloroplasts of plants and is especially concentrated in leaves and fruits. Abscisic acid inhibits growth and so works antagonistically to auxins and gibberellins. It appears to be produced in response to adverse conditions and so is sometimes referred to as the 'stress hormone'. Certainly it has been shown to increase in concentration up to 40-fold when a plant is subjected to drought conditions (section 6.19.3).

Abscission is a result of the stalk of leaves (petiole) or fruits becoming detached from the stem. This occurs in a series of stages:

- Valuable substances within the leaf, e.g. chlorophyll, are broken down and the products taken back into the body of the plant for future use. This causes the leaf to change colour from green to yellow-brown.
- Where the leaf stalk (petiole) joins the stem, an **abscission zone** develops, which is made up of:
  - a **separation layer** of small, thin-walled cells
  - a **protective layer** of cells with walls impregnated with the waterproof substance, **suberin**.
- Enzymes are produced that break down substances that hold together the walls of the cells in the separation layer.
- The protective layer is left on the stem as a ready-made shield against infection by organisms and loss of water from the plant.

What, then, controls the process of abscission? Despite the name, abscisic acid (ABA) plays little or no part in the actual abscission, but rather has a role in the ageing (senescence) of leaves. Abscisic acid acts antagonistically to auxins, and auxins stimulate growth. It follows that abscisic acid prevents growth and promotes ageing. It seems likely that the auxins prevent abscission and that a reduction in their level during autumn causes deciduous trees to lose their leaves and fruits. Abscisic acid levels do, however, rise in some plants before leaf and fruit

134

fall, although this seems likely to be in order to keep buds dormant (one of its effects) over winter. Spraying trees with large doses of abscisic acid increases leaf fall, although this is probably because it stimulates the production of another plant growth regulator, ethene, that is known to cause abscission.

6.19.3 Role of abscisic acid in the closing of stomata

Abscisic acid is sometimes referred to as the 'stress hormone' and has been shown to increase in concentration up to 40 times during drought conditions. It is this increase in abscisic acid that causes the closure of **stomata**. As stomata are the main means by which plants lose water vapour during **transpiration** (*Essential AS Biology for OCR*, unit 10.7), it follows that abscisic acid helps to reduce water loss. The response is rapid, as it needs to be if the plant is to survive, with stomata closing within a minute or two of abscisic acid being applied. The speed of this reaction rules out a mechanism involving regulating the expression of a **gene**. The normal mechanism for opening and closing stomata is described in the extension box. Although the exact mechanism of how abscisic acid operates is not yet understood, one suggested process is as follows:

- Abscisic acid combines with specific receptors on the cell surface membrane of the **guard cells** that surround stomata.
- This binding of abscisic acid inhibits the proton pump in some way.
- Hydrogen ions are therefore no longer pumped out of the guard cells.
- Potassium ions no longer enter the guard cells, neither does the water that would normally follow by **osmosis**. As a result the guard cells are less turgid and therefore the stomatal pore closes.

SUMMARY TEST 6.19

Among the many effects of the plant growth regulators called auxins is their ability to prevent development of lateral buds – a condition called (1). The mechanism is unclear, but probably involves other plant growth regulators such as abscisic acid. This regulator is made in the (2) of plants. It inhibits growth and therefore works in the opposite way, otherwise known as (3), to auxins and gibberellins. Abscisic acid may play an indirect role in leaf fall, or (4) as it is alternatively called, through the process of (5) in leaves. Leaf fall occurs when two layers develop where the (6) of a leaf joins the main stem. The (7) layer has small thin-walled cells and is where the leaf will become detached. The (8) layer will form a barrier against infection and water loss. Abscisic acid is sometimes called the (9), as it is produced during adverse conditions such as drought, when it causes the (10) cells that surround the opening known as a (11) to close and therefore conserve water.

EXTENSION
The mechanism of stomatal opening

It is known that stomata open and close in response to certain stimuli. For example, they usually open in light and close in the dark. One suggested mechanism for the opening and closing of stomata (Fig 6.37) is:

- a particular stimulus such as light activates ATPase, an enzyme that increases the production of ATP by the chloroplasts in the guard cells
- these chloroplasts only have photosystem I (section 2.3.4) and no Calvin cycle enzymes, hence ATP is produced in cyclic photophosphorylation but not used up in the Calvin cycle
- this ATP is therefore available to provide more energy for the active transport of potassium (K^+) ions into the guard cells
- the solute concentration of the guard cells increases, due to the increase in K^+ ions reducing water potential and causing water to enter them by osmosis
- the extra water causes the guard cells to become more turgid and to swell
- the thinner outer and thicker inner walls of the guard cells means that when they swell they bow outwards, and so widen the stomatal aperture.

Stoma is closed in the dark, but in the presence of light, ATPase is stimulated to convert ADP to ATP, which provides the energy to pump out hydrogen ions (protons) from the guard cells. These protons return on a carrier which also brings chloride ions (Cl^-) with it. At the same time, potassium ions (K^+) also enter the guard cells

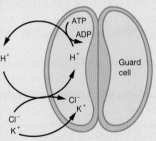

As a result of this influx of ions, the water potential of the guard cells becomes more negative (lower), causing water to pass in by osmosis. The resulting increase in water potential causes the stoma to open

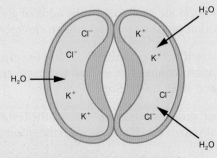

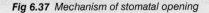

In the dark, the movement of ions and water is reversed

Fig 6.37 *Mechanism of stomatal opening*

135

abiotic an ecological factor that makes up part of the non-biological environment of an organism. Examples include temperature, pH, rainfall and humidity. See also *biotic*.

abscisic acid *plant growth regulator* that affects plant growth largely by inhibiting it.

abscission the falling of leaves or fruits from a plant.

absorption spectrum a graph that results from plotting the degree of absorption of light of different wavelengths by a pigment such as chlorophyll.

acetylcholine one of a group of chemicals, called *neurotransmitters*, released by *neurones*. It diffuses across the gap (*synapse*) between adjacent neurones and so passes an impulse from one neurone to the next.

action potential change that occurs in the electrical charge across the membrane of a *neurone* when it is stimulated and a nerve impulse passes.

action spectrum graph displaying the proportion of each wavelength of light that is used in a process such as photosynthesis.

activation energy energy required to bring about a chemical reaction. The activation energy is lowered by the presence of enzymes.

active transport movement of a substance from a region where it is in a low concentration to a region where it is in a high concentration. The process requires the use of ATP.

adenosine triphosphate (ATP) an activated nucleotide found in all living cells that acts as an energy carrier. The *hydrolysis* of ATP leads to the formation of adenosine diphosphate (ADP) and inorganic phosphate, with the release of energy.

adipose tissue a form of connective tissue that is made up of cells storing large amounts of fat.

adrenaline a hormone produced by the adrenal glands in times of stress that prepares the body for an emergency.

aerobic connected with the presence of free oxygen. Aerobic respiration requires free oxygen to release energy from glucose and other foods. See also *anaerobic*.

aleurone layer protein-rich layer beneath the testa of a cereal seed that makes amylase during germination.

allele one form of a *gene*. For example, the gene for the shape of pea seeds has two alleles, one for 'round', one for 'wrinkled'.

allopatric speciation the formation of a new species as a result of *populations* of a parent species becoming geographically isolated. See also *sympatric speciation*.

allopolyploidy having more than two sets of chromosomes that come from two different species.

anabolism an energy-requiring process of metabolism in which small molecules are combined to make larger ones.

anaerobic connected with the absence of free oxygen. Anaerobic respiration releases energy from glucose or other foods without the presence of free oxygen. See also *aerobic*.

antibiotic resistance the development in populations of microorganisms of mechanisms that prevent antibiotics from killing them.

antibody a protein produced by lymphocytes in response to the presence of a specific *antigen*.

antidiuretic hormone (ADH) a hormone produced by the *hypothalamus* that passes to the posterior *pituitary gland* from where it is secreted. ADH reduces the amount of water in urine by increasing water reabsorption in the kidneys.

antigen a molecule that triggers an immune response by causing lymphocytes to produce specific *antibodies* which bind to it.

ATP see *adenosine triphosphate*.

autonomic nervous system part of the nervous system, controlling the muscles and glands, that is not under voluntary control.

autopolyploidy having more than two sets of chromosomes that come from the same species.

autotrophic nutrition form of feeding in which an organism uses energy from light or chemicals to build up complex organic molecules from simple inorganic substances. See also *heterotrophic nutrition*.

auxin a *plant growth regulator* that affects plant growth by stimulating cell division and enlargement.

axon a process extending from a *neurone* that conducts *action potentials* away from the cell body.

biochemical oxygen demand (BOD) a measure of the rate at which oxygen in a volume of water is used up. It is used to measure the level of organic pollution in water; the higher the BOD the more polluted the water. It is defined as the difference in the volume of dissolved oxygen before and after incubation for five days at 20°C.

biodiversity the range and variety of living organisms within a particular area.

biological control a specific means of limiting the numbers of a pest organism by using its natural predators or *parasites*.

biomass the total mass of living material in a specific area at a given time; it is usually measured as dry mass because the amount of water in an organism is very variable.

biosensor equipment that uses biological molecules to measure the levels of certain chemicals.

biotic an ecological factor that makes up part of the living environment of an organism. Examples include food availability, competition and predation. See also *abiotic*.

Bowman's capsule see *renal capsule*.

Calvin cycle a biochemical pathway that forms part of the *light independent reaction* of photosynthesis during which carbon dioxide is reduced to form carbohydrate.

cardiac muscle type of muscle found only in the heart. It has fewer striations than skeletal muscle and can contract continuously throughout life without stimulation by nerve impulses. See also *smooth muscle*.

carrying capacity the maximum *population* that can be sustained in a particular *habitat* over a long period.

catabolism chemical reactions of metabolism involving the breakdown of large molecules.

chemiosmosis the synthesis of *ATP* in mitochondria and chloroplasts using energy that is stored as a hydrogen ion concentration gradient across a membrane.

chitin tough, nitrogen-containing polysaccharide that forms the walls of fungi and the exoskeleton of insects.

cholinesterase enzyme that breaks down and therefore inactivates the *neurotransmitter*, *acetylcholine*, in the nerve *synapse*.

chromatid one of the two strands, joined by a centromere, that make up a chromosome.

chromatography technique by which substances in a mixture are separated according to their different solubilities in a solvent.

cilium (plural **cilia**) short projection from the surface of a *eukaryotic cell* that has an internal 9 + 2 arrangement of microtubules.

climax community the organisms that make up the final stage of ecological succession.

co-dominance condition in which both alleles for one gene in a *heterozygous* organism contribute to the phenotype.

codon a sequence of three adjacent *nucleotides* in mRNA that codes for one amino acid.

community all the living organisms present in an ecosystem at a given time.

conservation method of maintaining ecosystems and the living organisms that occupy them. It requires planning and organisation to make best use of resources while preserving the natural landscape and wildlife.

continuous variation variation in which organisms do not fall into distinct categories, but rather there are gradations from one extreme to the other, e.g. height in humans. See also *discontinuous variation*.

coppicing the cutting down of a tree close to the ground in order that many new shoots grow from the stump. These are harvested every 5–10 years to be used as fuel or to make fencing or furniture.

counter-current system a mechanism by which the efficiency of exchange between two substances is increased by having them flowing in opposite directions.

covalent bond type of chemical bond in which two atoms share a pair of *electrons*, one from each atom.

crop rotation system of changing the crop grown on a particular area of land over a sequence of three to five years in order reduce pests and maintain soil fertility.

crossing over the process whereby a *chromatid* breaks during *meiosis* I and rejoins to the chromatid of its *homologous chromosome* so that their *alleles* are exchanged.

cuticle exposed non-cellular outer layer of certain animals and the leaves of plants. It is waxy and therefore helps to reduce water loss.

cytokinins group of plant growth regulators that stimulate cell division.

deamination removal of an amino group ($-NH_2$) from a compound, particularly an amino acid.

deflected climax condition in which ecological succession is prevented from reaching its *climax community* by a natural event (e.g. landslide or volcanic activity) or the activities of an organism, usually humans. Grazing animals, for example, prevent grassland in the UK from developing into deciduous woodland.

denaturation permanent changes to the structure, and hence the 3-dimensional shape, of a protein due to factors such as changes in temperature or pH.

dendrite a process, usually branched, extending from the cell body of a *neurone* that conducts impulses toward the cell body.

denitrifying bacteria bacteria that convert nitrates to nitrogen gas as part of the nitrogen cycle.

depolarisation temporary reversal of charges on the cell surface membrane of a *neurone* that takes place when a nerve impulse is transmitted.

diabetes metabolic disorder in which there is abnormal thirst and the production of large amounts of urine. Diabetes mellitus is caused by a reduction or absence of *insulin* production by the pancreas or insensitivity of insulin receptors on cells, leading to a rise in the blood glucose level.

diploid (2n) a term applied to cells in which the nucleus contains two sets of chromosomes. See also *haploid*.

directional selection selection that operates towards one extreme in a range of variation.

discontinuous variation variation shown when the characters of organisms fall into distinct categories, e.g. blood groups in humans. See also *continuous variation*.

diuretic drug used to increase the output of urine, especially in the treatment of high blood pressure and oedema.

ecological niche all of the ranges of environmental conditions and resources required for an organism to survive, reproduce and maintain a viable population.

ecosystem more or less self-contained functional unit in ecology made up of all the interacting *biotic* and *abiotic* factors in a specific area.

ectotherm an organism that uses the environment to control body temperature.

electron negatively charged sub-atomic particle that orbits the positively charged nucleus of all atoms. See also *proton*.

endemic describes any disease that is always present in a particular region or amongst a particular population. See also *epidemic*.

endergonic a chemical reaction in which the products contain more energy than the reactants so that, if the reaction is to proceed, free energy must be provided from outside. See also *exergonic*.

endocytosis the inward transport of large molecules through the cell surface membrane. See also *exocytosis*.

endosperm a storage tissue found in the seeds of plants such as cereals.

endothermic see *endergonic*.

epidemic describes any disease that spreads rapidly through a population to affect a large number of individuals. See also *endemic*.

ethene plant growth regulator concerned with the ripening of fruit.

eukaryotic cell a cell with a membrane-bound nucleus that contains chromosomes. The cells also possess a variety of other membranous organelles such as mitochondria and endoplasmic reticulum. See also *prokaryotic cell*.

eutrophication consequence of an increase in nutrients, especially nitrates and phosphates, in fresh-water lakes and rivers, which often leads to a decrease in *biodiversity*.

excretion the removal of metabolic waste products.

exergonic a chemical reaction in which the products contain less free energy than the reactants and so free energy is released during the reaction. See also *endergonic*.

exocytosis the outward movement of materials through the cell surface membrane. See also *endocytosis*.

exothermic see *exergonic*.

facilitated diffusion diffusion of molecules across a cell membrane that involves carrier protein molecules transporting other molecules through specific channels within them. It is a passive process.

flagellum long, whip-like extension of a cell used as a means of locomotion.

ganglion collection of nervous tissue made up of cell bodies and *synapses*, often enclosed in a fibrous sheath of *myelin*. The role of the ganglion is that of integration.

gene length of DNA on a chromosome normally coding for one or more polypeptides.

gene pool total number of *alleles* in a particular *population* at a specific time.

gene technology general term that covers the processes by which *genes* are manipulated, altered or transferred from organism to organism. Also known as *genetic engineering*.

generator potential *depolarisation* of the membrane of a receptor cell as a result of a stimulus.

genetic engineering see *gene technology*.

genetically modified organism (GMO) organism that has had its DNA altered as a result of *gene technology*.

genotype the genetic composition of an organism. See also *phenotype*.

gibberellins *plant growth regulators* that stimulate cell division, stem elongation and germination.

glomerulus a cluster of blood capillaries enclosed by the *renal (Bowman's) capsule* in the kidney.

glucagon a hormone produced by α cells of the *islets of Langerhans* in the pancreas that increases blood glucose levels by initiating the breakdown of glycogen to glucose.

glycolysis first part of cellular respiration in which glucose is broken down anaerobically in the cytoplasm to two molecules of pyruvate.

glycoprotein substance made up of a carbohydrate molecule and a protein molecule. Part of cell surface membrane and certain hormones are glycoproteins.

granum (plural **grana**) a stack of *thylakoids* in a chloroplast that resembles a pile of coins.

greenhouse gases gases such as methane and carbon dioxide which in the atmosphere cause more heat energy to be trapped, so raising the temperature at the Earth's surface.

guard cell one of a pair of cells that surround a *stoma* in plant leaves and control its opening and closing.

habitat the place where an organism normally lives and which is characterised by physical conditions and the types of other organisms present.

haemoglobin globular protein in mammalian blood that readily combines with oxygen to transport it around the body. It comprises four polypeptide chains, each with an iron-containing haem group.

haploid term referring to cells that contain only a single copy of each chromosome, e.g. the sex cells or gametes. See also *diploid*.

heterotrophic nutrition form of feeding in which the organism consumes complex organic material. See also *autotrophic nutrition*.

heterozygous condition in which the *alleles* of a particular *gene* are different.

histones proteins associated with the DNA in chromosomes. They function to condense chromatin and coil the chromosomes during cell division.

homeostasis the maintenance of a more or less constant internal environment.

homologous refers to structures that may have different functions but which have a common evolutionary origin.

homologous chromosomes a pair of chromosomes that have the same *gene loci* and therefore determine the same features. They are not necessarily identical, however, as individual *alleles* of the same genes may vary, e.g. one chromosome may carry the allele for blue eyes, the other the allele for brown eyes. Homologous chromosomes are capable of pairing during *meiosis* 1.

homozygous condition in which the *alleles* of a particular *gene* are identical.

human genome project international scientific project to map the entire sequence of the 3000 million base pairs of the 30 000 genes in a single human cell. The first draft of the genome was published in June 2000.

humus dark brown organic substance formed from the partial decay of plant and animal remains.

hydrolysis the breaking down of large molecules into smaller ones by the addition of water molecules.

hypothalamus region of the brain adjoining the *pituitary gland* that acts as the control centre for the *autonomic nervous system* and regulates body temperature, fluid balance, thirst, hunger and sexual activity.

industrial melanism the evolutionary process in which the frequency of organisms that are initially light coloured becomes less, and the frequency of those that are dark increases, as a result of natural selection in areas blackened by pollution.

insulin a hormone, produced by the β cells of the *islets of Langerhans* in the pancreas, that decreases blood glucose levels by, amongst other things, increasing the conversion of glucose to glycogen.

intercropping the practice of growing one crop among a crop of a different kind, usually in the space between the rows.

interspecific competition competition between organisms of different species.

intraspecific competition competition between organisms of the same species.

intrinsic proteins proteins of the cell surface membrane that completely span the *phospholipid* bilayer from one side to the other.

ion an atom or group of atoms that have lost or gained one or more *electrons*. Ions therefore have either a positive or negative charge.

islets of Langerhans groups of cells in the pancreas comprising large α cells that produce the hormone *glucagon*, and small β cells that produce the hormone *insulin*.

isotope variations of a chemical element which have the same number of *protons* and *electrons* but different numbers of *neutrons*. While their chemical properties are similar, they differ in mass. One example is carbon, which has a relative atomic mass of 12 and an isotope with a relative atomic mass of 14.

Krebs cycle series of aerobic biochemical reactions in the matrix of the mitochondria of most *eukaryotic cells* by which energy is obtained through the oxidation of acetyl coenzyme A produced from the breakdown of glucose.

light dependent reaction stage of photosynthesis in which light energy is required to produce ATP and reduced NADP.

light independent reaction stage of photosynthesis which does not require light energy directly but does need the products of the *light dependent reaction* to reduce carbon dioxide and so form carbohydrate.

link reaction the process linking *glycolysis* with *Krebs cycle* in which pyruvate is dehydrogenated and decarboxylated to form acetyl coenzyme A in the matrix of the mitochondria.

locus the position of a *gene* on a DNA molecule.

loop of Henlé the portion of a *nephron* that forms a hairpin loop which extends into the medulla of the kidney. It has a role in the reabsorption of water.

meiosis the type of nuclear division in which the number of chromosomes is halved.

mitosis the type of nuclear division in which the daughter cells have the same number of chromosomes as the parent cell and as each other.

motor neurone *neurone* that transmits *action potentials* from the central nervous system to an effector such as a muscle or gland.

multiple alleles term used to describe a *gene* that has more than two possible *alleles*.

mutagen any agent that induces a mutation.

mutation a permanent change in the amount or arrangement of a cell's DNA.

mutualism a nutritional relationship between two species in which both gain some advantage.

mycelium a mass of fungal hyphae.

myelin a fatty substance that surrounds *axons* and *dendrites* in certain *neurones*.

NAD (nicotinamide adenine dinucleotide) a molecule that carries high energy *electrons* and hydrogen ions from oxidised molecules to pathways that produce *ATP* during *aerobic* respiration.

negative feedback a series of changes, important in *homeostasis*, that result in a substance being restored to its normal level. See also *positive feedback*.

nephron basic functional unit of the mammalian kidney responsible for the formation of urine.

neurone a nerve cell, comprising a cell body, *axon* and *dendrites*, that is adapted to conduct *action potentials*.

neurotransmitter one of a number of chemicals that are involved in communication between adjacent nerve cells or between nerve cells and muscles. Two important examples are *acetylcholine* and noradrenaline.

neutron uncharged sub-atomic particle that occurs in the nucleus of an atom.

niche see *ecological niche*.

nitrifying bacteria microorganisms that convert ammonium compounds to nitrites and nitrates.

nitrogen fixation incorporation of atmospheric nitrogen gas into organic nitrogen-containing compounds. It can be brought about by lightning, industrial processes and by both free-living and *mutualistic* bacteria.

node of Ranvier a gap in the *myelin* sheath that surrounds the *axon* of a *neurone*.

nucleotides complex chemicals made up of an organic base, a sugar and a phosphate. They are the basic units of which the nucleic acids DNA and RNA are made.

oestrus the period in the oestrous cycle immediately after ovulation when the female is most fertile.

operon a group of *genes* that codes for one or more proteins and control its/their production.

osmoregulation the process by which the concentration of body fluids is controlled.

osmosis the net passage of water from a region of higher water potential to a region of lower water potential, through a partially permeable membrane as a result of the random motion of the water molecules.

oxidative phosphorylation the formation of *ATP* in the electron transport system of *aerobic* respiration.

palisade mesophyll cells long, narrow cells, packed with chloroplasts, found in the upper region of a leaf and which carry out photosynthesis. See also *spongy mesophyll cells*.

parasite an organism that lives on or in a host organism. The parasite gains a nutritional advantage and the host is harmed in some way.

petiole the stalk of a leaf.

phenotype the characteristics of an organism, usually visible, resulting from both its *genotype* and the effects of the environment.

phospholipid lipid molecule in which one of the three fatty acid molecules is replaced by a phosphate molecule. They are important in the structure and functioning of all cell membranes.

photoautotroph organism that uses light energy to convert inorganic molecules into organic ones. All algae, plants and some bacteria are photoautotrophs.

photolysis splitting of a water molecule by light such as occurs during the *light dependent reaction* of photosynthesis.

photon 'particle' of light with a quantum of energy.

photosystem an organised group of chlorophyll and other pigment molecules situated in the *thylakoids* of chloroplasts that traps *photons* of light in a process called light harvesting.

pioneer species a species that can colonise bare rock or ground.

pituitary gland master gland of the endocrine (hormone) system situated at the base of the brain.

plant growth regulator chemicals produced by plants in tiny amounts that affect their growth or development. Examples include *auxins, gibberellins, abscisic acid, cytokinins* and *ethene*.

plasmid small circular piece of DNA found in bacterial cells and used as a *vector* in *gene technology*.

podocyte cell from the inner lining of the *renal capsule* that has many processes and is adapted to help *ultrafiltration*.

polymerase chain reaction (PCR) process of making many copies of a specific sequence of DNA or part of a *gene*. It is used extensively in *gene technology* and genetic fingerprinting.

polymerisation production of large molecules called polymers that are made of numerous similar sub-units.

polyploidy the possession of three or more sets of chromosomes.

population a group of individuals of the same species that occupy the same space at the same time.

positive feedback process which results in a substance that departs from its normal level becoming further from its norm. See also *negative feedback*.

primary succession the progressive colonisation of bare rock or other barren terrain by living organisms.

producer an organism that synthesises organic molecules from simple inorganic ones such as carbon dioxide and water (an *autotrophic* organism). Most producers are photosynthetic and form the first *trophic level* in a food chain.

prokaryotic cell a cell, belonging to the kingdom Prokaryotae, which is characterised by being less than 5 μm in diameter and which lacks a nucleus and membrane-bound organelles. See also *eukaryotic cell*.

promoter the portion of an *operon* to which *RNA polymerase* attaches to begin the *transcription* of mRNA from the structural *genes*.

proton positively charged sub-atomic particle found in the nucleus of the atom. See also *electron*.

pseudopodium a temporary cytoplasmic extension of a cell.

reaction centre a molecule of chlorophyll *a* that collects light energy that has been absorbed from the surrounding accessory pigments in the *photosystem*.

recessive the condition in which the effect of an allele is apparent in the phenotype of a diploid organism **only** in the presence of another identical allele.

reflex arc the nerve pathway in the body taken by an *action potential* that leads to a rapid, involuntary response to a stimulus.

refractory period period during which the membrane of a *neurone* cannot be *depolarised* and no new *action potential* can be initiated.

regulator gene portion of DNA coding for a protein that controls the expression of another *gene*.

renal capsule the cup-shaped portion at the start of a *nephron* that encloses the *glomerulus*.

repolarisation return of the *resting potential* in a *neurone* after an *action potential*.

respiratory quotient a measure of the ratio of carbon dioxide evolved by an organism to the oxygen consumed over a certain period.

resting potential the difference in electrical charge maintained across the cell membrane of a *neurone* when not stimulated.

RNA polymerase enzyme that joins together *nucleotides* to form messenger RNA during *transcription*.

saltatory conduction propagation of an nerve impulse along a *myelinated dendron* or *axon* in which the *action potential* jumps from *node of Ranvier* to node of Ranvier.

saprobiont also known as a saprophyte, a saprobiont is an organism that obtains its food from the dead or decaying remains of other organisms. Many bacteria and fungi are saprobionts.

Schwann cell cell around a *neurone* whose cell surface membrane wraps around the *dendron* or *axon* to form the *myelin* sheath.

secondary succession the further colonisation of an area after the *pioneer species* have established themselves and created a less hostile habitat.

selection process that results in the best adapted individuals in a *population* surviving to breed and so pass their favourable *alleles* to the next generation.

senescence process of ageing.

sensory neurone a *neurone* that transmits an *action potential* from a sensory receptor to the central nervous system.

sere successional stage of an ecological *community* that ultimately results in a *climax community*.

sickle cell anaemia inherited blood disorder in which abnormal *haemoglobin* leads to red cells becoming sickle-shaped and less able to carry oxygen.

smooth muscle also known as involuntary or unstriated muscle, smooth muscle is found in the alimentary canal and the walls of blood vessels. Its contraction is not under conscious control.

sodium–potassium pump protein channels across cell surface membranes that use *ATP* to move sodium *ions* out of the cell in exchange for potassium ions that move in.

speciation the evolution of two or more species from existing ones.

spongy mesophyll cells irregularly shaped cells in the lower half of a leaf. They have many air spaces and are important in exchanging gases between the atmosphere and the rest of the leaf. See also *palisade mesophyll cells*.

stabilising selection selection that tends to eliminate the extremes of the *phenotype* range within a *population*. It arises when environmental conditions are constant.

steroid a lipid, of which cholesterol is an example, that does not contain fatty acids.

stoma (plural stomata) a pore, surrounded by two *guard cells*, mostly in the lower epidermis of a leaf, through which gases diffuse in and out of the leaf.

stroma matrix of a chloroplast where the *light independent reaction* of photosynthesis takes place.

suberin a waxy, waterproof substance found in certain plant cell walls such as endodermal cells of the root.

surrogacy the process whereby a female bears the offspring for another female, by the implantation of either a fertilised egg from the other female or her own egg fertilised by the other female's partner.

sustainable yield the removal of a renewable resource at a rate that is equal to, or less than, the rate at which it is produced. A sustainable yield can be taken indefinitely.

symbiosis any nutritional relationship between two organisms. The term covers *parasitism*, commensalism and *mutualism*.

sympatric speciation the formation of new species that occurs when organisms that are living together become reproductively isolated, e.g. different *populations* may have different breeding seasons. See also *allopatric speciation*.

synapse a junction between *neurones* in which they do not touch but have a narrow gap, the synaptic cleft, across which a *neurotransmitter* can pass.

tendon tough, flexible, but inelastic, connective tissue that joins muscle to bone.

threshold level/value the minimum intensity that a stimulus must reach in order to trigger an *action potential* in a *neurone*.

thylakoid series of flattened membranous sacs in a chloroplast that contain chlorophyll and the associated molecules needed for the *light dependent reaction* of photosynthesis.

transcription formation of messenger RNA molecules from the DNA that makes up a particular *gene*. It is the first stage of protein synthesis.

transducer cells cells that convert a non-electrical signal, such as light or sound, into an electrical (nervous) signal and *vice versa*.

transduction the process by which one form of energy is converted into another. In microbiology, the natural process by which genetic material is transferred between one host cell and another by a virus.

translation process whereby the code on a section of messenger RNA is converted to a particular sequence of amino acids which will go on to make a polypeptide and ultimately a protein.

transpiration evaporation of water from a plant.

trophic level the position of an organism in a food chain.

ultrafiltration filtration under pressure. A term applied to the first stage of urine formation in the kidney.

urea organic molecule, $CO(NH_2)_2$, that is the main nitrogenous excretory product in mammals.

uric acid insoluble nitrogenous waste product produced mainly by insects, reptiles and birds.

vector a carrier. The term may refer to something such as a *plasmid*, which carries DNA into a cell, or to an organism that carries a *parasite* to its primary host.

vegetative propagation form of asexual reproduction in higher plants involving the separation of a piece of the original plant (stem, root or leaf), which then develops into a separate plant.

voltage-gated channel protein channel across a cell surface membrane that opens and closes according to changes in the electrical potential across the membrane.

water potential measure of the extent to which a solution gives out water. The greater the number of water molecules present, the higher (less negative) the water potential. Pure water has a water potential of zero.

xerophyte a plant adapted to living in dry conditions.

SUMMARY TEST 1.2

The main energy currency of cells is **(1)** which is usually abbreviated to ATP. The removal of the first phosphate group releases **(2)** kJmol^{-1} of energy. ATP is made by adding inorganic phosphate to **(3)**. The process is catalysed by the enzyme called **(4)** and is known as phosphorylation of which there are three types. Where it occurs in chlorophyll-containing plant cells, it is called **(5)**. If it takes place on the mitochondrial membranes of plant and animal cells it is called **(6)**. Where phosphate groups are transferred from donor molecules to ADP, it is known as **(7)**.

SUMMARY TEST 1.5

During the processes of glycolysis and **(1)**, hydrogen atoms are produced. Most of these become combined with a hydrogen carrier called **(2)**, although a single pair combine with another hydrogen carrier called **(3)**. These hydrogen atoms are passed from one carrier to the next with the aid of enzymes known as **(4)**. In the process, energy is released in the form of **(5)**. At first hydrogen atoms are carried but they later split into **(6)** and **(7)**, which are then transported separately. Finally, the component parts of the hydrogen atoms combine with **(8)** to form **(9)** with the aid of an enzyme called **(10)**, which can be inhibited by cyanide. The whole process is called oxidative phosphorylation and takes place on the **(11)** of the mitochondria.

SUMMARY TEST 1.7

To measure the rate of respiration by calculating the volume of oxygen taken up by an organism, an instrument called a **(1)** can be used. This consists of two chambers, one containing the organism(s) and the other some inert, non-respiring material of equal **(2)**. The two chambers are connected by a U-shaped tube called a **(3)**, which contains a liquid. This type of respirometer is sometimes called a differential respirometer because it has a built-in **(4)**. It functions by the living organism(s) taking in oxygen and breathing out carbon dioxide. The carbon dioxide is absorbed by a chemical such as **(5)** and so the volume of gas in the experimental chamber is reduced due to the uptake of oxygen. The pressure in the control chamber is therefore **(6)** than that in the experimental chamber and the liquid in the U-shaped tube is displaced. We can measure the volume of oxygen taken up using the equation **(7)**, where h is the distance the liquid moves and r is the internal **(8)** of the tube. The respiratory quotient (RQ) is a measure of the ratio of **(9)** given out by an organism to the **(10)** consumed. For carbohydrates, the RQ is normally equal to **(11)**, whereas for lipids it is usually a value of **(12)**. Calculate the RQ for each of the following substances:

$C_{16}H_{32}O_2$ **(13)** $C_5H_{10}O_5$ **(14)** $C_4H_6O_5$ **(15)**.

SUMMARY TEST 2.1

Organisms, such as green plants, that use light to synthesise complex organic molecules from simple ones are called **(1)**. Those that use chemical energy rather than light energy to perform the same task are called **(2)**. The process of photosynthesis can be divided into three main stages. The first stage is the capture of light by pigments such as **(3)** and **(4)**. The second stage called **(5)** involves the splitting of water into hydrogen ions and oxygen, while the final stage called **(6)** involves using the hydrogen ions to reduce **(7)**. In measuring the effect of light intensity on the rate of photosynthesis an instrument called an Audus photosynthometer can be used. This measures the volume of **(8)** produced under various conditions. A chemical called **(9)** can be used to provide the aquatic plant used in the experiment with carbon dioxide.

SUMMARY TEST 2.4

The light dependent stage of photosynthesis occurs in the **(1)** of the chloroplasts. It uses light energy to make ATP from ADP and **(2)** in a process called photophosphorylation and also to split water – a process called **(3)**. Photophosphorylation is the generation of ATP by the flow of **(4)** through the channels in the **(5)** of the thylakoid membrane. This is known as the **(6)** process. When light is collected by a reaction centre chlorophyll molecule, one of its electrons is raised to an **(7)** state. This electron may return directly to the chlorophyll molecule via **(8)** – a process known as **(9)** photophosphorylation, in which case the useful product is **(10)**, which passes into the light independent reaction. This process involves only photosystem **(11)**. Alternatively, electrons from both photosystems may finally be taken up by **(12)** that carries them to the light independent reaction. These electrons are replaced by others from the splitting of water, which also yields **(13)** that enters the light independent reaction, as well as **(14)** that does not.

SUMMARY TEST 3.1

A population is a group of freely interbreeding individuals of the same **(1)** occupying the same place at the same time. The growth of a population such as that of bacteria follows a characteristic growth curve known as a **(2)** growth curve. This has four phases, the first of which is called the **(3)** phase when growth is slow. This is followed by rapid growth known as the **(4)** phase which leads into the **(5)** phase when new cells produced equal those that die. The final phase is called the **(6)** phase during which the living population steadily falls. The maximum size of a population is called the **(7)** and is determined by limiting factors that are collectively called the **(8)**.

SUMMARY TEST 3.2

Interspecific competition occurs between individuals of different species. No two species can occupy the same **(1)** indefinitely when resources are limiting. This is called the **(2)** principle. This principle was illustrated by the Russian scientist, C. F. Gausse, who experimented with species of the unicellular organism belonging to the genus **(3)**. In another experiment, two species of barnacles were studied. Those belonging to the genus **(4)** can survive at most levels on the seashore but are restricted to the upper shore due to competition from barnacles of the genus **(5)**. Competition between members of the same species is called **(6)** competition.

SUMMARY TEST 3.4

Succession is the change in species of organisms that occupy an area over time. When bare rock or barren terrain is first colonised it is known as **(1)** succession. Such inhospitable environments are first colonised by organisms such as **(2)**, which are called **(3)** species. Typically these species produce vast numbers of **(4)**, germinate and spread quickly, obtain 'food' by the process of **(5)**, fix **(6)** from the atmosphere, tolerate extreme conditions and compete well for resources. Each stage of succession is called a **(7)**, the final one of which is called the **(8)**. In lowland UK, this final stage is usually **(9)**. During succession the number of species increases, leading to greater **(10)** and increased **(11)**. Sometimes the activities of humans, such as the grazing of sheep, arrest the natural succession at an intermediate stage. This is known as **(12)**.

SUMMARY TEST 3.8

Natural fertilisers are also known as **(1)** fertilisers and the advantages to the soil of their use include increased **(2)**, improved crumb structure and **(3)** as well as the maintenance of its **(4)** both directly and by encouraging the activities of earthworms. Artificial fertilisers have the advantages of being easy to **(5)**, handle and apply. They are also relatively cheap, easy to obtain and do not spread **(6)**. The over-use of nitrogen fertilisers can have harmful effects including an increase in soil **(7)**, reduced **(8)**, pollution of **(9)** and a build up of salts in bodies of water – a process known as **(10)**.

SUMMARY TEST 4.2

Every adult cell of a species contains chromosomes that usually comprise pairs, one of which is provided by each parent. These are called (1) pairs. During meiosis these pairs are separated and so the (2) number of chromosomes is halved to give the (3) number. In humans this means that the chromosome number is changed from (4) to (5). During prophase of the first meiotic division the chromosome pairs come together in a process called (6) to form a (7). The chromatids of these chromosomes wrap around one another and may break and swap portions at points called (8) in a process called (9). This is one way in which meiosis produces variety. Others include the (10) of chromosomes at metaphase I and of the (11) at metaphase II, as well as the production of gametes that fuse (12) at fertilisation.

SUMMARY TEST 4.6

In humans there are (1) pairs of chromosomes. All except one pair are identical and are known as (2). The pair that may differ are the sex chromosomes. In females there are two X chromosomes whereas in males there is one X chromosome and one (3) chromosome. Males are therefore referred to as the (4) sex. Haemophilia is a sex linked disease resulting from a recessive allele carried on the (5) chromosome. As a result, it is almost always the (6) sex that have the symptoms which they invariably inherit from their (7).

SUMMARY TEST 4.7

Co-dominance occurs when both alleles of a gene are expressed in the (1). An example occurs in the snapdragon plant where a cross between a homozygous parent with red flowers and a homozygous one with white flowers, the flowers of the offspring are all (2) in colour. Where a gene has more than two alleles, the condition is called (3). An example is the inheritance of human ABO blood groups where the (4) gene (abbreviated to 'I') has three alleles. Allele I^A and allele I^B which are (5) as well as allele I^o which is (6) to the other two. The offspring of one parent who is blood group O and one who is blood group AB will either be blood group (7) or blood group (8).

SUMMARY TEST 4.10

Any change to the quantity or the structure of DNA is known as a (1). The condition in which an organism has three or more whole sets of chromosomes is known as (2). Sometimes individual chromosomes fail to segregate during the (3) stage of meiosis. This is known as (4) and results in an organism having one or more additional chromosomes. An example of this type of mutation in humans is (5). Gene mutations take a number of forms. Additions and deletions result in a (6) in the DNA code, leading to every triplet of bases that follows the change being altered. An example of a deletion mutation in humans is (7). A substitution mutation occurs if a (8) in a DNA molecule is replaced by another that has a different base. An example of a substitution mutation in humans is the disease called (9), in which a gene producing the β-amino acid chain in the (10) molecule has an adenine base substituted by a (11) base. As a result red blood cells have an abnormal crescent shape.

SUMMARY TEST 4.13

The human genome project has resulted in the sequencing of every one of the 3.2 billion (1) that make up each human's DNA. It indicates that we each have a total of around (2) genes. The information can be used to help cure many genetic diseases but also raises a number of dilemmas. These include whether companies should be able to require individuals to take a (3) test before making a job offer or before deciding on the premium for (4).

SUMMARY TEST 5.1

Members of a single species are capable of breeding to produce offspring that are themselves **(1)**. They also occupy the same **(2)**, have very similar **(3)** and have a common **(4)**. In the binomial system of naming organisms, the first name, called the **(5)** name is shared by close relatives while the second name, called the **(6)** name is unique to that species. The grouping of organisms is called **(7)** and its study is known as **(8)**. Natural classifications are based the evolutionary descent of organisms otherwise known as **(9)**. In hierarchical order, from the largest downwards, the taxonomic ranks used in classification are kingdom, **(10)**, **(11)**, order, **(12)**, **(13)** and species.

SUMMARY TEST 5.3

Plants are multicellular, **(1)** organisms that possess **(2)** and other pigments. They feed **(3)** by photosynthesis, have cell walls made of **(4)** and store carbohydrate as **(5)**. Animals are multicellular, have organelles with membranes and feed **(6)**. They do not have cell walls and store carbohydrate as **(7)**. They possess a **(8)** that allows them to coordinate activities. In the following examples, state the group (phylum) to which each organism belongs; snail **(9)**, moss **(10)**, flowering plant **(11)**, flatworm **(12)**, mammal **(13)** and insect **(14)**.

SUMMARY TEST 5.10

As species adapt to different environments they develop variations that may lead to reproductive isolation and hence **(1)**. As a consequence, organisms develop structural adaptations to different environments. For example, plants in dry regions develop **(2)** features to reduce transpiration. These include a thick waxy **(3)** on leaves, extensive **(4)** systems and **(5)** that are reduced in number or confined to pits or grooves. Mammals like the kangaroo rat that live in dry regions have extremely long **(6)** in their kidneys that help to produce very concentrated **(7)**.

SUMMARY TEST 6.1

In multicellular animals, there are usually two coordination systems. One is rapid and called the **(1)** system, the other is slower and called the **(2)** system. Most multicellular organisms maintain a relatively constant internal environment by means of homeostasis. Homeostasis maintains the make-up and volume of the blood and body fluids within narrow limits called **(3)**. Although fluctuations in fluid composition do occur, these take place around a fixed level called a **(4)**. Homeostasis is important because it allows organisms to have some degree of independence of the **(5)** environment and so have a wider **(6)** range. It also prevents large changes to the **(7)** of the internal fluids, which might otherwise cause cells to burst due to water entering by **(8)**. Enzymes are kept within narrow ranges of temperature and pH to keep them from being **(9)**. Homeostasis involves a control mechanism in which a **(10)** detects any deviation of a factor from the normal level. Information is passed to a **(11)** that coordinates the information it receives and sends appropriate instructions to an **(12)** that produces changes which return the factor to its normal level. This return to normality forms a feedback loop of which there are two types. **(13)** feedback turns the system off, bringing it back to the normal level, while **(14)** feedback results in an even greater deviation from the norm.

SUMMARY TEST 6.4

Blood enters the kidney through the **(1)** which branches to form about one million **(2)** arterioles each one of which enters a renal capsule where it divides to form a group of capillaries known as a **(3)**. These capillaries then reunite to form the **(4)** arteriole. As a result of the diameter of the arteriole leaving the renal capsule being narrower than that entering it, a **(5)** pressure is created forcing substances out of the capillaries to form a filtrate. This process is called **(6)** and is assisted by special cells called **(7)**, that form the inner layer of the renal capsule. Most of the filtrate is reabsorbed in the **(8)**.

SUMMARY TEST 6.7

Neurones are adapted to carry electrochemical changes called (1). Each neurone comprises a cell body from which extends a single long fibre called an axon and smaller branched fibres called (2). Many axons are surrounded by (3) that protect and provide (4) because their membranes are rich in a lipid known as (5). These cells also act as (6) in removing cell debris and are important in peripheral nerve (7).

SUMMARY TEST 6.9

The nervous system has two main divisions: the central nervous system (CNS) comprising the (1) and (2) and the peripheral nervous system (PNS). The peripheral nervous system is made up of the (3) nervous system that carries nerve impulses away from the CNS and the (4) nervous system that carries nerve impulses towards the CNS. A spinal reflex is an (5) response that involves the spinal cord. An example is the withdrawal reflex such as the withdrawing of the hand from a hot object. The sequence of events begins with the heat from the hot object that acts as the (6) which is detected by (7) in the skin on the back of the hand. Provided the (8) value is exceeded, these produce a (9) potential that leads to an action potential passing along a (10) neurone into the spinal cord via the (11) root. The action potential then passes to a (12) neurone that does not have insulating (13) around it. These neurones occur in the central region of the spinal cord, which therefore appears (14) in colour. The action potential then passes across a (15) to a (16) neurone that leaves the spinal cord via the (17) root. This neurone stimulates the effector, in this case the (18) muscle of the forearm, which contracts, resulting in the (19) in which the hand is moved away from the hot object.

SUMMARY TEST 6.11

The 'movement' of an action potential along an axon should be more accurately be called (1) of the action potential as it is reproduced at different points along the axon, rather than anything physically moving from one place to another. At resting potential the concentration of sodium ions is greater on the (2) of the axon membrane. The overall concentration of positive ions is greater on the outside and in this state the axon membrane is said to be (3). An appropriate stimulus causes a temporary reversal of the charges on the axon membrane. This is called the (4) and in this state the membrane is said to be (5). This change causes the opening of the sodium (6) channels in the adjacent region of the axon, which in turn has a temporary reversal of charge due to the influx of (7). Behind this region, (8) ions begin to leave the axon along their (9) gradient, causing the axon to become (10).

SUMMARY TEST 6.14

When an action potential arrives at the end of the presynaptic neurone, (1) ions enter the synaptic knob. These ions cause (2) to fuse with the presynaptic membrane so releasing acetylcholine, by the process of (3), into the (4). Channels on the postsynaptic neurone have receptor sites to which acetylcholine fuses, causing them to open and allowing (5) ions to move in by the process of (6). The influx of these ions generates a new action potential known as the (7) potential.

SUMMARY TEST 6.15

Hormones are produced by endocrine glands and are carried by (1) to the cell, tissue or organ on which they act, called the (2) cell/organ. Hormones often have widespread and (3) effects and are usually proteins although some are (4). The pancreas produces digestive secretions that it passes along its pancreatic duct and, as such, it acts as an (5) gland. It is also an endocrine gland, producing the hormone insulin from (6) cells found in the groups of endocrine cells called the (7). Another type of cell, called (8) cells produce the hormone (9). Both hormones act together to control (10).

Answers to summary tests

Summary Test 1.1

1 work
2 kinetic
3 potential
4 anabolic
5 active transport
6 (high) body temperature
7 activation

Summary test 1.2

1 adenosine triphosphate
2 30.6
3 adenosine diphosphate (ADP)
4 ATP synthase
5 photophosphorylation
6 oxidative phosphorylation
7 substrate-level phosphorylation

Summary Test 1.3

1 cytoplasm
2 glucose
3 phosphate
4 ATP
5 hexose (fructose) bisphosphate
6 triose phosphate
7 hydrogen
8 NAD (nicotinamide adenine dinucleotide)
9 pyruvate
10 ATP

Summary Test 1.4

1 glycolysis
2 matrix
3 active transport
4 decarboxylation
5 dehydrogenation
6 acetyl coenzyme A
7 fatty acids
8 oxaloacetate
9 citrate
10 nicotinamide adenine dinucleotide (NAD)

Summary Test 1.5

1 Krebs cycle
2 NAD
3 FAD
4 dehydrogenases
5 ATP
6
7 } hydrogen ions (protons) / electrons
8 oxygen
9 water
10 cytochrome oxidase
11 cristae (inner membrane)

Summary Test 1.6

1 oxidative phosphorylation (electron transport system)
2 NAD
3 yeast
4 carbon dioxide
5 ethanol
6 alcoholic
7 lactate
8 2
9 32
10 glycogen
11 lipids
12 protein

Summary Test 1.7

1 respirometer
2 volume
3 manometer
4 control
5 soda-lime
6 greater / higher
7 $\pi r^2 h$
8 radius
9 carbon dioxide
10 oxygen
11 1.0
12 0.7
13 0.7 (0.696)
14 1.0
15 1.33

Summary Test 2.1

1 photoautotrophs
2 chemoautotrophs
3
4 } chlorophyll / carotenoids
5 light dependent reaction / photolysis
6 light independent reaction
7 carbon dioxide
8 oxygen
9 sodium / potassium hydrogencarbonate

Summary Test 2.2

1 palisade (mesophyll)
2 stomata
3 xylem
4 phloem
5 sugars / sucrose
6 envelope
7
8 } DNA / ribosomes
9 stroma
10 light independent
11 starch
12 thylakoids
13 grana
14 light dependent

Summary Test 2.3

1 carotenoids
2 porphyrin
3 hydrophilic
4 hydrophobic
5 absorption spectrum
6 reaction
7 proteins
8 accessory
9 antenna complex
10 700 nm
11 inter-granal lamellae
12 680 nm
13 granal lamellae

Summary Test 2.4

1	thylakoids	8	electron carriers
2	inorganic phosphate	9	cyclic
3	photolysis	10	ATP
4	protons	11	I
5	stalked particles	12	NADP
6	chemiosmotic	13	hydrogen ions / H^+ (protons)
7	excited	14	oxygen

Summary Test 2.5

1 Calvin
2 ribulose bisphosphate (RuBP)
3 glycerate 3-phosphate (GP)
4
5 } ATP / reduced NADP ($NADPH + H^+$)
6 light dependent
7 triose phosphate
8 hexose / 6-carbon
9 polymerisation

Summary Test 2.6

1	limiting factor	5	} red / blue
2	carbon dioxide	6	
3	oxygen	7	0.04
4	light compensation point	8	0.1

Summary test 3.1

1	species	5	stationary
2	sigmoid (population)	6	death/decline
3	lag	7	carrying capacity
4	exponential/log	8	environmental resistance

Summary test 3.2

1	(ecological) niche	4	*Chthamalus*
2	competitive exclusion	5	*Balanus*
3	*Paramecium*	6	intraspecific

Summary Test 3.3

1	extinction	4	rise / increase / recover
2	diverse / various	5	(Canadian) lynx
3	fall / decrease	6	10

Summary Test 3.4

1 primary
2 lichens
3 pioneer
4 seeds / spores
5 photosynthesis
6 nitrogen
7 sere
8 climax community
9 deciduous (oak) woodland
10
11 } biomass / biodiversity
12 deflected climax / plagioclimax

Summary Test 3.5

1 moraines
2 community
3
4 } bacteria (cyanobacteria) / lichens
5 pioneer
6 *Dryas (mountain avens)*
7 alder
8 nitrogen fixation
9 spruce
10 less
11 fewer

Summary Test 3.6

1 density
2 abundant / common / frequent
3 cover
4 10
5 pin
6 point
7 dense
8 seashore
9 interrupted / ladder

Summary Test 3.7

1 deflected climax / plagioclimax
2 higher / greater
3
4 } genetic / species
5 habitats
6 hedges
7 ponds / marshes / wetlands
8 monoculture
9 pesticides
10 effluent / waste
11
12 } crop rotation / intercropping

Summary test 3.8

1	organic	6	disease
2	water retention	7	acidity
3	drainage	8	species diversity
4	air content	9	(drinking) water
5	transport	10	eutrophication

Summary Test 3.9

1	renewable	8	hardwood
2	sustainable yield	9	paper / furniture / packaging
3	biodiversity	10	ecology
4	carbon dioxide	11	selective felling
5	nutrient cycling	12	clear felling
6	afforested	13	coppicing
7	softwood	14	pollarding

Summary Test 4.1

1 homologous
2 bivalent
3 chiasmata
4 crossing over
5 metaphase I
6 equator
7 anaphase I
8 spindle fibres
9 nuclear envelope
10 nucleolus
11 tetrad

Summary Test 4.2

1 homologous
2 diploid
3 haploid
4 46
5 23
6 synapsis
7 bivalent
8 chiasmata
9 crossing over
10 independent assortment
11 chromatids
12 randomly

Summary Test 4.3

1 genotype
2 mutation
3 phenotype
4 modification
5 nucleotides
6 polypeptides
7 homozygous
8 heterozygous
9 recessive

Summary Test 4.4

1 higher
2 lower
3 recessive
4 encircled / put in a circle
5 Punnett square
6 monohybrid
7 first filial / F_1
8 green
9 second filial / F_2
10 green
11 yellow

Summary Test 4.5

1 phenotype
2
3 } heterozygous / homozygous dominant
4 test
5 homozygous recessive
6 alleles
7 heterozygous
8 homozygous dominant
9 large / greater in number

Summary test 4.6

1 23
2 autosomes
3 Y
4 heterogametic
5 X
6 male/heterogametic
7 mother

Summary test 4.7

1 phenotype
2 pink
3 multiple alleles
4 immunoglobulin
5 codominant
6 recessive
7
8 } A/B

Summary Test 4.8

1 dihybrid
2 dominant
3 recessive
4 recessive
5 dominant
6 round
7 yellow
8 alleles
9
10
11 } (RG) / (Rg) / (rG) / (rg)
12
13 round
14 yellow
15 wrinkled
16 green
17+18
19+20 } round and yellow / wrinkled and yellow

Summary Test 4.9

Class (category)	Observed (O)	Expected (E)	O − E	$(O - E)^2$	$\dfrac{(O - E)^2}{E}$
Normal wings	30	36	−6	36	1.0
Vestigial wings	18	12	+6	36	3.0
					$\Sigma = 4.0$

With two classes of results there is one degree of freedom. The value of 4.0 lies between 3.84 and 5.41, i.e. between probabilities of 0.05 and 0.02, which means that the probability that the deviation is due to chance is less than 5%. The deviation is therefore significant and we must therefore assume that there is some other explanation than that the parents are heterozygous.

Summary Test 4.10

1 mutation
2 polyploidy
3 anaphase
4 non-disjunction
5 Down's syndrome
6 frame shift
7 cystic fibrosis
8 nucleotide
9 sickle cell anaemia
10 haemoglobin
11 thymine

Summary Test 4.11

1 environment
2 genotype
3 enzyme
4 melanin
5 (recessive) allele
6 above
7 extremities / tips / any suitable example
8 black / dark
9 altitude
10
11 } height / number of leaves / overall size / shape / survival rate
12 genotype
13 range / extent / limit
14 environment

Summary Test 4.12

1 glucose
2 respiratory
3 } glucose / galactose
4
5 *lac* operon
6 structural
7 operator
8 promoter

9 mRNA
10 regulator
11 operator
12 RNA polymerase
13 repressor protein
14 lactose permease
15 β-galactosidase

Summary test 4.13

1 nucleotides
2 25 000–30 000
3 genetic
4 life insurance

Summary test 5.1

1 fertile
2 (ecological) niche
3 genes
4 ancestry
5 generic
6 specific
7 classification

8 taxonomy
9 phylogeny
10 phylum
11 class
12 family
13 genus

Summary Test 5.2

1 bacteria
2 membranes
3 70S
4 murein
5 eukaryotic
6 heterotrophically

7 chlorophyll
8 hyphae
9 mycelium
10 chitin
11 glycogen

Summary test 5.3

1 eukaryotic
2 chlorophyll
3 autotrophically
4 cellulose
5 starch
6 heterotrophically
7 glycogen

8 nervous system
9 mollusca
10 bryophyta
11 angiospermophyta
12 platyhelminthes
13 chordata
14 arthropoda

Summary Test 5.4

1 } height / mass
2
3 normal distribution curve
4 polygenic
5 environment
6 one / a single
7 blood groups
8 mutation
9 recombinants
10 prophase I
11 independent assortment

12 metaphase
13 mating
14 species
15 fusion of gametes

Summary Test 5.5

1 Alfred Wallace
2 more
3 constant / stable
4 intraspecific (competition)
5 genetically
6 alleles / genes
7 offspring
8 antibiotic
9 pesticide
10 penicillin
11 DDT
12 warfarin
13 melanic
14 polymorphism
15 camouflaged / less conspicuous
16 industrial melanism

Summary Test 5.6

1 binary fission
2 24 hours
3 spores
4 pollen
5 ovules

6 clutch / litter
7 intraspecific
8 breed
9 genetic variation

Summary test 5.7

1 selection pressures/environmental resistances
2 gene pool
3 disruptive
4 stabilising
5 directional

Summary Test 5.8

1 gene pool
2 allelic frequency
3 selection
4 substituted / replaced
5 red (blood) cells
6 co-dominant

7 $Hb^S Hb^S$
8 oxygen
9 crystallise
10 stabilising
11 directional

Summary Test 5.9

1 speciation
2 reproductively
3 hybrid
4 polyploidy
5 deme
6 adaptive radiation
7 allele frequencies
8 species

9 allopatric
10 sympatric
11 prezygotic
12 donkey
13 mule
14 (prophase I of) meiosis
15 hybrid

Summary test 5.10

1 speciation
2 xeromorphic
3 cuticle
4 root
5 stomata
6 loops of Henlé
7 urine

Summary Test 5.11

1 selective breeding
2 lowered / less / reduced
3 heterozygotes
4 } inbreeding / outbreeding
5
6 pedigree
7 progeny testing
8 vagina
9 artificial insemination
10 embryo transplantation

Summary Test 6.1

1 nervous
2 endocrine
3 normal ranges
4 set point
5 external
6 geographical
7 water potential
8 osmosis
9 denatured
10 receptor
11 controller
12 effector
13 negative
14 positive

Summary Test 6.2

1 elimination
2 water
3 carbon dioxide
4 most
5 amino
6 water
7 energy / ATP
8 deamination
9 carbon dioxide
10 ornithine
11 uric acid
12 } birds / reptiles
13
14 (fibrous) capsule
15 cortex
16 medulla
17 nephrons
18 renal artery
19 ureter

Summary Test 6.3

1 renal (Bowman's) capsule
2 glomerulus
3 afferent
4 podocytes
5 proximal
6 cuboid
7 microvilli
8 loop of Henlé
9 distal
10 collecting duct
11 peritubular

Summary test 6.4

1 renal artery
2 afferent
3 glomerulus
4 efferent
5 hydrostatic
6 ultrafiltration
7 podocytes
8 proximal convoluted tubule

Summary Test 6.5

1 hairpin
2 medulla
3 proximal (first) convoluted tubule
4 descending
5 descending
6 ascending
7 low
8 osmosis
9 lowest
10 counter-current multiplier
11 pH
12 } mitochondria / microvilli
13

Summary Test 6.6

1 2500
2 2300
3 respiration
4 urine
5 sweat
6 homeostatic
7 distal (second) convoluted tubule
8 sweating
9 fall / reduce / decrease
10 hypothalamus
11 posterior pituitary
12 permeability
13 urea
14 rises / increases
15 negative feedback

Summary test 6.7

1 nerve impulses
2 dendrites
3 Schwann cells
4 insulation
5 myelin
6 phagocytes
7 regeneration

Summary Test 6.8

1 perception
2 (mechanical) pressure
3 receptor
4 transducers
5 sodium
6 generator
7 action potential
8 all or nothing

Summary Test 6.9

1 } brain / spinal cord
2
3 motor (efferent)
4 sensory (afferent)
5 involuntary
6 stimulus
7 (heat) receptors
8 threshold
9 generator
10 sensory
11 dorsal
12 relay / intermediate
13 myelin
14 grey
15 synapse
16 motor / effector
17 ventral
18 biceps
19 response

Summary Test 6.10

1 electrical
2 50–90
3 65
4 polarised
5 positively
6 40
7 depolarised

Summary Test 6.11

1 propagation
2 outside
3 polarised
4 action potential
5 depolarised
6 voltage-gated
7 sodium ions
8 potassium
9 electrochemical
10 repolarised

Summary Test 6.12

1 0.5
2 120
3 slower
4 lower / less
5 diffusion
6 speeds up / increases
7 Ranvier
8 saltatory conduction
9 (voltage-gated) channels
10 absolute
11 relative
12 threshold value

Summary Test 6.13

1 dendrite
2 cleft
3 20–30
4 presynaptic
5 neurotransmitter
6 synaptic vesicles
7 postsynaptic
8 unidirectional
9 junctions
10 summation
11 } memory / learning
12 }

Summary test 6.14

1 calcium
2 synaptic vesicles
3 exocytosis
4 synaptic cleft
5 sodium
6 diffusion
7 excitatory postsynaptic

Summary test 6.15

1 blood
2 target
3 permanent
4 steroids
5 exocrine
6 β
7 islets of Langerhans
8 α
9 glucagon
10 blood sugar (level)

Summary Test 6.16

1 ATP
2 90
3 homeostasis
4 brain
5 osmotic
6 carbohydrates
7 glycogen
8 muscle
9 amino acids
10 gluconeogenesis
11 glycogen
12 respiration
13 endocrine
14 islets of Langerhans
15 smaller
16 insulin
17 lower / reduce / fall
18 glucagon
19 antagonistically
20 adrenaline

Summary Test 6.17

1 sugar
2 higher
3 } thirst / hunger
4 }
5 urinate
6 } insulin dependent / juvenile onset
7 }
8 β
9 islets of Langerhans
10 autoimmune
11 protein
12 hypoglycaemia
13 } insulin independent / mature onset
14 }
15 glycoprotein
16 75
17 carbohydrate
18 exact / identical
19 rapid
20 immune
21 infections / diseases
22 cheaper
23 tolerance

Summary Test 6.18

1 chlorophyll
2 } touch / gravity
3 }
4 stems
5 dominant
6 enzyme
7 testa and pericarp
8 embryo
9 aleurone
10 α-amylase
11 endosperm
12 starch
13 glucose
14 respired
15 cellulose

Summary Test 6.19

1 apical dominance
2 chloroplasts
3 antagonistically
4 abscission
5 ageing / senescence
6 petiole / leaf stalk
7 separation
8 protective
9 stress hormone
10 guard
11 stoma

Examination Questions

Chapter 1

1 The figure shows a simple respirometer, **A**, that can be used to measure the rate of respiration of small

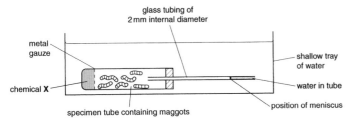

After assembling, the apparatus is lowered into a shallow tray of warm water. The open end of the glass tubing is kept out of the water for 10 minutes. At the end of this period of time the tubing is completely submerged and the position of the meniscus noted. A thermometer is used to monitor the temperature of the water.

a Name the chemical **X**. *(1 mark)*

b State the function of this chemical. *(1 mark)*

c Explain why the apparatus is left for 10 minutes before readings are taken. *(2 marks)*

A second respirometer, **B**, is set up in exactly the same way as the first, but with glass beads replacing the maggots.

d Explain the purpose of this second respirometer. *(2 marks)*

The table shows a typical set of student results obtained with the respirometers. The student measured the distance moved by the meniscus in **each minute** over a ten minute period.

respirometer	contents	distance moved by the meniscus in **each minute**/mm										
A	maggots	2.0	2.5	2.0	2.5	2.0	2.0	1.5	2.0	2.0	1.5
B	glass beads	0.5	0.0	0.5	0.0	0.5	0.0	0.0	0.5	0.0	0.0

e Calculate the **mean** distance moved by the meniscus per minute in each respirometer. *(2 marks)*

f Calculate the mean rate of oxygen uptake by the maggots in $mm^3\ min^{-1}$. Show your working.

The internal diameter of the glass tubing is 2mm.
$\pi r^2 h$ = volume of a cylinder (r = radius, h = distance)
π = 3.14 *(3 marks)*

g A second student carried out the same experiment. State **two** factors, **other than temperature**, that should be controlled to achieve comparable results. *(2 marks)*

h State **one** way in which the apparatus should be modified to measure the rate of respiration in leaves **and** give a reason for your answer. *(2 marks)*

i State the role of oxygen in respiration. *(1 mark)*

(Total 16 marks)

OCR 2804 Jan 2004, B, No. 1

2 **a** Aerobic respiration of glucose requires enzymes. The process is divided into four stages: glycolysis, the link reaction, Krebs cycle and oxidative phosphorylation.

Complete the table to indicate the **precise location** of the four stages.

respiratory stage	location in cell
glycolysis	
link reaction	
Krebs cycle	
oxidative phosphorylation	

(4 marks)

b Liver cells are frequently used as a source of mitochondria. These cells are homogenised in a sucrose solution and the mitochondria isolated. The suspended mitochondria are then placed in an oxygen electrode where the oxygen uptake of these organelles can be measured over a given time period.

The figure shows a print-out from this apparatus. At point **A** the respiratory substrate glucose was added. At points **B**, **C** and **D** equal quantities of ADP were added.

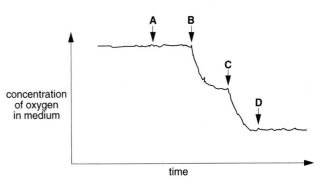

Explain the results,

(i) between points **A** and **B**; *(2 marks)*

(ii) between points **B** and **C**; *(2 marks)*

(iii) after point **D**. *(2 marks)*

c In this question, one mark is available for the quality of written communication.

Describe the main features of the Krebs cycle. **No credit will be given for a flow diagram of the cycle.**
(7 marks)

(QWC 1 mark)

(Total 18 marks)

OCR 2804 Jun 2003, B, No. 3

3 The figure shows the structure of ATP.

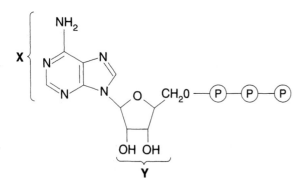

a (i) Name the nitrogenous base labelled **X** on the diagram. *(1 mark)*

(ii) Name the sugar labelled **Y** on the diagram. *(1 mark)*

ATP is often described as the 'universal energy currency of cells'.

b Explain what is meant by the term 'universal energy currency of cells'. *(4 marks)*

c List **three** roles of ATP in **plant cells**. *(3 marks)*

Most of the ATP is produced by a process known as oxidative phosphorylation within the mitochondrion.

d (i) State the exact location, within the mitochondrion, of this process. *(1 mark)*

(ii) Describe the main features of this process.
(5 marks)

(Total 15 marks)

OCR 2804/01 Jun 2002, B, No. 1

4 The figure shows the relationship between various metabolic processes.

GLUCOSE

$CO_2 + H_2O \leftarrow^{C}$ PYRUVATE $\xrightarrow{B}$ LACTATE

(A points from GLUCOSE down to PYRUVATE)

a (i) Identify the three metabolic processes (**A, B, C**).
(3 marks)

(ii) State the letter of the pathway in which acetyl coenzyme A is involved. *(1 mark)*

(iii) State the letter of the pathway in which ATP is utilised. *(1 mark)*

In an investigation, mammalian liver cells were homogenised (broken up) and the resulting homogenate centrifuged. Portions containing only nuclei, ribosomes, mitochondria and cytosol (residual cytoplasm) were each isolated. Samples of each portion, and of the complete homogenate, were incubated in four ways.

1 with glucose;   3 with glucose plus cyanide;

2 with pyruvate;   4 with pyruvate plus cyanide.

Cyanide inhibits carriers in the electron transport chain, such as cytochromes. After incubation the presence or absence of carbon dioxide and lactate in each sample was determined.

The results are summarised in the table at the bottom of the page.

b (i) With reference to this investigation, name **two** organelles not involved in respiration. *(1 mark)*

(ii) Explain why carbon dioxide is produced when mitochondria are incubated with pyruvate but **not** when incubated with glucose. *(3 marks)*

(iii) Explain why, in the presence of cyanide, lactate production does occur, but not carbon dioxide production. *(3 marks)*

This investigation may be repeated using yeast cells instead of liver cells.

c State the products that would be formed by the incubation of glucose with cytosol from yeast. *(1 mark)*

(Total 13 marks)

OCR 2804 Jan 2002, B, No. 1

		complete		nuclei only		ribosomes only		mitochondria		cytosol only	
		carbon dioxide	lactate	carbon dioxide	lactate	carbon dioxide	lactate	carbon dioxide	lactate	carbon dioxide	lactate
1.	glucose	✓	✓	✗	✗	✗	✗	✗	✗	✗	✓
2.	pyruvate	✓	✓	✗	✗	✗	✗	✓	✗	✗	✓
3.	glucose and cyanide	✗	✓	✗	✗	✗	✗	✗	✗	✗	✓
4.	pyruvate and cyanide	✗	✓	✗	✗	✗	✗	✗	✗	✗	✓

samples of homogenate

✗ = absent   ✓ = present

5 The figure shows some of the reactions which occur during aerobic respiration in an animal cell.

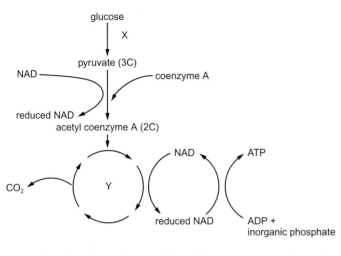

a (i) Identify pathways **X** and **Y**. *(2 marks)*

(ii) State precisely where pathway **X** occurs. *(1 mark)*

b Explain why one of the enzymes involved in the conversion of pyruvate to acetyl coenzyme A is called pyruvate dehydrogenase. *(2 marks)*

c State what is meant by the term decarboxylation. *(1 mark)*

d (i) State the site of oxidative phosphorylation in an animal cell. *(1 mark)*

(ii) Describe in outline the production of ATP in oxidative phosphorylation. *(5 marks)*

(Total 12 marks)

OCR 2804 2000 Specimen paper, B, No. 1

Chapter 2

1 The light dependent stage of photosynthesis takes place on thylakoid membranes in chloroplasts. These membranes surround the thylakoid space (lumen) and are arranged into stacks known as grana. The diagram summarises the processes that take place at the thylakoid membrane.

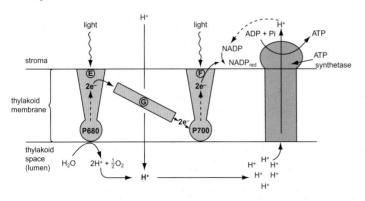

a State the general name of the pigment complexes shown as **E** and **F** on the diagram. *(1 mark)*

b Name the pigment represented by P680 and P700. *(1 mark)*

c Name the type of molecule represented by **G**. *(1 mark)*

d State, **using the information in the diagram above**, why the pH of the thylakoid space (lumen) is lower than that of the stroma. *(1 mark)*

e Explain the function of this pH gradient. *(3 marks)*

f Herbicides (weedkillers), such as diquat and paraquat, act on the chloroplast thylakoids. They interfere with electron transport by accepting electrons and prevent the light dependent stage of photosynthesis from taking place. Explain how this causes plants to die. *(5 marks)*

g Some weed species are **not** killed when herbicides are applied. Suggest why. *(2 marks)*

(Total 14 marks)

OCR 2804 Jan 2004, B, No. 2

2 The rate of photosynthesis at different wavelengths of light can be measured and plotted on a graph. This is called an action spectrum and is shown on the figure below.

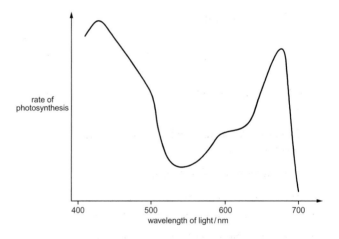

a Describe the effects of different wavelengths of light on the rate of photosynthesis. *(3 marks)*

b In the chloroplasts of green plants, pigment molecules are organised into photosynthetic units called photosystems.

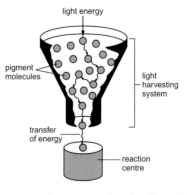

(i) Name **two** pigment molecules found in chloroplasts. *(2 marks)*

(ii) State **one** role of pigment molecules in a photosystem. *(1 mark)*

(iii) State the location of photosystems within the chloroplast. *(1 mark)*

c The production of ATP in chloroplasts is known as photophosphorylation. There are two types of photophosphorylation, cyclic and non-cyclic.

(i) Complete the following table comparing the two types of photophosphorylation.

	cyclic	non-cyclic
photosystem(s) involved		
end product(s)		

(4 marks)

(ii) Explain the role of ATP in the light **independent** stage of photosynthesis. *(3 marks)*

d Some chloroplasts have been shown to possess photosystem 1 only.
Explain why these chloroplasts are unable to form sugars. *(3 marks)*

(Total 17 marks)
OCR 2804 Jan 2003, B, No. 1

3 Figure **A** shows an apparatus used to investigate the effect of light intensity on photosynthesis.

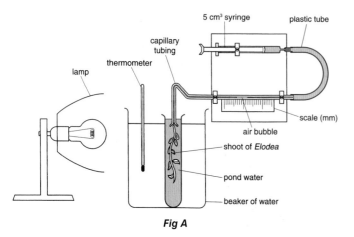

Fig A

a Describe how the investigation would be carried out. *(6 marks)*

A student using apparatus similar to the above investigated the effect of two environmental factors on the rate of photosynthesis. Figure **B** shows the results from one of the experiments.

b With reference to Fig. **B**,

(i) describe the results obtained for the two different light intensities; *(4 marks)*

(ii) explain the differences in the results. *(4 marks)*

c Suggest why the volume of oxygen released does not give the true rate of photosynthesis. *(1 mark)*

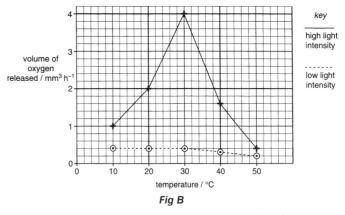

Fig B

(Total 15 marks)
OCR2804/01 June 2002, B, No. 2

4 The figure is an electronmicrograph of a chloroplast.

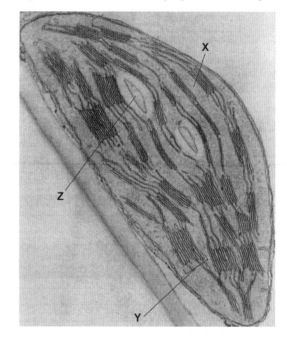

a (i) Name **X** to **Z**. *(3 marks)*

(ii) On the above figure indicate with a label line marked with the letter **W** where photophosphorylation takes place. *(1 mark)*

b Describe in detail how chloroplasts are specialised for photosynthesis.

QWC (1 mark)
(8 marks)

The figure below gives an outline of the Calvin cycle.

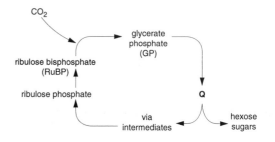

c (i) Indicate on the figure, by using the letter **P**, where the ATP from photophosphorylation is utilised in the Calvin cycle. *(2 marks)*

(ii) Name the enzyme involved in the fixation of carbon dioxide. *(1 mark)*

(iii) Name substance **Q**. *(1 mark)*

(iv) State **two** macromolecules, other than carbohydrates, that can be formed from substance **Q**. *(2 marks)*

(Total 18 marks)

OCR 2804 Jan 2002, B, No. 2

5 T.W. Engelmann investigated the effect of different wavelengths of light on photosynthesis. He placed a filamentous green alga into a test tube along with a suspension of motile bacteria which move to regions of high oxygen concentration. He allowed the bacteria to use up the available oxygen and then illuminated the alga with light that had been passed through a prism to form a spectrum. After a short time, he observed the results shown in the figure A. Bacteria, which are indicated by the tiny rectangles, were evenly distributed throughout the test tube at the start of the experiment.

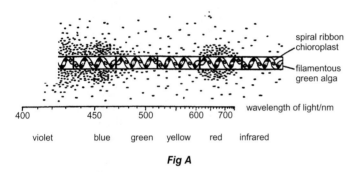

Fig A

a With reference to the passage and to the above figure, sketch a graph on the axes provided below, to show how the rate of photosynthesis varies with the wavelength of light. Label the axes on figure B.

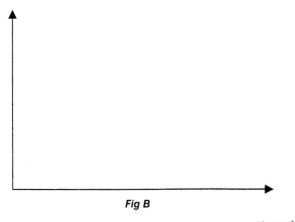

Fig B

(2 marks)

b Explain the reasons for results observed in Figure A.

(4 marks)

c Explain the role of the Calvin cycle in fixing carbon dioxide to form carbohydrates.

QWC (1 mark)

(8 marks)

(Total 14 marks)

OCR 2804, 2000 Specimen paper, B, No.7

Chapter 3

1 Two species of mite were kept in a laboratory. One species, **X**, feeds on oranges, and the other, **Y**, is a predator of **X**.

The figure shows the changes in the populations of these two mites when species **Y** was introduced to a population of **X** feeding on a single orange. The introduction occurred in day 18.

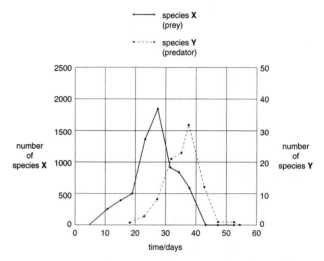

a Complete the following table using data from the figure above.

	species	
	X	**Y**
maximum population size		
time when maximum population was recorded/days		

(2 marks)

b Explain the changes in the population of species **Y** during the course of the experiment. **Credit will be given for reference to the data.**

(6 marks)

(Total 8 marks)

OCR 2804 Jun 2003, B, No. 7

2 The collared dove, *Streptopelia decaoto*, is a recent addition to the British list of breeding birds. At the start of the 20th century, this bird was a rare visitor. It spread across northern Europe and breeding pairs were first seen in

Britain in the early 1950s. The collared dove is now widespread throughout Britain.

The figure is a record of its population growth.

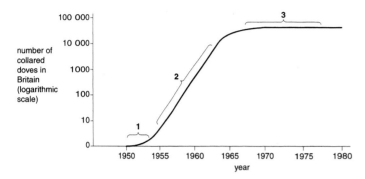

a Name the stages labelled **1** to **3** on the figure above.
(3 marks)

b Suggest why the number of collared doves in Britain remained constant between 1970 and 1980. (3 marks)

c In this question, one mark is available for the quality of written communication.

The figure below shows the population curve of unicellular photosynthetic organisms (algae) in a freshwater lake in southern England.

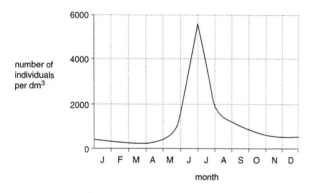

Explain how a change in environmental factors could account for the sudden rise and fall of this population between May and September. (7 marks)
QWC (1 mark)
(Total 14 marks)
OCR 2804 Jan 2003, B, No. 3

3 a Explain the term *primary succession*. (2 marks)

The figure shows a primary succession in a temperate climate.
X represents an example of deflected succession.

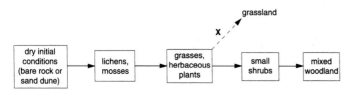

b Explain the role of pioneer plants in succession on a bare rock or sand dune. (3 marks)

c Suggest how deflected succession **X** could be caused. (2 marks)

d Explain how biomass changes during a primary succession. (2 marks)

e Using timber production in temperate countries as an example, explain how ecosystems can be managed in a sustainable way.
(6 marks)
QWC (1 mark)
(Total 16 marks)
OCR 2804/01 Jun 2002, B, No. 3

4 a Explain what is meant by the term *intraspecific competition*. (2 marks)

Wheatgrass, *Agropyron spicatus*, was the dominant plant species on the semi-arid grasslands of north western USA prior to the introduction of European species. These species were introduced to improve the productivity of the grassland for grazing. One such species was cheatgrass, *Bromus tectorum*, which invaded and dominated land previously colonised by wheatgrass.

An experiment was carried out in which seeds from the two species were mixed together in different proportions and sown in plots of equal area. The sowing density was the same in all plots. The mean root lengths of each species were determined when they were grown separately and in mixtures of different proportions. The table below shows the results of this experiment carried out on the two grasses.

	mean root length/cm	
	wheatgrass	cheatgrass
grown separately	64.4	82.8
4 wheatgrass : 1 cheatgrass	56.9	85.4
1 wheatgrass : 1 cheatgrass	47.2	91.1
1 wheatgrass : 4 cheatgrass	41.0	82.1

b With reference to the table,
  (i) state **two** conclusions that can be drawn from the data; (4 marks)
  (ii) suggest how cheatgrass outcompetes wheatgrass.
(2 marks)
(Total 8 marks)
OCR 2804 Jan 2002, B, No. 3

Chapter 4

1 The bacterium, *Escherichia coli (E. coli)*, can use either glucose or lactose as a respiratory substrate.

When grown in a medium containing lactose, but no glucose, the genes coding for the enzymes required to utilise lactose are switched on.

These genes are located together in the *lac* operon as shown in the figure below.

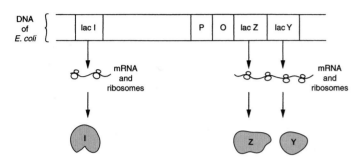

a Complete the table below stating the functions of the parts of the *lac* operon. The function of lac 1 has been done for you.

part of the *lac* operon	function
lac 1	controls production of repressor protein
O – operator	
P – promoter	
I – repressor molecule	
Z – beta galactosidase	
Y – lactose permease	

(5 marks)

b Explain why beta galactosidase and lactose permease are not produced when lactose is absent. *(3 marks)*

c Describe the events that occur within *E. coli* when lactose is the only respiratory substrate available.
(5 marks)
(Total 13 marks)
OCR 2804 Jan 2004, B, No. 5

2 The table shows the diploid chromosome number in different organisms.

name of organism	diploid chromosome number (2n)
yeast	34
broad bean	12
fruit fly	8
domestic cat	72
human	46

a State the number of chromosomes present in the following:

domestic cat sperm cell; human white blood cell; broad bean companion cell; fruit fly zygote *(4 marks)*

b In diploid organisms, haploid cells or gametes are produced by meiosis.
The figure below shows diagrams of an animal cell at various points in the first division of meiosis. The diagrams are **not** in the correct sequence.

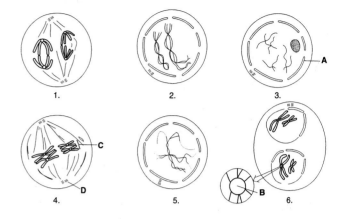

(i) Write the numbers of the diagrams to show the correct meiotic sequence. *(1 mark)*

(ii) Identify the structures labelled **A** to **D**. *(4 marks)*

c Explain how meiosis **and** fertilisation produce variation within a population. *(4 marks)*
(Total 13 marks)
OCR 2804 Jan 2003, B, No. 2

3 In certain breeds of domestic fowl the gene determining feather colour has two alleles that are codominant. The allele C^B when homozygous produces black feathers; the allele C^W when homozygous produces white feathers.

The gene for feather shape also has two codominant alleles. The allele A^S when homozygous produces straight feathers; the allele A^F when homozygous produces frizzled feathers.

The heterozygote for feather colour is grey and the heterozygote for feather shape is mildly frizzled. The two genes involved are **not** sex linked.

a (i) State what is meant by each of the following terms:

codominant   *heterozygote*   *(2 marks)*

(ii) Draw a genetic diagram to show the results of a cross between a grey, mildly frizzled hen and a white, frizzled cockerel.

parental phenotypes	grey, mildly frizzled hen	white, frizzled cockerel
parental genotypes		
gametes		
offspring genotypes		
offspring phenotypes		
phenotypic ratio		

(5 marks)

A breeder wishes to obtain domestic fowl which are all grey in colour and mildly frizzled.

b List the **two** crosses that will produce such a population. *(2 marks)*

c The figure shows a diploid cell with two pairs of chromosomes.
Complete the diagram to show the possible combinations of these chromosomes in the four gametes produced by meiosis.

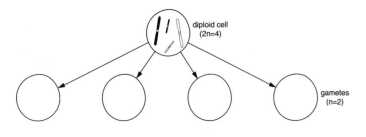

(2 marks)

d List **three** sources of variation in the process of meiosis. *(3 marks)*

(Total 14 marks)

OCR 2804/01 Jun 2002, B, No. 4

4 a Explain the meanings of the following terms:

allele   recessive   sex linkage

(6 marks)

In humans a certain rare sex linked recessive allele results in a change to the shape of the iris. This condition is known as a cleft iris.

b Using the symbols **B** and **b** show all the possible genotypes and phenotypes of the children of a man with a cleft iris and a woman who has only the normal allele.
parental genotypes
gametes
offspring genotypes
offspring phenotypes *(4 marks)*

A woman with a normal iris who is a carrier of the cleft iris allele becomes pregnant by a man with a normal iris.

c State the probability that their first child will have a cleft iris. *(1 mark)*

(Total 11 marks)

OCR 2804 Jan 2002, B, No. 4

5 Guinea pigs, which were homozygous for long, black hair were crossed with ones which were homozygous for short white hair. All the F_1 offspring had short, black hair.

a (i) Using suitable symbols, draw a genetic diagram to explain this result. *(3 marks)*

(ii) Draw a genetic diagram to show the results of interbreeding the F_1 offspring. *(5 marks)*

b State the ratio of phenotypes expected in the F_2 offspring. *(1 mark)*

(Total 9 marks)

OCR 2804 2000 Specimen paper, B, No. 4

Chapter 5

1 a Explain the meaning of the term *species*. *(3 marks)*

A recent study of populations of the house mouse, *Mus musculus*, on the island of Madeira resulted in the following observations:

- there are six distinct populations
- the mice are associated with human settlements
- the populations are located in different valleys separated by steep mountains
- each population has a different diploid number of chromosomes.

As a result of these observations, it has been suggested that speciation is taking place.

The figure below is a schematic representation of Madeira showing the distribution of the six populations.

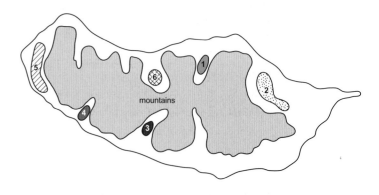

b Using the information in the above figure, state the likely isolating mechanism and the type of speciation taking place. *(2 marks)*

c 'It has been suggested that speciation is taking place.' Explain how this process is occurring in the house mouse populations of Madeira. *(5 marks)*

d Explain the likely outcome of individuals from two separate populations being mated in captivity. *(4 marks)*

(Total 14 marks)

OCR 2804 Jan 2004, B, No. 4

2 In biological classification, there are seven principal taxonomic groups. For garlic, a flowering plant, they are listed below, but not in the correct sequence.

number	taxonomic group	classification of garlic
1	order	Liliales
2	kingdom	Plantae
3	genus	*Allium*
4	phylum	Spermatophyta
5	family	Liliaceae
6	species	*sativum*
7	class	Monocotyledoneae

a Using the numbers 1–7, place the taxonomic groups in the correct sequence starting with the highest group. The first one has been done for you.

(1 mark)

Garlic is a member of the kingdom Plantae, which are all eukaryotic organisms.

b List the other **three** kingdoms that contain eukaryotic organisms. *(3 marks)*

c State **three** features of the kingdom Plantae, other than being eukaryotic. *(3 marks)*

d Cytochrome c is a protein that is found in all living organisms. Analysis of the amino acid sequences of proteins, such as cytochrome c, provides data that taxonomists use to produce more accurate classifications. Explain how analysing the amino acid sequences of proteins provides useful data for taxonomists. *(4 marks)*

e Since the late 19th century, taxonomists have been able to describe phylogenies. Explain the term *phylogeny*. *(2 marks)*

(Total 13 marks)
OCR 2804 Jun 2003, B, No. 4

3 Between 1976 and 1978, a study of the relationship between beak size and diet was carried out on a population of a single species of ground finch, *Geospiza fortis*, living on one of the Galapagos Islands.

In 1976 the beak depth of 751 birds was measured.

In 1977 there was a severe drought that reduced the mass of seeds available. The seeds that were produced that year were larger than in 1976.

In 1978 the beak depth of 90 birds was measured.

Ground finches with smaller beaks are better at opening small seeds, whereas ground finches with larger beaks are better at opening large seeds.

Data from this study are shown in Fig. 3.1 as follows:
A – number of *G. fortis* between 1976 and 1978
B – total mass of seeds available between 1976 and 1978
C – beak depth of *G. fortis* in 1976 and 1978.

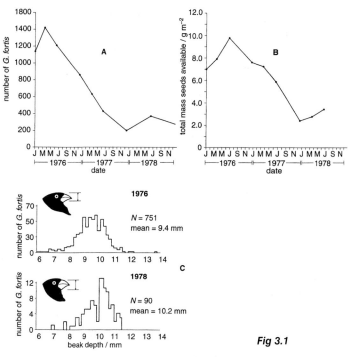

Fig 3.1

a Using figure 3.1**C**, calculate the % increase in mean beak depth of *G. fortis* between 1976 and 1978. Show your working. *(2 marks)*

b In this question, one mark is available for the quality of written communication.

Using the information and the data in Figure 3.1 **A**, **B** and **C**, describe the changes in the numbers of the population of *G. fortis* and the size of beaks. Explain the reasons for the changes. *(9 marks)*
QWC (1 mark)
Total 12 marks)
OCR 2804 Jan 2003, B, No. 5

4 In sickle cell anaemia, the presence of the mutant allele Hb^S in place of the normal Hb^A results in the substitution of one amino acid at a critical position in the haemoglobin molecule. The frequency of Hb^S is much higher on the West Coast of Africa than in most parts of the world. The frequency of the allele is correlated with the distribution of malaria. It has been shown that heterozygotes possess an advantage in childhood over normal individuals as they have increased resistance to malaria. They also have sufficient amounts of normal haemoglobin in the blood to prevent severe anaemia.

a (i) Using the information given in the passage, state whether the likely life expectancy is high or low in West Africa for individuals with the following genotypes. In each case give a reason for your answer:

$Hb^A Hb^A$ $Hb^A Hb^S$ $Hb^S Hb^S$ *(6 marks)*

(ii) Explain how a change in the structure of DNA can lead to an alteration in the haemoglobin molecule. *(4 marks)*

b Explain why populations of West African descent living in the USA have a decreased frequency of the Hb^S allele compared with present day West African populations. *(4 marks)*

(Total 14 marks)

OCR 2804 Jan 2002, B, No. 5

5 a (i) State **three** ways in which meiosis can lead to variation. *(3 marks)*

(ii) Explain why variation is important in selection. *(2 marks)*

Rye, *Secale cereale*, is a cereal crop which is widely cultivated. It is believed to have originated over 2500 years ago in Asia Minor from *Secale ancestralis*, a wild species with a fragile stem but fairly large grains. When the cultivation of wheat, *Triticum sp.*, spread, wild rye accompanied the wheat as a weed. The ability of wild rye to thrive on poor soil, and to resist frost and drought better than wheat, resulted in it being subjected to selection pressures such that it yielded a crop when the wheat failed. Climatic and soil factors eliminated the wheat, leaving rye as the sole cereal crop in northern upland regions. Artificial selection of rye has favoured the varieties with the highest grain yield.

b Explain why *Secale ancestralis* and *Secale cereale* are classified within the same genus but as separate species. *(2 marks)*

c With reference to the passage,

(i) Explain what is meant by the term *selection pressure*. *(2 marks)*

(ii) Suggest how natural selection has led to rye becoming 'the sole cereal crop in northern upland regions'. *(3 marks)*

d Explain how artificial selection of rye could have been achieved. *(4 marks)*

(Total 16 marks)

OCR 2804 2000 Specimen paper, B, No.5

Chapter 6

1 Figure **A** shows the changes in membrane potential associated with an action potential in a mammalian neurone.

The changes in potential difference are due to the movement of potassium and sodium ions through specific ion channels.

a In this question, one mark is available for the quality of written communication.

Describe how movements of sodium and potassium ions across the membrane of a neurone produce an action potential.

Use the letters A to E on Figure A to help structure your answer. *(7 marks)*

QWC *(1 mark)*

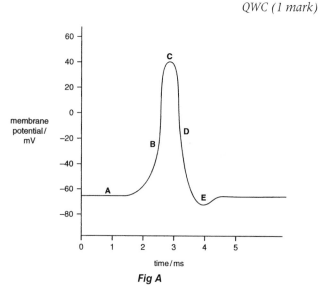

Fig A

b Some degenerative diseases, such as multiple sclerosis, are caused by a breakdown of the myelin sheath.

Explain the effect that the breakdown of the myelin sheath will have on the transmission of nerve impulses. *(3 marks)*

c Describe the role of calcium ions at the synapse. *(3 marks)*

(Total 14 marks)

OCR 2804 Jan 2004, B, No. 3

2 Below is a diagram of the spinal reflex arc.

a Identify the structures labelled **P** to **S**.

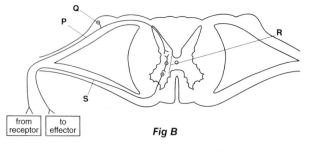

Fig B

(4 marks)

b Explain how synapses determine the direction of nerve impulse transmission in the reflex arc shown in figure **B**. *(2 marks)*

c Botulinum toxin stops nerve impulse transmission at synapses. Suggest how this may occur. *(3 marks)*

(Total 9 marks)

OCR 2804 Jun 2003, B, No. 1

3 The figure below shows diagrams of nephrons from the kidneys of three different mammals, **X**, **Y** and **Z**.

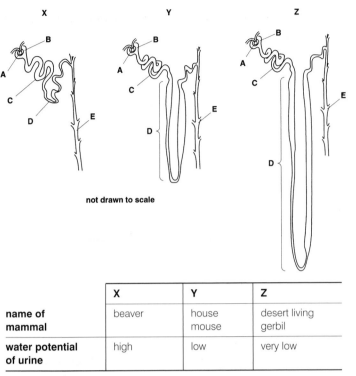

not drawn to scale

	X	Y	Z
name of mammal	beaver	house mouse	desert living gerbil
water potential of urine	high	low	very low

Fig A

a Name parts **A** to **E**. *(5 marks)*

b Explain the relationship between the length of part **D** and the water potential of the urine in the three mammals. *(4 marks)*

The figure below is a drawing of a cell from part **C** of the diagram of the nephrons shown in the figure above.

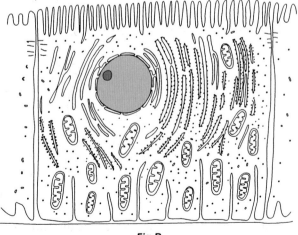

Fig B

c State **three** structural features **visible** in this cell which help in selective reabsorption from the glomerular filtrate. *(3 marks)*

d In this question, one mark is available for the quality of written communication.

Explain how the composition of the fluid flowing through part **C** of the nephrons shown in Fig. **A** is altered by cells of the type shown in Fig. **B**. *(7 marks)*

QWC (1 mark)

(Total 20 marks)

OCR 2804 Jun 2003, B, No. 5

4 Plant growth substances are important in controlling the life cycles of flowering plants. Changes in the concentration of plant growth substances in cells can regulate the expression of specific genes. One such substance is abscisic acid, ABA.

The concentration of ABA was measured during development of cotton fruits.

Fig. **C** shows the change in concentration of ABA as cotton fruits develop. Fig **D** shows a mature cotton fruit.

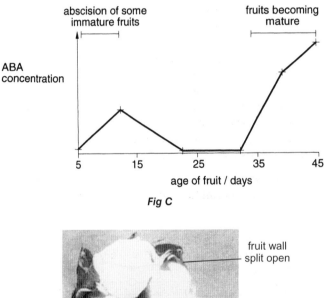

Fig C

Fig D

a With reference to **C**, describe the relationship between fruit development and ABA concentration. *(3 marks)*

b Suggest a way in which ABA acts within plant cells to bring about changes. *(2 marks)*

c ABA concentrations have also been measured in the leaves of broad bean seedlings grown in outdoor experimental plots. It has been observed that the concentration of ABA increases on hot, dry and breezy summer days.

Explain

(i) why these environmental conditions lead to an increase in the concentration of ABA; *(2 marks)*

(ii) the effect of raised ABA concentrations on the leaf. *(2 marks)*

(Total 9 marks)

OCR 2804 Jan 2003, B, No. 4

5 In one form of diabetes, the pancreas is unable to make sufficient insulin. In an investigation, twenty people were divided into two groups. Group **A** contained ten people with this form of diabetes, while Group **B** contained ten people without diabetes (control group).

Blood samples were taken from each person at 30 minute intervals, and the amounts of glucose, insulin and glucagon measured. After one hour, each person ate a meal containing a large amount of carbohydrate. Mean concentrations were calculated for each substance at each sampling time. The results are shown in the figure below.

a (i) State **one** difference between Groups **A** and **B** in the way in which **glucagon** secretion responds to the intake of carbohydrate. *(1 mark)*

(ii) State **two** differences between Groups **A** and **B** in the way in which **insulin** secretion responds to the intake of carbohydrate. *(2 marks)*

b Explain the changes in blood glucose concentration in

(i) **Group A** *(3 marks)*

(ii) **Group B** *(3 marks)*

c Suggest what would happen to the blood glucose concentration of people in Group A, if they ate no carbohydrate for another 24 hours. Explain your answer. *(3 marks)*

(Total 12 marks)

OCR 2804 2000 Specimen paper, B, No. 2

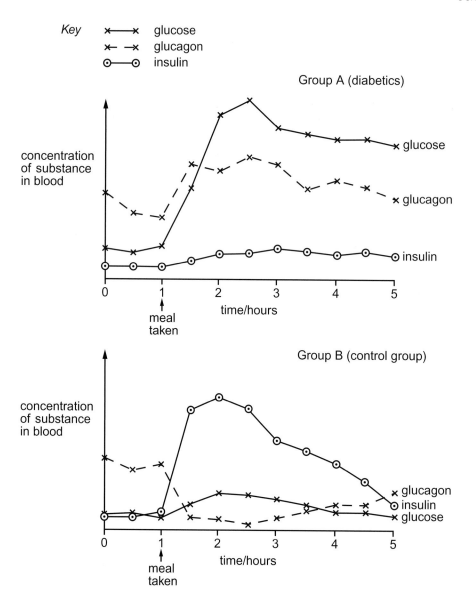

Acknowledgements

The authors and publishers are grateful to Oxford, Cambridge and RSA Examinations (OCR) for kind permission to reproduce the examinatiion questions.

Photograph acknowledgements
The author and publishers are grateful to the following:

Cover image: Leaf Vein X-ray by D Roberts/Science Photo Library

Ardea London Ltd/Jean-Paul Ferrero p170; **Biological Photo Service**/Clare A Hasenkampf pp50 & 51; **Bruce Coleman**/Kim Taylor p36; **Corel 103** (NT) p20 (bottom); **Corel 451** (NT) p17; **Digital Vision 2** (NT) p77 (bottom); **Digital Vision 3** (NT) p20 (top); **Digital Vision 5** (NT) p19 (bottom & top), 81 (right), 98 (top); **Digital Vision 15** (NT) p31; **Digital Vision JA**/Gerry Ellis (NT) p98 (bottom); **Digital Vision LU**/Stephen Frink (NT) p81 (left); **Ecoscene**/DT Grewcock p48; **Frank Lane Picture Library**/Leonard Lee Rue p95 (top); **Holt Studios**/Richard Antony p45, Nigel Cattlin p44 (bottom); **Oxford Scientific Films**/M Austermann, Animals Animals p95 (bottom); **Photodisc 6** (NT) p98 (middle); **Science Photo Library**: p23 Dr Jeremy Burgess; 40 (bottom left & right), 41, 75 (right), 77 (4) Simon Fraser; 49 (bottom) Robin Scagell; 60 Biophoto Associates; 70 (top) BSIP Laurent/Gluck; 70 (middle) John Beatty; 70 (bottom) John Eastcott & Yva Momatiuk; 73 Dr Gopal Murti; 75 (left) Klaus Guldbrandsen; 77 (3) Claude Nuridsany & Marie Perennou; 77 (top) Dr Kari Lounatmaa; 77 (2) Eric Grave; 79 (top) Alex Rakosy, Custom Medical Stock Photo; 84 John Durham; 85 (top & bottom) Michael W Tweedie; 87 Jeanne White; 90 Eye Of Science; 96 (top) BSIP, Fife; 103 Prof P Motta/Dept Of Anatomy/University "La Sapienza", Rome; 105 VVG; 111 VVG; 128 JC Revy; 131 Saturn Stills; 96 (bottom), 97 Peter Menzel; 102 (top), 127 Astrid & Hanns-Frieder Michler; 102 (bottom), 121, 122 CNRI.

Every effort has been made to trace all copyright holders, but if any have been overlooked the publisher will be pleased to make the necessary arrangements at the first opportunity.

Index

Bold page references refer to illustrations, figures or tables.

test crosses 58–9, **58**
tetrads 51, **51**, 53
thermodynamics 6
threshold level 113, 120–1, **121**
thylakoid membranes 24, **25**, 26, **27**
thylakoids 22, **23**
timber production 48–9, **48**, **49**
transduction 20, 112, 113
transects 43
transfusions 63
transplants 63
triose phosphate 11, **11**, **28**, 29

ultrafiltration 104, **105**
unmyelinated nerves 118, **119**
urea 100, **100**, 108
ureter 101, **101**
uric acid 100, **100**
urine 106, 109, **109**

variation 82–3
  genetic 51, 52–3, 83
  and natural selection 87, **87**
visual acuity 113
voltage-gated channels 117
  and action potentials 117, **117**
  and impulse propagation **119**
  refractory period 120

Wallace, Alfred 84
waste products 100, **100**

water
  in the body 108–9, **109**
    kidneys 105, 106–7, **106**
    as waste product 100, **100**
  and desert animals 95, 109, **109**
  eutrophication of **46**, 47
  in photosynthesis 20, **20**, 21
    light dependent stage 26, 27, **27**
  pollution of 47
water potential 98, 108–9, **109**
  and reabsorption 106, **106**, 107
wavelength in photosynthesis 21
  in photosystems 25, 26
  and rate 31
  spectra 24, **25**
woodland 38, **38**, 39
  and glacier retreat 41, **41**
  timber production 48–9, **48**, **49**

xanthophylls 24
X chromosomes 60–1, **60**, **61**
xeromorphic features 95
xylem 22, **23**

Y chromosomes 60–1, **60**, **61**
yeast 16, **16**

Z-scheme 27, **27**
zygotes 52